DATE			

The Brown Rot Fungi of Fruit

THEIR BIOLOGY AND CONTROL

The Brown Rot Fungi of Fruit
THEIR BIOLOGY AND CONTROL

by

R. J. W. BYRDE

Reader in Plant Pathology,
Long Ashton Research Station,
University of Bristol, U.K.

and

H. J. WILLETTS

Associate Professor,
School of Botany,
University of New South Wales,
Kensington, N.S.W.

PERGAMON PRESS
Oxford . New York . Toronto . Sydney . Paris . Frankfurt

U.K.   Pergamon Press Ltd., Headington Hill Hall, Oxford
                   OX3 0BW, England

U.S.A.   Pergamon Press Inc., Maxwell House, Fairview Park,
                   Elmsford, New York 10523, U.S.A.

CANADA   Pergamon of Canada Ltd., 75 The East Mall,
                   Toronto, Ontario, Canada

AUSTRALIA   Pergamon Press (Aust.) Pty. Ltd., 19a Boundary Street,
                   Rushcutters Bay, N.S.W. 2011, Australia

FRANCE   Pergamon Press SARL, 24 rue des Ecoles, 75240 Paris,
                   Cedex 05, France

WEST GERMANY   Pergamon Press GmbH, 6242 Kronberg-Taunus,
                   Pferdstrasse 1, Frankfurt-am-Main, West Germany

Copyright © 1977 Pergamon Press Ltd.

First edition 1977

Library of Congress Catalog Card No. 76-47898

*In order to make this volume available as economically and rapidly as possible the author's type-
script has been reproduced in its original form. This method unfortunately has its typographical
limitations but it is hoped that they in no way distract the reader.*

Printed in Great Britain by A. Wheaton & Co. Exeter
0 08 019740 (Hardcover)

And so, from hour to hour we ripe and ripe,

And then from hour to hour we rot and rot,

And thereby hangs a tale.

As You Like It : Act II, Scene vii

CONTENTS

LIST OF ILLUSTRATIONS

PREFACE

Rotting of plant tissues, frequently with the formation of dark brown areas, is a common symptom of diseases in plants. Often the term 'brown rot' is used to refer specifically to diseases caused by several *Monilinia* (= *Sclerotinia*) spp., which include *M. fructigena, M. fructicola, M. laxa* and *M. laxa* forma *mali*. This book is concerned mainly with these fungi, but occasional references are also made to related forms that are less well-known, and restricted in their distributions.

The brown rot fungi are found in most temperate regions where apples, pears and stone fruits are grown. They have often caused considerable losses and damage to fruit crops and to the trees themselves. Because of their economic importance, they have been widely studied. Also they provide excellent models for mycological studies and for investigations of some of the fundamental principles of plant pathology. An extensive literature, in many languages and often in obscure journals, has accumulated and yet the only comprehensive account of these fungi is that written by Wormald (1954), which is the standard text today. Since 1954, many new techniques have been developed and these have contributed to a better understanding of the development, ultrastructure, physiology, biochemistry and ecology of living organisms, including fungi. Also new chemicals are now used to control the brown rot diseases. The purpose of this book is to integrate and discuss the available data to give a comprehensive and up-to-date account of the fruit-rotting Monilinias.

R.J.W. Byrde
H.J. Willetts

FOREWORD

The damage that the brown rot fungi (*Monilinia* spp.) do to rosaceous fruits and fruit trees has stimulated an impressive volume of research in an attempt to reduce losses caused by these fungi. This research is recorded in an extensive literature, including a number of monographs and reviews. Notable among these is Wormald's comprehensive account published in 1954. Since then new lines of investigation have been pursued and much new information has become available. In spite of all this effort, adequate control of brown rot has not yet been achieved.

Modern plant pathology is becoming increasingly directed towards control of plant disease by methods other than the use of toxic chemicals. It is also generally recognised nowadays that in planning control methods information is required, not only relating to the response of the pathogen to particular fungicides, but also to every detail of its structure (including ultra-structure), physiology, metabolism, ecology and relations with its host plant. The present volume collects together all the currently available information about the brown rot group of related pathogens. The importance of such a many-faceted study cannot be over-estimated.

The two authors are both actively engaged in research on various aspects of the brown rot fungi, and their work is well-known internationally. Their collaboration has produced a volume which should stimulate plant pathologists to consider new approaches to control of the brown rot diseases and at the same time should direct the attention of mycologists in general to the study of these fungi as organisms of outstanding biological interest and as models of the relationship between fungus pathogen and plant host. It is to be hoped that this will lead to the filling in of the gaps, which still remain, in our knowledge, and hence to a better control of these destructive organisms.

Lilian E. Hawker
Emeritus Professor of Mycology
University of Bristol

July, 1976.

ACKNOWLEDGEMENTS

We are grateful to many colleagues at Long Ashton Research Station and at the University of New South Wales for their interest and help. Particular mention must be made of Mrs. L. Brengman, Dr. A.T.K. Corke, Mr. A.H. Fielding, Miss J.A. Hutcheon, Mr. R.W. Marsh O.B.E., Mr. W.J. Redmond, Mr. S. Teague, Ms Jane Tarran, Miss E. Turner, Dr. R.S. Vickery, Mr. J.T. Waterhouse and Dr. A.-L. Wong.

We also wish to thank Drs S.A. Archer, P.F. Kable, D. Lewis, T.R. Swinburne and M.S. Wolfe for helpful comments on parts of the text, and in particular Emeritus Professor L.E. Hawker, who has given unstinting help and support to both authors and was responsible for one (H.J.W.) first becoming involved in work on the brown rot fungi.

H.J.W. thanks the British Council, the Agricultural Research Council, U.K. and the University of New South Wales for financial support which enabled him to spend a year at Long Ashton Research Station. We thank the Directors of the Station, Professor J.P. Hudson, G.M., C.B.E. and Professor J.M. Hirst, D.S.C., F.R.S. for making facilities available and Professor D.J. Anderson, Head, School of Botany, University of New South Wales for his active support.

Finally, we are greatly indebted to Miss Jeanne Ogborne who typed this text with such care and skill.

Chapter **1**

INTRODUCTION

Plant pathologists and mycologists often use the term 'brown rot' in a very general sense to describe a variety of plant diseases that may be caused by fungi or bacteria and, sometimes, disorders that are of a physiological nature. On these occasions the name describes a general symptom of disease and gives no indication of the causal agent. In the present text the term ' the brown rot fungi or organisms' is used in a much more restricted sense and refers to a group of fungal pathogens that causes considerable damage to cultivated fruit trees, particularly apples, pears and stone fruits, in the temperate regions of the world. The group includes:

Monilinia fructicola (Wint.) Honey (= *Sclerotinia fructicola* (Wint.) Rehm),

Monilinia fructigena (Aderh. & Ruhl.) Honey (= *Sclerotinia fructigena* Aderh. & Ruhl.),

Monilinia laxa (Aderh. & Ruhl.) Honey (= *Sclerotinia laxa* Aderh. & Ruhl.)

and the forma specialis

Monilinia laxa (Aderh. & Ruhl.) Honey forma *mali* Wormald sensu Harrison (= *Sclerotinia laxa* Aderh. & Ruhl. forma *mali* Wormald sensu Harrison).

Several related but less well known fungi could also be included as members of the brown rot group, and references are made to them elsewhere in the text.

A large volume of literature has accumulated on the brown rot fungi with much of the early work published in obscure journals and in a variety of languages. Fortunately there are a few good reviews available on these fungi. The most recent was by Wormald entitled "The Brown Rot Diseases of Fruit Trees", published in the United Kingdom in 1954. Wormald has made many valuable, original contributions to our understanding of these fungi and he has included much of this work in his review article together with details of most of the significant work carried out in Europe up to 1954. Roberts & Dunegan (1932) outlined the early work on the brown rot fungi in America, while Harrison (1928) published an interesting account of the brown rot of fruits and associated diseases in Australia. Harrison later extended his studies to the brown rot diseases of fruits in Europe and America and presented a detailed historical review and critical remarks on the taxonomy and nomenclature of the group (Harrison, 1933). These reviews contain a wealth of interesting and valuable information, and their extensive bibliographies are very useful sources of reference.

HISTORY

The brown rot diseases of fruits have been extensively studied in Europe for over 150 years, in North America for about 100 years, and more recently in other parts of the World, particularly in Australia, New Zealand and Japan. Much of the history of this group of fungi is inextricably bound up with mycological work on their taxonomy and nomenclature and has been referred to in more detail in Chapter 2.

Europe

There are references to diseases of fruits in early European literature that could be attributed to the brown rot fungi, such as the statement by Langley (1729) that Royal plum cultivars were '... subject to rot upon the Tree before ripe in wet Lands'. However, the first authentic description of a brown rot fungus on fruits in Europe was published by Persoon (1796). During the 19th Century there was a greater awareness of fungal diseases of plants in Europe and the number of morphological publications, including those concerned with the brown rot fungi on fruits, increased accordingly. By the end of the 19th Century it had been established that there were two brown rot species in Europe (*Monilia fructigena* and *M. laxa*) but the perfect stages were not reported until several years later (Aderhold & Ruhland, 1905).

North America

Brown rot on fruits was described as troublesome in the U.S.A. from the beginning of the 19th Century (Tilton, 1807) but the rotting was thought to be something inherent in the fruit that only became troublesome under moist conditions. Thus the fungus on the diseased fruit was considered to be the result of this rotting and not the cause of it. The fungal origin of the disease was recognized by Kirtland (1855) and he attempted to identify the causal agent. At first the fungus was thought to be one of the European species but later it was found to be different and was given the specific epithet *fructicola*.

Jackson (1915) recorded the imperfect stage of one of the European brown rot fungi on pears in the American State of Oregon. The fungus was named *Monilia oregonensis* by Barss (1923) but was later shown to be *M. laxa*. The disease quickly spread in fruit-growing areas along the Pacific coast and became firmly established as a pathogen of stone fruits in several regions of North America.

Australia

The history of fruit growing and the first report of brown rot on fruit trees in Australia is an interesting story and one that has been described by Harrison (1928). Fruit trees from England, Rio de Janeiro and South Africa were taken to Australia by the first fleet sent from Britain. The trees flourished and initially they were relatively free from disease. The fruits which grew best in Australia were peaches, apricots, nectarines and plums. These were grown commercially within a radius of about 45 miles to the West and North of Sydney, New South Wales. Soon the supply of fruits outstripped their demand, and it became unprofitable to grow fruit for market. Consequently many orchards were left unattended and fruit was not harvested. In 1896 brown rot was found by McAlpine (1902) in orchards near Melbourne, Victoria, where fruit growing had also become established. The damage caused by the disease included rotting of peaches, plums, apricots and cherries, blighting of twigs and withering of blossoms. Cobb (1897) was concerned about the possibility of a build-up of fruit diseases in the large acreages of unattended orchards grown under the warm, moist summer conditions of Sydney. He appealed for the destruction of unused trees, but his warnings were unheeded and soon brown rot was causing considerable damage to all types of stone fruits in the orchards of New South Wales (Cobb, 1904). By 1909, the disease was severe and, in addition to losses to fruits, death of nectarine and peach trees was reported (Froggatt, 1909). Brown rot of stone fruit was reported as 'the commonest fruit disease in our markets ... produced by *Monilia fructigena*'

(Johnston, 1910). Thus Cobb's fears were justified and brown rot has been a severe fruit disease of orchard trees and fruits in Eastern Australia since the beginning of the present century. The disease is also present in the Murrumbidgee Irrigation Areas (M.I.A.) of south-western New South Wales where there is large-scale cultivation of stone fruits. Brown rot was first observed in one locality in the M.I.A. during the 1933-34 season; by 1946 the disease was present throughout the area and in that year 25% of the peach crop was lost. Serious losses have been reported since on numerous occasions although, from experience in America (Roberts & Dunegan, 1932), the semi-arid conditions of the region would be expected to be unfavourable for epiphytotics.

Harrison (1922) found apothecia of a *Sclerotinia* causing brown rot of fruits in a suburb of Sydney. He suggested that the organism producing the apothecia was *S. fructigena*, but a biologic form distinct from both the European and American species. However, after obtaining further data Harrison (1928; 1933) concluded that *Sclerotinia fructicola* (Wint.) Rehm was the correct name to apply to the species present in the eastern areas of Australia.

The only brown rot species recorded in Australia was *Monilinia* (= *Sclerotinia*) *fructicola* until Jenkins (1965*a*) isolated a fungus with the cultural characteristics of *M. laxa* (Aderh. & Ruhl.) Honey on blossoms, twigs and fruits of stone fruits in southern Victoria. This species has now been reported in South Australia (Moller & Carter, 1975) and New South Wales (Penrose, Tarran & Wong, 1976).

New Zealand

The conidial stage of a brown rot fungus was first recorded in New Zealand by Kirk (1905). However, the disease appears to have become troublesome in New Zealand later than in Australia, as it was not regarded as important there until the spring of 1915 when extensive damage was reported on blossoms of fruits (Cunningham, 1922*a*). Brown rot was described by Cunningham (1922*a*) as 'the most destructive disease with which the grower of stone fruits in this country (New Zealand) has to contend. It attacks blossoms, shoots, leaves and fruits, causing the death of blossoms, formation of cankers on the shoots, perforations in the leaves and rotting of fruits. The effects of the disease are not limited to the orchard, as fruit commonly becomes infected during transit and opens up in the market in a badly-rotted condition'. Cunningham (1922*b,c*) found the ascigerous stage of the fungus, which he called *Sclerotinia cinerea* Schröter. The fungus was identified as *S. fructicola (S. americana)* by Wormald (1927). This was the only species reported in New Zealand until Boesewinkel & Corbin (1970) and Boesewinkel (1972) identified *S. (= M.) laxa* as a cause of blossom blight, twig canker and fruit rot of stone fruits.

Japan

Many of the present-day hosts of the brown rot fungi originated from Eastern Asia and, probably, details of the history of the brown rot diseases in that region could provide an insight into the evolution of the *Monilinia* group. This is discussed in Chapter 10. Records of these fungi from the Far East are few, and those that are available usually cannot be studied in detail by workers in other parts of the world because of language difficulties.

Both *M. laxa* and *M. fructigena* have been reported as common pathogens on a variety of hosts in Japan (Takahashi, 1911; Miura, 1929; Wormald, 1927). The first record of *M. fructicola* in Japan was by Terui & Harada (1966*a*) who have made cultural studies on the fungus (Terui & Harada, 1970, 1971). In addition to these species, related forms have been described and they appear to be indigenous to Japan. Takahashi (1911) described a cherry disease caused by *Sclerotinia kusanoi* and a blossom blight of apple. The latter produces symptoms that are similar to those caused by *M. laxa* f. *mali* but the Japanese species possesses disjunctors (small structures that separate mature conidia within a conidial chain and promote the break up of the chains, thereby facilitating dispersal) and these distinguish the European species from the Japanese fungus. *Sclerotinia malicora* Miura causes apple blossom wilt but the fungus was considered by Shima (1936) to be synonymous with *Sclerotinia mali* Tak. (= *Monilinia mali* (Tak.) Whetzel). (The Japanese species referred to above were placed in the genus *Monilinia*, section Disjunctoriae by Honey (1936). Shima (1936) described the symptoms on apples as blighting of blossoms, leaves and woody tissues and fruit rot. The ecology and control of *M. mali* was described by Kimura (1967) and cultural studies on this species have been carried out by Terui and Harada (1963, 1964, 1965).

SYMPTOMS

The brown rot fungi infect aerial parts of host plants to give a variety of symptoms, which include blighting of blossoms and leaves, cankers on woody tissues and rotting of fruits. Table 1.1 summarizes the main symptoms produced by these fungi on some important commercial crops; Fig. 1.1 illustrates some examples.

Blossom blight

When the brown rot fungi attack blossoms of cultivated fruit trees there may be extensive crop losses, which are only exceeded by the damage caused by rotting of fruits. Blossom blight is the first infection of the spring and develops when spores (conidia or ascospores) land on and penetrate flowers of susceptible plants. Moist, moderately warm weather favours an outbreak of blossom blight, and if these conditions continue there may be severe damage to the flowers. Blighting of flowers results in a reduction in the set of fruit and also infection of fruitlets, but the latter may not become apparent until later in the season. Any part of the flower, the stigma, stamens, petals or sepals can be the first site of infection. The infected tissue turns dark brown and the discoloration may extend through all the flower parts, down the pedicel and into the young fruit. If the fungus reaches the tissues of the spur, other flowers in the cluster may wilt. However, the fungus is often confined to the sepals and petals. The discoloured flower parts wither to give a typical blighted appearance (Fig. 1.1). Some infected blossoms fall to the ground but others can remain attached to the tree for long periods, and during moist weather the pathogen within the withered flowers produces tufts of conidiophores over the infected tissues. The chains of conidia, which are borne on the sporogenous hyphae, provide the inoculum for other parts of the same or neighbouring trees.

Twig and leaf blight

Twig blight and cankers are often a sequel to blossom blight. The fungus grows from the floral parts through the peduncle into the twigs where the infected tissues are seen as brown, collapsed areas. These gradually extend up and down the twig. Gum accumulates on the surface of infected tissues.

TABLE 1.1.   BROWN ROT SYMPTOMS ON SOME COMMERCIAL FRUIT CROPS
(summarized mainly from Harrison (1928), Roberts & Dunegan (1932) and Wormald (1954))

Host	*M. fructigena*	*M. laxa*	*M. fructicola*
Apple	Fruit rot is very common and destructive; sometimes the fungus spreads into branches from the fruit and gives rise to cankers. Black apples.	Fruit rot phase of disease is not important. *M. laxa* f. *mali* causes blossom wilt which is occasionally severe and cankering of branches may develop. Black apples.	Fruit rot but not serious; blighting of spurs sometimes takes place. Black apples.
Pear	Fruit rot - severe on occasions.	Fruit rot has been recorded on rare occasions; blossom wilt sometimes observed but usually confined to the spurs and extensive cankering of branches does not develop.	Fruit rot reported on injured or ripe fruits but rare in commercial orchards.
Plum	Fruit rot - considerable losses reported; often present with *M. laxa* in same fruit cluster.	Severe fruit rot; leaves can become infected and fungus sometimes extends into terminal shoot which withers (wither tip); spur blight and small cankers; blossom wilt sometimes severe.	Severe fruit rot; twig blight and blossom wilt also severe.

cont'd ..

TABLE 1.1 (cont'd)

Host	*M. fructigena*	*M. laxa*	*M. fructicola*
Cherry	Fruit rot which appears just before ripening as flowers not attacked by this species.	Blossom wilt is common and a contributing factor to the severe fruit rot which sometimes develops; twig blight, leaf infection and wither tip not common.	Severe blossom wilt and fruit rot; infection of other parts of the tree of lesser importance.
Peach and Nectarine	Fruit rot but not usually severe.	Fruit rot, blossom wilt, twig blight and cankers often severe.	Rotting of fruit, blossom wilt, twig blight and cankers often severe; leaves also infected.
Apricot	Fruit rot but not often severe.	Fruit rot, blossom wilt, twig blight and cankers sometimes very destructive.	Fruit rot, blossom wilt and cankers severe; twig blight, but less common than peach.
Quince	Common fruit rot in Europe.	Reported on fruits, blossoms, leaves and twigs.	Fruit rot can be severe; twig blight.

Fig. 1.1. Typical infections.

    (A)   Of apple fruit by *M. fructigena*, showing concentric rings of
           pustules (p).

    (B)   Of peach fruit by *M. fructicola*.

    (C)   Of plum spur by *M. laxa* showing gumming (g), and wilted
           blossoms (b) through which infection occurred.

On most fruit trees, infection of leaves is uncommon, except from blighted
twigs. A brown discoloration spreads through the leaf until most, or sometimes all, of the lamina is affected. The leaf shrivels and dies to give a
blighted appearance (Fig. 1.1). When infection is restricted to localized
lesions, a shot-holing effect may be produced as the diseased areas dry out.
Although leaves are killed sometimes by the brown rot fungi, the damage due
to reduction of foliar surface does not significantly lower fruit yield.
When the weather is warm and humid spores develop on infected leaves.

On plums, and sometimes cherries, leaves on young shoots can be infected
directly, often through an injury, and the subsequent spread of the fungus
into the shoot results in a 'wither tip' symptom (Wormald, 1954).

Stem cankers

Cankers seldom develop from direct penetration through the external surfaces
of the plants even when injuries have been caused by frosts, sprays or other
agencies. Stem cankers develop usually from blighted twigs or fruit spurs by
growth of mycelium into larger limbs of the tree. In the early stages of canker formation the bark in the infected area dies, the tissue beneath the bark
becomes sunken and discoloured and finally an open wound develops. Gum is
often exuded in the diseased area. Usually callus tissue develops around
the canker and restricts further growth, so that the cankers heal up. Occasionally the wounds continue to develop for several years and extensive damage
or even death of the tree may be caused, but this is often the result of invasion by other organisms. If environmental conditions are suitable for sporulation, active cankers sometimes produce conidia and thereby provide a source
of inoculum.

Fruit rot

Fruit rot is the most destructive phase in the life cycles of the brown rot
fungi. Infection of young fruits can take place early in the season following blossom blight as described above or at any stage during fruit development.
Green fruits are more resistant to the brown rot fungi than are those approa-
ching the ripening stage. Various reasons have been suggested for this, and
are discussed in more detail in Chapter 7. Post-harvest rotting of fruits can
cause considerable losses in transit, storage or the market.

The first indication of fruit infection is the development of a small, superficial, circular brown spot which gradually extends outwards. As the disease
progresses from small lesions, conidiophores rupture the epidermis of the
fruit to form small tufts over the surface; conidia are produced on the sporogenous hyphae. Often the conidiophores are arranged in concentric bands around
the source of infection to give a characteristic appearance (Fig. 1.1). Under
moist conditions and on soft, ripe fruit, almost all the surface is covered
with conidial tufts or vegetative mycelium, but when the relative humidity is
low and/or the fruits are not ripe, no mycelium and very few or no conidial
tufts develop. Eventually the whole fruit becomes discoloured and water is
lost so that a shrivelled, wrinkled 'mummy' is formed. The dry type of rot
which develops in fruits infected by the brown rot fungi is referred to as
mummification. Infection often spreads from a diseased fruit to healthy ones
in the same cluster. Several mummies become joined firmly together by the
drying out of mucilage that exudes from fruits during the rotting process.
Mummies hang on branches of trees until spring or, alternatively, mummified
fruits fall to the ground where they remain through the winter months, partly
or completely buried beneath soil or leaf litter.

The role of pectolytic enzymes in the rotting of fruit by the brown rot fungi is discussed in detail in Chapter 7. Mummification of fruits by the brown rot fungi produces a dry, firm rot and although juices may be exuded under certain conditions a wet, soft rot of the type produced by some other fruit pathogens such as *Botrytis cinerea* and *Penicillium expansum* does not develop. The dry type of rot results from a comparatively early inhibition of pectolytic activity by oxidized polyphenolic fruit constituents so that there is incomplete dissolution of the tissue (Cole & Wood, 1961*b*). By contrast, *P. expansum* has the ability to inhibit polyphenol oxidation (Walker, 1969) and pectolysis proceeds further (Cole & Wood, 1961*b*).

Black apple

This term refers to another form of rot which sometimes develops when apples are infected by any of the species of the brown rot fungi. The colour of the rot is brown at first, but it becomes jet black as the rot progresses. The skin of the apple takes on a shiny appearance, the surface is smooth and unruptured by conidiophores, and the amount of shrinking of the apple tissue is insignificant until the late stages of black apple development. The condition is found most frequently in stored fruits. Storage of infected fruits in complete darkness appears to be one of the factors that induces black apple (Hall, 1933; Wormald, 1945) but this is only part of the explanation as the condition has been observed in the orchard. Storage of infected apples in sealed preserving jars with only occasional illumination will also produce black apple (H.J. Willetts, unpublished).

HOSTS

Under suitable environmental conditions, the brown rot fungi will probably infect all drupaceous and pomaceous species and also many other members of the Rosaceae may serve as hosts to these fungi. Only rarely are members of other families attacked by the brown rot organisms. The extensive cultivation of fruit trees in temperate regions and their long life-span ensure that the hosts are readily available.

The main commercial crops that are hosts to *M. fructicola*, *M. fructigena* and *M. laxa* include apple *(Malus pumila* Mill.), pear *(Pyrus communis* L.), quince *(Cydonia oblongata* Mill.), the *Prunus* species peach and nectarine *(P. persica* (L.) Batsch), apricot *(P. armeniaca* L.), plum *(P. domestica* L.), sweet cherry *(P. avium* L.), sour cherry *(P. cerasus* L.) and almond *(P. amygdalus* Batsch). The host range of *M. laxa* f. *mali* is narrow, and in the orchard damage is confined to apple blossoms and spurs. The economic importance of the diseases is discussed in Chapter 8.

There are many records of the brown rot fungi attacking other plants. Details, with relevant references, of naturally-infected plants and some which have been found to provide a suitable substratum for growth of the fungi after artificial inoculations, have been given by Harrison (1928), Roberts & Dunegan (1932), Wormald (1954), Lovisolo (1956), and Negru, Mircea & Crişan (1958). Some of the hosts are medlar, hazel (develops nut drop), grape, gourd, blackberry, strawberry, hawthorn, blackcap *(Rubus occidentalis)*, rose hip, loquat, persimmon, tomato, guava, and many ornamental trees and shrubs. Other hosts include fig (Walker & McLeod, 1970) and rhododendron (Boerema, Van Kesteren, Dorenbosch & de Weert, 1971).

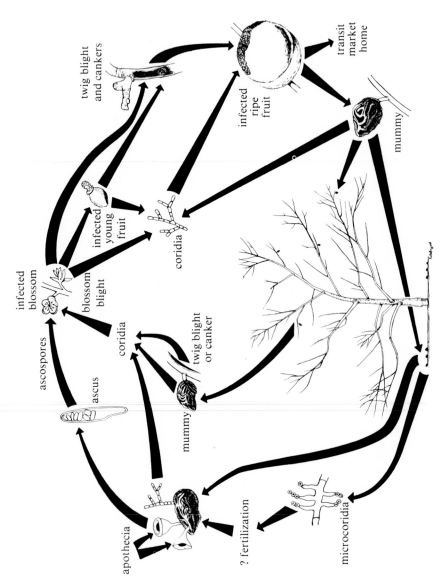

Fig. 1.2. Life cycle of *M. fructicola*

LIFE CYCLES

The life cycles of the 3 brown rot fungi are similar except for the greater importance of the perfect stage in *M. fructicola* than in the other species. A generalized life cycle is given in Fig. 1.2.

The fungi overwinter in or on diseased fruit mummies or in infected tissues on trees such as twigs, peduncles and cankers on branches. In the spring when temperatures, day-length and relative humidities are suitable for sporulation tufts of conidiophores bearing chains of asexual spores (conidia) develop on the surfaces of mummies and infected areas of the host. This is the imperfect or *Monilia* stage of the fungus.

Sexual spores (ascospores) are produced by *M. fructicola* in North America and Australia, but their production is erratic. There are only a few records of the development of the perfect stage by *M. fructigena* and *M. laxa*. Apothecia are produced in spring on mummies which have overwintered on the ground. Mummified fruits which remain on the tree do not produce apothecia. The liberation of ascospores normally coincides with the emergence of young shoots and blossoms of plants. When spores alight on susceptible tissues infections are initiated under favourable environmental conditions.

In addition to the conidium and ascospore, a third type of spore is produced by the brown rot fungi and many other Ascomycetes. This spore is known as a microconidium because of its small size. Unlike the conidium (macroconidium) and the ascospore, the microspore does not have the functions of propagation and dispersal. Drayton (1934) showed that microconidia of *Sclerotinia gladioli* are functional spermatia and a similar role has been attributed to microconidia of several other fungi belonging to the family Sclerotiniaceae (Drayton, 1937; Gregory, 1938, 1941; Groves & Drayton, 1939). Possibly microconidia of the brown rot fungi also function as spermatia, although experimental proof of this is lacking. Microconidia of the brown rot species are produced in abundance within small cavities and on the surfaces of fruit mummies.

Mycelium of the fungus spreads via blossoms to fruit peduncles, young fruits and woody tissues. Older fruits are usually infected by conidia. After initial penetration of fruits there is active mycelial growth, and the hyphae in the outer tissues of the fruit become closely interwoven to form a stroma (pl. stromata). This has an outer rind, a medulla containing both hyphae and host cells and an inner rind. The tissues in the centre of the fruit rot away leaving a hollow sclerotial sphere of leathery or rubbery consistency usually enclosing the seed or unrotted core of the fruit. Fruits may become infected at harvest time and then fruit rots develop during the post-harvest period.

The mycelia within mummified fruits survive long periods of adverse environmental conditions, particularly those of winter. The fungus also survives in twigs, cankers and other infected tissues. When conditions become favourable after a dormant period, spores are produced on infected tissues and the fungus is dispersed and propagated. Thus a new cycle of infection is started and this coincides with early spring growth of host plants.

GEOGRAPHICAL DISTRIBUTION

A detailed account of the areas of the World where the different brown rot fungi had been found up to the early 1950's was given by Wormald (1954). To illustrate the distribution of the species he included copies of the Distri-

bution Maps of these fungi published by the Commonwealth Mycological Institute
in the 1940's. Also many references from a large number of countries were
quoted by Wormald. These have not been repeated in this account. Third edi-
tions of the Distribution Maps of *M. fructicola*, *M. fructigena* and *M. laxa*
were published by the Commonwealth Mycological Institute in 1965 and much of
the information given below was taken from these maps. Some recent references
that have extended the distribution of members of the group to new areas have
also been included.

M. fructigena

This species is found throughout Western and Southern Europe and extends into
the Scandinavian countries, Eastern Europe and the U.S.S.R.; Egypt, Morocco;
Turkey, Israel and Iran; India (Punjab), Korea, China, Japan; and the South
American countries of Uruguay (Koch de Brotos & Boasso, 1955) and Brazil.

M. laxa

M. laxa is found throughout Europe, except for the most northerly areas; in
the U.S.S.R. the species has been reported in many regions including Central
Asian S.S.R. (Doshumov, 1958); Turkey, Israel (Cohen, 1955) and Syria in the
Middle East; Afghanistan; Manchuria and the Kiangsu, Chekiang and Szechwan
Provincesof China; Japan; the Cape Province of South Africa (Heyns, 1968);
the western seaboard of North America from California to British Columbia,
and in the States of New York (Kable & Parker, 1963), Wisconsin and Michigan
and in Canada (Creelman, 1962); the Central American State of Guatemala;
Argentina, Brazil, Chile (English, Moller & Nome, 1967); and Uruguay (Koch de
Brotos & Boasso, 1955) in South America.

Reports of *M. laxa* from Australia and New Zealand suggest that the species has
spread more widely in recent years. When Jenkins (1965a) found the species in
Australia in 1962 it was thought that it was confined to a small area of the
State of Victoria. However, it has now been found in South Australia (Moller
& Carter, 1975) and New South Wales (Penrose, Tarran & Wong, 1976).
Boesewinkel & Corbin (1970) isolated the species in the South Island of New
Zealand, and later it was found to be widely distributed in the country
(Boesewinkel, 1972). Possibly, *M. laxa* has been established in Australia for
some time but it had not been distinguished from *M. fructicola* until recently.

M. laxa f. *mali*

The forma specialis of *M. laxa* appears to be present in Europe but has not been
reported elsewhere.

M. fructicola

This brown rot species is present in fruit growing areas of Australia, New
Zealand, U.S.A., Canada, Central America and in the South American countries
of Argentina, Bolivia (Bell & Alandia, 1957), Brazil (Drummond-Goncalves, 1956)
and Peru. These are all countries of the New World. Recently Heyns (1967)
reported *M. fructicola* in South Africa, while Ali & Morsy (1972) have claimed
it is present in Egypt. Wormald (1954) also referred to several records of
M. fructicola in Africa. A brown rot fungus isolated from stone fruits in
north-eastern Japan was identified by Terui & Harada (1966a) as *M. fructicola*.

Thus, *M. fructigena* and *M. laxa* are essentially Old World species, although
the distribution of the latter has been extended during the 20th Century:
M. fructicola is almost restricted to the New World with only a few records

from elsewhere. Wormald (1954) referred to reports in the United States
Department of Agriculture's lists of intercepted plant pests that both
M. *laxa* and M. *fructigena* have been introduced into the United States in consignments of fruits from Europe. He also gave instances of the importation
of M. *fructicola* into Britain. Doubtless, many undetected consignments of
infected fruits have been imported into countries where the diseases have not
been reported, especially before quarantine regulations were imposed. Specu-
lation on reasons for the restricted distribution of the brown rot fungi has
been made in Chapter 10.

Chapter 2

TAXONOMY AND NOMENCLATURE

GENERAL

The brown rot fungi are classified in the Discomycetes, a sub-division of the
Ascomycetes. The main diagnostic feature of the Discomycetes is the apothecium or fruiting body in which the sexual spores (ascospores) are produced.
The apothecium (Fig. 3.4(G)) is cup- or disc-shaped and derives its name from
the Greek *apotheke*, meaning storehouse. It bears large numbers of asci and
paraphyses in a hymenium on the upper surface of the disc or head. In most
species the hymenium, when mature, is exposed to facilitate ascospore discharge. Those Discomycetes which produce ascocarps above ground (epigean) com-
prise two large groups: the inoperculate group, in which the asci have no regular pore but burst open at their tips to release the ascospores or dehisce
through an apical pore or slit, and the operculate group in which there is a
hinged, lid-like cap (operculum) at the tip of each ascus for the release of
ascospores. The spores are usually forcibly discharged by a puffing action
which is affected by environmental factors such as humidity, temperature and
light. The brown rot fungi are inoperculate Discomycetes, and are usually
included in the Order Helotiales, family Sclerotiniaceae.

The inoperculate Discomycetes form a very large group of economically important
fungi. Unfortunately mycologists have not been able clearly to delimit the
families although many studies have been carried out on them. The main difficulties are: the absence of monographic works on some of the genera; inconsis-
tent descriptions of the species; inadequate micro-anatomical details; the
availability of only small amounts of original material, much of which is
poorly preserved and scattered in many parts of the World; the rarity of some
species; and the small sizes of the fruit bodies which are therefore difficult
to find in the field. Also, great confusion has been caused by the description
of the same fungus under different generic and specific names.

In an attempt to reduce this confusion, important contributions to the taxonomy
and nomenclature of the brown rot fungi have been summarized, in chronological
order, below. This arrangement results in some duplication of information, but
provides a useful source of reference for a discussion of the nomenclature of
these organisms.

Summary of important work on the nomenclature of the brown rot fungi

References	Notes on the events	Names given to the fungi
Persoon, 1796	First description of a brown rot fungus found on decaying fruits of pear, plum and peach. The conidial pustules were *grey*.	*Torula fructigena*

Persoon, 1801	Published a further description of the conidial stage of the fungus and changed the generic name.	*Monilia fructigena* – this name is still used for the imperfect or conidial stage of the fungus which produces *buff-coloured* pustules.
Kunze & Schmidt, 1817; also Schmidt, 1819	Presented a clear description of the fungus with *buff* pustules.	*Oidium fructigenum* – this name was used by several leading British mycologists until late in the 19th Century.
Ehrenberg, 1818	Described a brown rot fungus on apricots with *grey* pustules.	*Oidium laxum* – later changed to *Monilia laxa* Sacc. & Vogl.
Persoon, 1822	Described a brown rot fungus which produced *grey* pustules. Apparently, Persoon thought this fungus was generically different from the one he had originally described.	*Acrosporium fructigenum* – this binomial does not represent a generic transfer.
Wallroth, 1833	Distinguished between the brown rot fungi with 'ochraceous' and 'griseis' pustules.	*Oospora fructigena* ('ochraceous') *O. laxa* ('griseis')
Bonorden, 1851	Proposed name of *Monilia cinerea* for a brown rot fungus on cherries.	*Monilia cinerea* – this name is still used by some European workers for the *grey Monilia* on plums and cherries.
von Thümen, 1875 & 1879	Drew attention to the economic importance of the fruit-rotting *Monilias*; emphasized the differences between the two European brown rot fungi; and extended their host range.	*Oidium fructigenum* and *O. laxum*
Peck, 1881	Gave the first adequate description of a brown rot fungus found in the U.S.A.	*Monilia fructigena* – reported as the cause of brown rot of fruits, blossom wilt and twig blight in America.
Winter, 1883	Described the perfect stage of a brown rot fungus found in Pennsylvania, U.S.A. by Eugene Rau on mummified peaches.	*Ciboria fructicola* – this appears to be the first record of the perfect stage of any brown rot fungus.

Saccardo & Voglino, 1886 (in Vol. IV of *Sylloge Fungorum*)	Listed three brown rot species; this reflected the general opinion of mycologists in Europe at that time.	*Monilia fructigena* (mainly pome fruits) *M. laxa* (apricots) *M. cinerea* (plums and cherries).
Schröter, 1893 (in Cohn's *Kryptogamic Flora*)	Transferred *Monilia fructigena* and *M. cinerea* to the genus *Sclerotinia* based on comparison of their conidial stages with other species of *Monilia* for which the ascigerous stage had been found.	*Sclerotinia fructigena* *S. laxa* – these names have no nomenclatural validity as they are based only on analogy.
Woronin, 1900	Presented convincing evidence that *Monilia fructigena* and *M. cinerea* can be distinguished by the morphology and physiology of the *Monilia* stages.	*Sclerotinia fructigena* *S. cinerea*

Woronin failed to find the perfect stages of the brown rot fungi although he had shown that a *Monilia* on young shoots of cowberry (*Vaccinium vitis-idaea*) was the imperfect form of a *Sclerotinia* which produced apothecia on the mummified fruit (Woronin, 1888) and that *S. padi* produced apothecia on *Prunus padus* and the perfect stage of *S. aucupariae* developed on *Pyrus aucuparia* (Woronin, 1895).

Norton, 1902	Discovered and described the apothecial stage of the common American brown rot fungus on peach mummies in a Maryland orchard.	*S. fructigena*
Bos, 1903	Described *Monilia* fungi on Morello cherries, plums, apples and pears.	*Stromatinia fructigena* *Stromatinia cinerea*

The generic name *Stromatinia* was proposed because of the presence of interwoven mycelia and host tissue in the medulla of the sclerotium.

Aderhold, 1904	Discovered apothecia of a brown rot fungus on apple mummies in Europe.

Aderhold & Ruhland, 1905	Described the perfect stage of brown rot fungi on mummified apples and on mummified apricots collected in Europe; also studied preserved apothecia from peaches sent by Norton from the U.S.A.	*Sclerotinia fructigena* (apples) *S. laxa* (apricots) *S. cinerea* (peaches) – last criticised because conidial stage was not studied but other two names accepted.

They germinated ascospores from apothecia; cultures from apple material were typical of the fungus described by Schmidt (1819) as *Oidium fructigenum*; cultures from apricot fitted Ehrenberg's (1818) description of *O. laxum*.

Saccardo, 1906	The American fungus named *Ciboria fructicola* by Winter (1883) was transferred to the genus *Sclerotinia* on the authority of Rehm.	*Sclerotinia fructicola*; also concluded that Norton's fungus should be called *S. cinerea*.
Reade, 1909 (unpublished thesis, Cornell University)	Concluded from work in America on the local species that *Sclerotinia fructigena* (Pers.) Nort. and *S. fructicola* (Wint.) Rehm were synonymous when referring to the common American brown rot fungus.	*Sclerotinia fructigena*
Pollock, 1909	Suggested the use of the name *S. fructicola* (Wint.) Rehm instead of *S. fructigena* (Pers.) Nort. for the American brown rot fungus.	*Sclerotinia fructicola*
Westerdijk, 1912	Found apothecia of a *Sclerotinia* on mummified sour cherries in Holland. *Monilia* stage not studied.	*Sclerotinia* sp. (probably *laxa*)
Jackson, 1915	First recorded the imperfect stage of one of the European brown rot fungi on pears in Oregon, U.S.A.	*Monilia* sp. (named *Monilia oregonensis* by Barss, 1923)
Wormald, 1919 & 1920	(i) Confirmed the presence of two species of the brown rot fungi in England and in Europe.	(i) *Monilia (Sclerotinia) fructigena* - *buff* spores on pome and stone fruits; *M. (S.) cinerea* - *grey* spores on stone fruits and producing blossom blight, twig wilt and fruit rot.

	(ii) Showed the presence of two biologically and physiologically different forms of *M. cinerea*.	(ii) *M. cinerea* forma *mali* (apple blossom blight) *M. cinerea* forma *pruni*
	(iii) Form of *Monilia* causing brown rot of fruits in N. America more closely related to *M. cinerea* than *M. fructigena*.	(iii) *M. cinerea* forma *americana*
Norton & Ezekiel, 1924	Confirmed difference between the American and European brown rot fungi.	*Sclerotinia americana* for the common American fungus.
Ezekiel, 1925	Suggested that the second brown rot fungus on the Pacific Coastal region was identical with *M. laxa* f. *pruni* of Europe - confirmed by Wormald (1927).	*Monilia cinerea* forma *pruni*
Roberts & Dunegan, 1927	Proposed use of the name *Sclerotinia fructicola* (Wint.) Rehm for the brown rot fungus generally found in fruit-growing regions of N. America.	*Sclerotinia fructicola*
Honey, 1928	Proposed the generic name *Monilinia* to include those members of *Sclerotinia* which produce monilioid conidia and pseudosclerotia.	*Monilinia* spp.
Harrison, 1933	Compared European, American and Australian brown rot fungi, including their host ranges and taxonomy.	Recommended the names *S. fructicola*, *S. laxa*, *S. laxa* f. *mali* for the European species; and *S. fructicola* for the American and Australian species.

GENERIC NAME

Long, branched chains of macroconidia, which develop on relatively simple conidiophores, form cushion-like tufts (sporodochia) on the surface of fruits infected with the brown rot fungi. Microscopic examination of the chains of conidia reveals lemon-shaped, oval or ellipsoidal spores which are arranged as beads on a string. This type of arrangement is known as *monilioid*, after the

Latin word *monile* for a necklace. The conidial stage was regularly observed by early workers who gave the fungus the generic name *Monilia*. This continues to be used for the conidial or imperfect form of the brown rot fungi.

Apart from the genus *Monilia*, the brown rot fungi have also been placed in the genera *Torula* and *Oidium* based on the characteristics of the conidial stage. When the perfect (apothecial) stage is used as the criterion, the main genera in which the fungi have been placed are *Sclerotinia*, *Ciboria*, *Stromatinia* and *Monilinia*. There is still some controversy regarding the generic name by which the brown rot fungi should be referred.

The genera *Sclerotinia* and *Ciboria* were first proposed by Fuckel (1869) who described members of the former as fungi which produced apothecia from true sclerotia while *Ciboria* species did not produce sclerotia and their apothecia were borne directly on vegetative mycelia. Five species were included in the genus *Sclerotinia* by Fuckel but he failed to name a type species. Karsten (1871) did not recognise the genus *Sclerotinia*; he created, among many others, a new genus *Rutstroemia* which was, however, discarded later (Karsten, 1885) since he concluded that *Rutstroemia* was synonymous in part with *Sclerotinia* Fuckel and *Ciboria* Fuckel, a view shared by Saccardo (1884, 1889). Rehm (1887-1896) also recognized the genus *Sclerotinia* and separated it into 2 sub-genera, *Stromatinia* for the species in which sclerotia developed in fruits, and *Eusclerotinia* in which the sclerotia were embedded in tissues of stems or leaves. Schröter (1893) also divided the genus *Sclerotinia* into two groups according to whether sclerotia developed in leaves and stems or in fruits.

Boudier's *Histoire et Classification des Discomycetes d'Europe* (1907) had a great impact on the nomenclature and classification of Discomycetes. Boudier provided a useful index for the allocation of all the binomials published as Discomycetes in Europe at that time, but he did not have a working knowledge of many of the species he included in the system. Boudier gave *Ciboria*, *Sclerotinia* and *Stromatinia* generic rank, the two former in the same manner as that used by Fuckel and the latter distinguished by a stroma covering infected organs but not forming a sclerotium composed only of hyphae.

When Winter (1883) gave the description of the perfect stage of a brown rot fungus, the name *Ciboria fructicola* was used. Soon after, workers in Europe associated the *Monilia* stage of several fungi with apothecia which had developed on stromatized plant tissues (Woronin, 1888; 1895) and these fungi were placed in the genus *Sclerotinia*. Schröter (1895), by analogy with these other *Monilia* fungi, also placed the European brown rot fungi in the genus *Sclerotinia* but at that time the perfect stage of the Old World species had not been found. Thus the nomenclature used by Schröter is not valid even though the perfect stages were found later by Aderhold & Ruhland (1905) as he had predicted in 1895.

The validity of the four genera *Ciboria*, *Sclerotinia*, *Rutstroemia* and *Stromatina*, all of which have been mentioned above, was thoroughly and critically discussed by Honey (1928). He came to the conclusion that it was difficult clearly to establish lines of demarcation for these genera. Honey (1928) suggested that 'in applying the principle of types ... both *Ciboria* and *Sclerotinia* have priority over *Rutstroemia*, while the presence of the sclerotium separates members of the genus *Sclerotinia* from that of *Ciboria*'. Honey proposed that the genus *Sclerotinia* as it existed at that time, should be divided into two sub-genera or two genera. The basis presented for this separation was the nature of the stroma and the type of conidial fructification. He proposed the generic name *Monilinia* to include those members of *Sclerotinia* which produce monilioid conidia and pseudosclerotia (sclerotia formed within the host and comprising both fungal and plant tissues) with *Monilinia fructicola* (Winter) Honey (= *Sclerotinia fructicola* (Winter) Rehm) as the type species. The genus proposed by Honey (1928) comprises a natural group of fungi; apart from the formation of pseudosclerotia and monilioid conidia, the life cycles of the fungi included in the genus are very similar and the members are all virulent pathogens which produce the same types of symptoms on blossoms, leaves and fruits.

The occurrence, grouping and life histories of the American species of *Monilinia* were described by Honey (1936). The presence or absence of disjunctors (Chapter 1) was used as a diagnostic character within the genus *Monilinia*. Two groups were suggested by Honey.

(i) Junctoriae - disjunctors absent; at maturity spores joined directly in the macroconidial chain (the brown rot fungi were included in this group).

(ii) Disjunctoriae - disjunctors present; macroconidia usually separated by disjunctors at the time of break up of the conidial chain.

A great contribution to the taxonomy of inoperculate Discomycetes has been made by Whetzel, who devoted a life-time to their study. Apart from the work he did personally, he also trained many mycologists who have added greatly to our knowledge of this group of fungi. At the time of his death in 1944, Whetzel was preparing a detailed account of the stromatic inoperculate Discomycetes. The work was completed by H.M. Fitzpatrick and published in 1945 (Whetzel, 1945). Unlike the earlier taxonomists who had concentrated on the apothecium as the main diagnostic feature of the Discomycetes, Whetzel used a number of characters. He suggested that, although there may be one outstanding character in a natural group, a combination of characters could be used to illustrate relationships but all members need not possess every character. This reasoning was used when Whetzel (1943) first proposed the new family, Sclerotiniaceae, for a group of discomycetous fungi. The members of this family produced stromata on which stalked apothecia developed under suitable conditions; their ascospores were generally ellipsoidal and their microconidia globose to slightly ovate (Whetzel, 1945). It was emphasized that all stromatic inoperculate fungi did not necessarily belong to the Sclerotiniaceae or that these characteristics were not found singly in other fungi. Whetzel included 15 genera in the new family, and amongst these were:

'Apothecia arising from a tuberoid sclerotium .... *Sclerotinia*

Apothecia arising from a thin, effuse, subcuticular sclerotium covering (i.e. manteling) the affected portion of
the suscept ... *Stromatinia*

Stroma of the hollow sphaeroid type: a conidial stage present; conidia borne in monilioid chains in sporodochia ... *Monilinia*'.

Ciboria and *Rutstroemia* were also named as genera in the Sclerotiniaceae.

Although Whetzel included the genus *Monilinia* in his classification, he did not agree with Honey's concept of the stroma as a pseudosclerotium but described it as 'a definite sclerotium of the hollow-sphaeroid type'.

Whetzel's synopsis of the genera and species of the Sclerotiniaceae provided some definite guide-lines for other workers in the field. However, difficulties have arisen because he did not follow the International Code of Botanical

Nomenclature such as sometimes not providing Latin diagnoses for his types and also, re-typifying genera when he considered it necessary. These re-typifications have been used by some later workers, thereby adding further confusion to the taxonomy of this group.

Buchwald, one of the European authorities on the inoperculate Discomycetes, in a review of the nomenclature of the Sclerotiniaceae (Buchwald, 1949) placed the brown rot fungi in the genus *Monilinia*, section Junctoriae.

Wormald (1954) in his monograph on the brown rot fungi acknowledged that *Monilinia* comprises a natural group but argued against its use because *Sclerotinia* has been used almost as a popular name for the brown rot fungi. He also questioned the significance of the pseudosclerotium as a diagnostic feature. Wormald suggested that possibly *Monilinia* could be adopted as a sub-genus of *Sclerotinia*. Wormald's influence on plant pathologists, particularly those in England, has been very great; this is one of the main reasons why the generic name *Sclerotinia* has continued to be used for these fungi by many British workers.

In a revision of the British Helotiaceae, Dennis (1956) recognized the genus *Monilinia*; his treatment of *Sclerotinia* was very conservative and embraced several sub-genera. Subsequently, in a book on the British Ascomycetes, Dennis (1968) again recognized the family Sclerotiniaceae 'in deference to current trends in systematics' with *Monilinia* and *Sclerotinia* as two of the genera in the family. However, he emphasized the difficulty of separating the Sclerotiniaceae from the Helotioideae, and suggested a return to Nannfeldt's classification of the Helotiaceae/Ciborioideae based on the anatomical characters of the apothecium.

In 1971, Dumont & Korf published the first paper in a series which will be the basis of a monograph of the Sclerotiniaceae. In this initial paper they discussed the typification, nomenclature and current taxonomic status of the 15 genera which Whetzel (1945) included in the Sclerotiniaceae. As with all recent taxonomic work on this group, the brown rot fungi have been included in the genus *Monilinia*. Dumont & Korf have, however, made significant changes to some of the taxonomic groupings used by Whetzel. The revision of the Sclerotiniaceae which is being made by these workers is very timely and, it is hoped, will remove some of the confusion associated with the nomenclature and taxonomy of the inoperculate Discomycetes.

In conclusion, it is evident that most authorities on the Discomycetes accept *Monilinia* as the generic name of the brown rot fungi. In the past, both authors of this book have published under the name *Sclerotinia*. However, throughout the general text of this treatise *Monilinia* will be used, except when referring to specific works, for the brown rot fungi, as obviously they belong to this valid, natural grouping. It is urged that other plant pathologists, particularly those in Britain and Europe, also use *Monilinia*, thereby achieving uniformity with fungal taxonomists and the majority of American plant pathologists and mycologists.

SPECIES NAMES

It is now generally considered that there are three species of brown rot which attack fruits and fruit trees. These three species are *Monilinia fructigena* (Aderh. & Ruhl.) Honey, *M. laxa* (Aderh. & Ruhl.) Honey and *M. fructicola* (Wint.) Honey. The main distinguishing characters between the species are:

the colour and appearance of the conidial pustules; the cultural characteristics of the colonies; the host range; and the parts of the plant infected. A summary of the major differences between the species is given in Table 2.1.

M. fructigena

As already stated, the species epithet *fructigena* was used first by Persoon (1796) for the conidial stage of what he claimed was a brown rot fungus in Europe. However, Harrison (1933) concluded 'that it is impossible with certainty to allocate Persoon's description to any of the present day species of Brown Rot fungi'. The first clear account of the fungus we now call *M. fructigena* was given by Kunze & Schmidt (1817) and they named it *Oidium fructigenum*. A descriptive collection of specimens of German fungi was issued by Schmidt (1819); Harrison (1933) studied the material which had been named *Oidium fructigenum* and confirmed that it was *Monilia fructigena*.

Aderhold & Ruhland (1905) were the first workers to describe the apothecia of this brown rot fungus and they also described the conidial stage which was obtained from ascospores isolated from the ascocarps. Their description of the imperfect form was very similar to the one given for *O. fructigenum* by Kunze & Schmidt (1817). *Sclerotinia fructigena* Aderh. & Ruhl. was the combination given by them and is valid for this fungus. However, the fungus became known as *Monilinia fructigena* (Aderh. & Ruhl.) Honey after Honey (1928) created the genus *Monilinia*.

M. laxa

The name *Oidium laxum* was used by Ehrenberg (1818) for the imperfect stage of the European brown rot fungus with grey conidial pustules on apricots. Later this was changed to *Monilia laxa* Sacc. & Vogl.. The specific epithet *cinerea* was given first by Bonorden (1851) for the European brown rot fungus which produced grey conidial pustules on plums and cherries. Thus, at the beginning of the present Century, apart from *M. fructigena*, two other brown rot species were thought to be present in Europe - *M. laxa* and *M. cinerea*. However, Wormald (1927) came to the conclusion that the latter species was conspecific and this was confirmed by Harrison (1933).

Aderhold & Ruhland (1905) published the first description of the perfect stage of this fungus; also they concluded that the conidial stage was similar to Ehrenberg's *Oidium laxum*. They named the fungus *Sclerotinia laxa*. The name, *S. cinerea*, was used first by Schröter (1893) but this was not valid as the perfect apothecia had not been found at that time. Wormald (1921), after obtaining apothecia on plums, also called the fungus with grey conidial pustules *S. cinerea* (Bon.) Schröter, but when *S. laxa* and *S. cinerea* were found to be conspecific then the valid name, on the basis of priority, became *S. laxa* Aderh. & Ruhl. This was changed to *Monilinia laxa* (Aderh. & Ruhl.) Honey by Honey (1928).

M. fructicola

At the turn of the last Century, the American brown rot fungus was usually given the specific epithet *fructigena*. In an unpublished thesis submitted to Cornell University in 1909 and referred to by Harrison (1933) in his review of the nomenclature of the brown rot fungi, J.M. Reade concluded that *S. fructigena* (Pers.) Nort. and *S. fructicola* (Wint.) Rehm were synonyms when used for the American brown rot fungus. Pollock (1909) suggested that, based on the rule of priority, the correct name should be *S. fructicola* (Wint.) Rehm.

TABLE 2.1. CHARACTERS USED TO DISTINGUISH THE FUNGAL SPECIES WHICH CAUSE BROWN ROT OF FRUIT AND FRUIT TREES

	M. fructigena	*M. laxa*	*M. fructicola*
Hosts and parts of plants infected	Fruit rot of pome, stone fruits, quince and medlar; spur blight and canker of apple and peach trees; nut-drop of hazel.	Fruit rot of stone fruits and on rare occasions of pears; blossom wilt, twig blight of stone fruits, pears and quinces; canker of apricot trees. Considered to be a pathogen of blossoms and twigs more than of fruit.	Fruit rot of stone fruits, quince and infrequently of apple; blossom wilt, twig blight and canker of stone fruit trees.
Pustules on fruit	Pustules about 1 mm in dia with a maximum dia of 1.5 mm; light buff on the basis of Ridgway's (1912) scheme of colours (Wormald, 1920).	Pustules about 0.4 mm in dia with a maximum of 0.8 mm; smoke-grey on Ridgway's standards (Wormald, 1920). (Well-defined sporodochia on twig infections in spring, a distinctive feature).	Pustules about the sizes of those of *M. laxa* and described as "pin-head type" by Harrison (1928); greyish-olive on Ridgway's colour scheme (Jenkins, 1965a); Harrison (1928) reported the pustules to be grey when young but becoming a bright fawn colour later.
Conidium production *in vivo*	Conidia not formed during the winter as higher temperatures (15-25°C) required - *M. fructicola* has similar requirements.	Sporulation from 5°C; conidia produced during winter and early spring but the spores are of smaller size than those formed during the summer.	Conidia produced when moisture content of tissues bearing the spores and other environmental conditions are favourable.
Dimensions of conidia	12-34 x 9-15 μm-av about 22 x 13 (from Wormald, 1954).	Summer conidia 8-23 x 7-16 μm - av about 19 x 13.5 μm (from Wormald, 1954)	8-28 x 6-19 μm (from Roberts & Dunegan, 1932).

TABLE 2.1 cont.

	M. fructigena	M. laxa	M. fructicola
Dimensions of conidia (cont.)		Winter conidia 5–19 x 4–12 µm – av about 11.5 x 8 µm.	
	Conidium size is not regarded as a useful taxonomic character – however, the spores of *M. fructigena* are, generally, larger than those of the other two species. For further information, see Chapter 3.		
Mode of branching of germ tube of conidium	Usually produces a long germ tube before branching (Fig. 3.2 (N)).	Germ tube branches close to the conidium and after about 20 hr it is often difficult to identify the original germ tube because of the scorpioid form (Fig. 3.2 (L & M)).	Long, unbranched germ tubes usually develop – often no branching is observed for 20 hr after germination.
Mode of growth on potato dextrose agar	Margins of colonies entire; concentric rings of conidiophores sometimes formed; stromata infrequently produced; large, black microconidial clusters not often observed macroscopically (Fig. 2.1 (A–C))	Margins of colonies characteristically lobed; sparse development of conidia over surface of cultures; mycelium sometimes becomes pigmented in the centre of cultures but organized stromata not often produced; black clusters of microconidia not generally discernible macroscopically (Fig. 2.1 (G–I))	Margins of colonies entire; abundant conidia, concentric rings of conidiophores usually formed; stroma formation sometimes extensive and often produced beneath sporulating regions of the colony; abundant microconidia apparent macroscopically as black raised areas, particularly at the edges of Petri dishes (Fig. 2.1 (D–F))

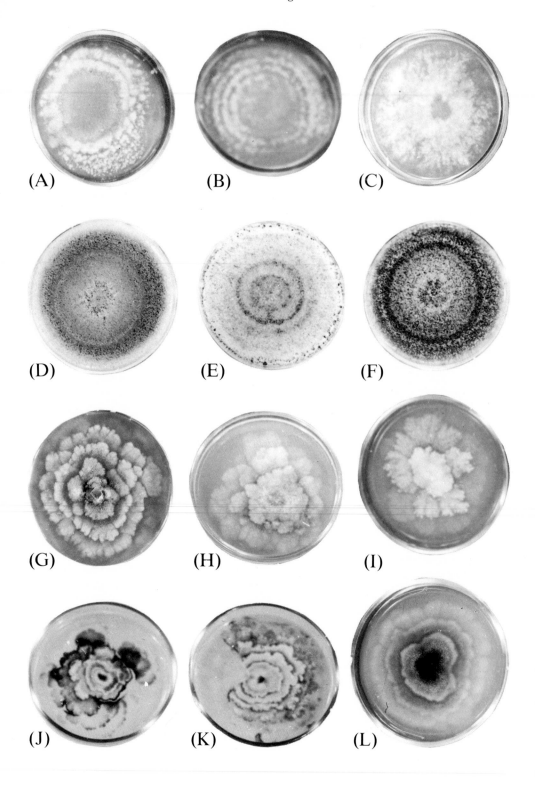

Nevertheless, at that time *S. cinerea* (Bon.) Schröt. continued to be used because Aderhold & Ruhland (1905) had concluded from their studies on the apothecia sent from America by Norton, that this was the name of the fungus. Cultural differences between the European and American isolates of *S. cinerea* prompted Wormald (1920) to propose the name *S. cinerea* forma *americana* for the American fungus; this was given species ranking by Norton & Ezekiel (1924) who proposed the combination *S. americana* (Wormald) Norton & Ezekiel. Roberts & Dunegan (1932) and Harrison (1933) supported the combination *S. fructicola* (Wint.) Rehm since this species epithet was the first applied to it, together with a good description of the fungus. The specific epithet *fructicola* is now universally accepted, combined either with the generic name *Sclerotinia* or with *Monilinia* (*M. fructicola* (Wint.) Honey). The term 'the American brown rot species' usually refers to *M. fructicola* although *M. laxa* is also present in parts of North America.

SUB-SPECIFIC FORMS

Considerable variation has been observed between different isolates within each of the brown rot species (Wormald, 1920; Roberts & Dunegan, 1932; Harrison, 1933; Thind & Keitt, 1949). Ezekiel (1924) noted wide variation in the cultural characteristics, effects on inoculated fruits, and the production of oxidase within *M. fructicola*. He classified his isolates into six varieties, according to cultural characteristics, but later workers have not accepted these as distinct varieties but as different strains similar to those found in most fungi.

Biologic forms have been shown only for *M. laxa*. Two forms were referred to by Wormald (1919 and 1920) as *M. laxa* forma *mali*, which was found to cause blossom wilt and canker of apple trees, and *M. laxa* forma *pruni* which would not infect the apple inflorescence except when flowers were artificially inoculated. Differences between the biologic forms are given in Table 2.2.

Fig. 2.1. Cultural characteristics of the brown rot fungi.

(A and B). *M. fructigena* grown in alternating light and darkness on PDA; note the bands of conidia in concentric rings. (C). A culture of *M. fructigena* grown on PDA in darkness.

(D-F). Cultures of *M. fructicola* grown in darkness. (D). Note the thick layer of conidia over most of the surface of the culture. (E). Numerous, small, black microconidial clusters can be seen near the edge of the Petri dish and the culture shows zonation. (F). A black stromatic layer in the medium beneath the aerial conidia gives the dark colour to the culture; note the zonation near the edge of the colony.

(G-I). Cultures of *M. laxa* grown on PDA. (G). Culture grown in light. (H and I). Cultures grown in the absence of light. Note the characteristic lobing of this species.

(J-L). Cultures of *M. laxa* f. *mali*. (J and K). Growth on malt agar in alternating light and darkness. (L). Growth on PDA in darkness.

TABLE 2.2.   CHARACTERS USED TO DISTINGUISH BETWEEN *M. laxa* and *M. laxa* f. *mali*

	M. laxa	*M. laxa* f. *mali*
Hosts	Wide host range (see Table 2.1) but rarely apple.	Confined to apple trees.
Parts of plant infected	Blossom wilt, twig blight, canker and fruit rot.	Blossom wilt, spur-kill and canker of apple trees. Will cause rotting of fruit after artificial inoculation but not naturally.
Secretions	Poor oxidation of tannins by enzymes extracted from the mycelium.	Good oxidation of tannins by an enzyme secreted from the mycelium.

Based on Wormald (1919, 1920)

However, Harrison (1933) regarded the use of the name forma *pruni* as undesirable and misleading as the fungus has a wide host range, and apart from infecting members of the genus *Prunus* it also attacks pears and quinces. Thus, the names *Monilinia laxa* (Aderh. & Ruhl.) Honey and *M. laxa* (Aderh. & Ruhl.) Honey forma *mali* (Wormald) Harrison are used for the two biologic forms, although the correct nomenclature of the former, under the International Botanical Code, would appear to be *M. laxa* (Aderh. & Ruhl.) Honey forma *laxa*, and of the latter *M. laxa* (Aderh. & Ruhl.) Honey forma *mali* Wormald sensu Harrison.

Killian (1921) studied cultures of *Sclerotinia cinerea* (= *Monilinia laxa*) isolated from cherries in Europe, and he distinguished two physiological forms, *S. cinerea* f. *avium* from sweet cherries and *S. cinerea* f. *cerasi* from acid cherries. These appear to be two culturally distinct strains comparable with the strains that have been noted in other species of the brown rot fungi.

PRESENT-DAY TAXONOMY OF BROWN ROT FUNGI

Taxonomic work on the brown rot fungi almost came to a halt after Harrison's contributions in 1933, although the need for further investigations was indicated by Wormald (1954). During the two decades that have passed since Wormald's review, new techniques and equipment, which can be applied to taxonomic studies, have become available. However, much useful data can be obtained from the use of older morphological, anatomical and physiological methods. This has been stressed by Korf & Dumont (1968), who suggested that information is needed on the microanatomy of the sterile elements of sporocarps of Discomycetes. Also, ontogenetic (developmental) studies are needed to clarify the taxonomy of Discomycetes (Van Brummelan, 1972; Kimbrough, 1972). The value of such studies was noted by Willetts (1968*b*) who was able to identify species of the brown rot fungi according to type of stroma development, while Willetts & Wong (1971) observed consistent differences in the ontogeny of the large sclerotia of *Sclerotinia sclerotiorum* and *S. trifoliorum* from that of the smaller sclerotium of *S. minor*.

In recent years, the molecular approach to fungal taxonomy has been developed and data on inter- and intra-specific differences of proteins can be used, preferably together with morphological and physiological criteria, to resolve taxonomic and phylogenetic problems. Proteins and nucleic acids have been claimed to have the greatest potentials as they have built-in evolutionary histories of their own (Zuckerkandle & Pauling, 1965; Turner, 1969).

Several techniques are now available for molecular studies.

Electrophoresis

This technique involves the use of an electric current to separate proteins, according to their size and charge, in a supporting medium such as paper, agar-(ose) gel, cellulose acetate, starch gel or polyacrylamide gel. The proteins are dispersed and concentrated in bands in the gel and then specific stains are used to detect the proteins. In recent years simplified apparatus, new synthetic support media, shorter time of analysis and new staining techniques have extended the use of electrophoresis for taxonomic investigations.

In recent years the taxonomy of many fungal groups has been studied by means of electrophoresis (Hall, 1973) and the method has proved valuable for species differentiation. Penrose, Tarran & Wong (1976) used polyacrylamide gel electrophoresis and traditional morphological criteria to distinguish between

M. fructicola and *M. laxa* in Australia. Detailed electrophoretic studies (J. Tarran, unpublished) on a range of brown rot fungi have indicated that the technique is very useful for identification at the species level.

Isoelectric focusing

The development of isoelectric focusing in polyacrylamide gel in 1968 provided a method of higher resolving power than that of gel electrophoresis for the analytical separation of proteins (Vesterberg, 1971). Carrier ampholytes are added to the polyacrylamide gel and these give a stable pH gradient between the anode and cathode. When an electric current is passed through the gel, proteins are separated according to their isoelectric points rather than their charge and size as in electrophoresis. After selective staining of the gels, highly resolved patterns are produced and these are used in diagnostic and genetic studies.

As yet, isoelectric focusing has had only limited use in fungal taxonomy. One of the few studies in which the technique has been used for this purpose has been on the brown rot fungi. Willetts, Byrde, Fielding & Wong (1976) used column isoelectric focusing to study differences between the forms of extracellular pectolytic enzymes of *M. fructigena*, *M. fructicola*, *M. laxa* and *M. laxa* f. *mali*. There were consistent and distinctive differences between the species regarding forms of their α-L-arabinofuranosidase enzyme; there was one enzymic form of pectin lyase (pI 9.1) which was characteristic for *M. laxa* and *M. laxa* f. *mali* and another (pI 8.3) which was observed only in extracts of *M. fructigena* and *M. fructicola*. It appears that isoelectric focusing, when used for protein analyses of the brown rot fungi, provides a useful means of distinguishing between species and also sub-species of the fungus.

Serology

Two main serological techniques are used in fungal taxonomic studies – double diffusion and immunoelectrophoresis in agar gels (Ouchterlony, 1968; Hall, 1969). In the double diffusion method, antigens and antibody solutions are placed in separate wells in an agar gel. Both diffuse outwards and where related forms of the antibody and antigen meet, reactions take place to give precipitin arcs. Immunoelectrophoresis requires that the antigen is first subjected to electrophoresis and then allowed to react with antibody solutions placed in a trough cut alongside the path of electrophoresis. The number of precipitin arcs which develop indicates the relatedness of isolates. Some workers claim that serological techniques are less useful than electrophoresis for fungal taxonomic studies (Renard & Meyer, 1969; Meyer & Renard, 1969; O'Hara & Nasuno, 1972).

Miscellaneous techniques

Other molecular methods are available for taxonomic studies on the brown rot fungi, but a search of the literature has not revealed any record of their use. They include molecular analyses of nucleic acids (Storck, 1966; Dutta & Ojha, 1972); comparative studies on the amino acid sequences of homologous proteins of related fungi (Sussman, 1974); and comparison of the composition of cell walls (Bartnicki-Garcia, 1968). Considerable experimental expertise is needed to use these techniques. It is desirable that, whenever possible, methods are developed which do not require elaborate and expensive equipment so that they can be used by field plant pathologists. Wong & Willetts (1975) suggested a method for the *Sclerotinia sclerotiorum* group of fungi which in-

volves observations of types of mycelial interactions that develop between
related species. Probably a similar method of identifying the brown rot fungi
could be developed by a detailed study of the mycelial reactions between species and sub-specific forms.

Apart from routine use of chemotaxonomic methods, a detailed study of the
variability within and between species isolated from selected regions of the
World could give a better understanding of the relationships within the group
and probably of its evolution (see Chapter 10). In the past, comparative
studies of all the species have been difficult because of the restricted distributions of the fungi and the need to enforce quarantine restrictions. Now
protein extracts can be prepared, passed through millipore filters, freeze-
dried and sent to regions where the disease is not found, without fear that
the disease will be spread to new areas. This should allow more detailed comparisons between forms, especially if international co-operation could be
arranged.

Chapter 3

STRUCTURE AND MORPHOGENESIS

The hypha is the structural vegetative unit of fungi. Hyphae branch repeatedly
to give rise to a mycelial colony or alternatively numerous hyphae may become
interwoven to form vegetative or fruiting bodies. The characteristic vegetative structure of the brown rot fungi is the stroma that develops *in vivo* within infected fruits and in culture as a plate of plectenchymatous (interwoven)
tissue beneath or on the surface of the medium.

THE HYPHA

The hypha of the brown rot fungi (Fig. 3.1(C)) shows no obvious characteristic
differences from those of other ascomycetous fungi. The walls of aerial vegetative hyphae are approx 0.15 μm thick and consist of an electron-transparent
inner layer with an electron-dense outer one that is probably of mucilaginous
origin (Willetts & Calonge, 1969*a*). The electron-dense layer is not normally
detected in hyphae that grow submerged in agar or liquid media. Septa develop
at regular intervals along the hypha. Each septum develops centripetally, and
when fully formed is complete except for a simple central pore through which
cytoplasm and hyphal organelles move freely.

Many nuclei are found in hyphal cells of the brown rot fungi. Hall (1963) observed up to 40 nuclei in some hyphal cells of *M. fructicola* and Hoffmann
(1970) as many as 100 in tip cells of *M. laxa* and *M. fructigena*. Nuclei are
more numerous in actively-growing hyphae, probably owing to their degeneration
or migration from older cells to areas of active growth. Cells in the aerial
mycelium and on sporulating hyphal branches have 20-30 nuclei. Heuberger
(1934) and Hall (1963) observed nucleoli that were centrally placed in the
nuclei. The latter worker concluded that there are four chromosomes in each
nucleus. Hoffmann (1972) carried out cytological studies on single conidial
cultures obtained from a large number of single hyphal isolations of wild
strains of *M. fructigena* and detected different morphotypes and subtypes.
Similar results were obtained for *M. laxa* by Hoffmann (1974) who concluded
that the mycelia of both species are di- or hetero-karyotic.

Other organelles found in the hyphal cells are globose mitochondria with
clearly-defined cristae, a rather sparse, irregular membrane system, vacuoles
and lysosomes. The main inclusions in mature hyphae are glycogen granules
and, as the hyphae age, abundant lipid globules.

Anastomoses (hyphal fusions) between hyphae are a common feature of all the
brown rot species (Willetts, 1968*a*; Hoffmann, 1970, 1972, 1974). Small protuberances that develop on one hypha often coincide with protuberances on a
neighbouring hypha or a branch of the same hypha; where these protuberances
meet the separating walls break down forming a connecting bridge. Also tip-
to-tip and tip-to-lateral hyphal fusions are sometimes observed. Nuclear migration between mycelia takes place following hyphal fusions and when different
mycelia are involved heterokaryosis may result. Other organelles and dissolved nutrients may be channelled *via* hyphal fusions.

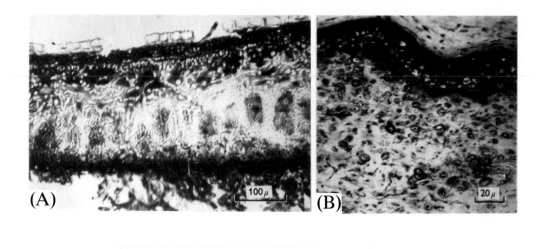

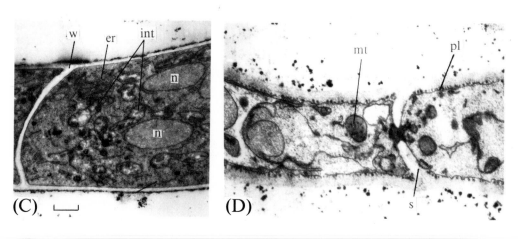

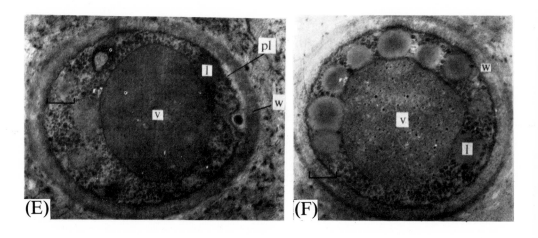

Dichotomous branching of hyphae of *M. fructicola* sometimes takes place but usually lateral branches develop from small outgrowths which are initiated behind the tips of the parent hyphae. Branches grow at an angle of about 45° to the main hyphae. Lateral branch formation is less frequent in hyphae of *M. fructigena* than in those of *M. fructicola*, although sometimes active branching by the former is observed near the tip of a relatively unbranched hypha. The hyphae of *M. laxa* grow in a different manner from those of the other two species (Wormald, 1920; Ezekiel, 1924; Willetts, 1968*b*) and the type of growth is described as scorpioid and geniculate. Frequent branching, with one branch growing much longer than the others, gives the scorpioid effect. Some branches grow in such a way as to form a partial or complete hoop.

THE MYCELIUM

As with other fungi, the conditions of growth both *in vivo* and *in vitro* greatly affect the form of *Monilinia* colonies. One of the most characteristic cultural features of the three species is the alternation of bands of relatively sterile mycelium with bands of sporogenous hyphae that bear chains of macroconidia to give zonation across the Petri dish or over the surface of the fruit. Light, nutrient status of the substratum and H-ion concentration of the medium have great influence on zonation (see Chapter 4). Sometimes there is an unzoned central region over which dense conidiophores and abundant conidia are formed and around this central mass of sporogenous mycelium several concentric rings develop. Occasionally the whole surface of an infected fruit or culture is covered by spores and zonation is not apparent.

Another characteristic feature of brown rot fungi is the development of plectenchyma in or on the surface of the substrata. The plectenchyma becomes darkly pigmented when the culture begins to mature and a stromatic plate or small discrete stromata are produced.

When fruits are infected by inoculum of the brown rot fungi, hyphae penetrate into the fruits and form a mass of interwoven hyphae that becomes organized into a stroma. Mycelial growth may be confined to the tissues of the host

---

Fig. 3.1.   Stromata of the brown rot fungi.

(A). Section through a stroma of *M. fructicola* in wheat grain showing the outer and inner rinds and the medulla of host cells and hyphae.

(B). Section of a stroma formed in culture showing the outer rind and medulla.

(C–F). Electron micrographs of longitudinal sections of: (C) vegetative hyphae; (D) metabolically active stromatic hypha; (E–F) storage medullary hyphae.

Symbols: w, hyphal wall; s, septum; mt, mitochondrion; n, nucleus; er, endoplasmic reticulum; l, lipid body; pl, plasmalemma; v, vacuole.

(A & B) Willetts (1968*b*); (C) Willetts & Calonge (1969*a*); (E & F) Willetts & Calonge (1969*b*).

without the production of aerial mycelium or, alternatively, a sparse, discontinuous mycelium grows over the surface of the fruit. However aerial mycelium is often abundantly produced under warm, humid conditions on soft juicy fruits to form a thick hyphal mat. The mat is produced from tufts of sporogenous hyphae that rupture the skin of the fruit and then, instead of producing chains of spores, branch profusely to give a compact mycelial layer (Willetts, 1968c). Superficially a mummy with a hyphal mat over its surface cannot be distinguished from one that has only a stroma in the host tissues.

In culture, the three brown rot species have characteristic growth patterns that are often used as criteria for identification purposes. However, as all species of the group are rarely found in the same region, only a few truly comparative studies have been carried out. It is very important always to state the conditions under which the fungi are grown, as the type of growth varies greatly according to the substratum and physical factors. Also there is variability between isolates of the same species. Both Wormald (1920) and Harrison (1928) recommended prune extract as a useful substratum for distinguishing between vegetative cultures of the European species.

The main cultural characteristics of the group are described below.

M. fructicola (Fig. 2.1 (D-F))

Most cultures of this species, when grown on potato dextrose agar at 25°C in the dark, form colonies with active growing, entire margins; the aerial vegetative mycelium is usually sparse but often denser bands of sporogenous tissue develop concentrically around the inoculum (Jenkins, 1965a; Willetts, 1969c). The bands are usually light buff in colour. When large numbers of conidia are formed and in old cultures, the circles take on a dark buff colour. Black stromatal crusts develop on the surface or in the medium but usually only after the mycelium has filled the culture dish. In ageing cultures, microconidial clusters become apparent as small, black, raised dots which are most abundant at the edges of the cultures, although often they are dispersed throughout the mycelium. There is considerable variation between isolates of M. fructicola, particularly in the amount of stromatal tissue and its arrangement; the abundance of microconidia; and in the density and arrangement of macroconidia. On media rich in carbon and nitrogen, conidia are produced in abundance and may cover the whole surface of the colony; on other occasions the fungus produces a continuous conidial cover in the centre of the culture and concentric rings of spores towards the edge of the colony. Ezekiel (1924) described in detail the formation by M. fructicola of hyphal masses consisting of pure white, densely interwoven, mainly sterile hyphae under which stromatic tissue does not develop; these masses were used to distinguish between isolates.

M. laxa (Fig. 2.1 (G-I))

The most characteristic cultural feature of this species is its lobed type of mycelial growth. Wormald (1920) described the zonate development of the mycelium of M. laxa on prune juice agar. Usually when the colony had half-filled the plate, but sometimes before this, he observed temporary inhibition of mycelial growth which was followed by the formation of 'flabelliform outgrowths of mycelium which eventually coalesced to form a definite zone'. Several distinct zones may be produced this way. On prunes and prune extract, Harrison (1928) observed the slow growth of a white cobweb-like mycelial mat upon which abundant, ashy-grey conidial tufts developed as the cultures aged; nigrescence did not develop. The grey colour of the conidia is used to distinguish between M. laxa and the other two species (Table 2.1). Conidia are only sparsely

produced on potato dextrose agar but in more abundance when the medium is acidified. Mixed vegetable juice agar (V8) is a good medium for the production of
spores by the European species; cultures of the three species cannot be distinguished on the medium. Stromatic tissue occasionally develops in culture, but
usually there is only nigrescence of the mycelium in the centres of the colonies. Small clusters of microconidia are usually found when colonies are examined microscopically but small black masses, discernible with the naked eye,
are not normally produced.

The sub-species, M. *laxa* f. *mali* (Fig. 2.1 (J & K)), is culturally similar to
M. *laxa* but it produces microconidia more readily than the other brown rot fungi
found in the Old World (Willetts, 1969c).

M. *fructigena* (Fig. 2.1 (A-C))

On prune juice agar the margins of colonies are entire and the mycelium grows
out uniformly to the edge of the culture plate (Wormald, 1920). Large, dome-
shaped, buff-coloured conidial tufts develop on autoclaved prunes (Harrison,
1928) and the buff-colour of the sporogenous tissue is a useful criterion to
distinguish between this species and M. *laxa*. On potato dextrose agar and in
alternating periods of light and dark, some isolates produce distinct concentric rings while others either do not sporulate or they form only indistinct
sporogenous bands; the colony margins of the cultures are entire; stromatic
tissue is formed infrequently but nigrescence of the mycelium is more common.
Small hyaline clusters of microconidia are dispersed throughout the cultures
but these are discernible only with magnification.

STROMATA

In mycological terms a stroma consists of a compact, mattress-like mass or matrix of vegetative hyphae, on which fructifications are often formed. In the
Sclerotiniaceae there are two main types of stromata: the sclerotial stroma,
which is usually referred to as the 'sclerotium', and the 'substratal stroma'
(Whetzel, 1945). A sclerotial stroma was described by Whetzel as 'a strictly
hyphal structure under the natural conditions of its development. While elements of the substrate may be embedded in its medulla, they occur there only
incidentally and do not constitute a part of the reserve food supply.' The substratal stroma is defined as having a medulla composed of a network of hyphae
enclosing and preserving a portion of the host or substrate which serves as a
food reserve. According to Whetzel, the stromata of the brown rot fungi are
true sclerotia but some workers (Aderhold & Ruhland, 1905; Honey, 1928) regarded them as 'substratal stromata' or 'pseudosclerotia' because of the occurrence of host cells in the medulla.

Biologically, sclerotia and stromatized portions of the substratum are extremely
important structures in the life cycles of those fungi that produce them. They
serve as vegetative reproductive bodies; reproductive structures, asexual and
sexual, may develop from them; and they are able to survive severe conditions
for long periods, much longer than do most other resistant fungal bodies.

Structure of stroma

In culture, stromata of the brown rot fungi do not usually become visible macroscopically until the vegetative colony has filled the plate or is about 10 or
more days old.

The stromata of M. *fructicola* (Fig. 3.1 (A & B)) may develop as a continuous plate of hyphal tissue or as small discrete structures; M. *laxa* and M. *fructigena* usually produce only limited stromatic areas. In fruits, a well-developed stroma takes the form of a more or less complete hollow sphere enclosing the core or seed of the fruit. Two regions can be distinguished in the stroma of these fungi, a black or dark-coloured rind which covers all exposed surfaces, and a medulla of interwoven, unpigmented hyphae.

Rind. Cells of the rind fit closely together to form a pseudoparenchymatous tissue, three or more cells across. There is a grading of intensity of pigmentation from black to light brown to almost hyaline from the outside in towards the medulla. Studies on the surfaces of stromata of the brown rot fungi with light and scanning electron microscopes have shown that there is an almost continuous skin or crust of dried-up pigmented aerial hyphae over the surface (Willetts, 1968*d*). Gaps in this crust reveal thickened tips of rind cells beneath. This type of arrangement is seen both in stromata obtained from agar cultures and in fruits, although often in the latter the epidermis of the host must be torn before the structure of the stromatal rind can be studied. The appearances of the surfaces of stromata of the brown rot fungi and of sclerotia of *Botrytis cinerea* are very similar (Willetts, 1969*a*). The walls of the rind cells beneath the crust are often greatly thickened but some cytoplasmic contents may be retained (Willetts & Calonge, 1969*b*).

Whetzel (1945) attributed the dark colour of sclerotial rind cells to impregnated oxidation products of the dead protoplasmic contents. Willetts (1968*b*) suggested that a rind forms on all exposed parts of the stroma of the brown rot fungi in contact with air following drying or autolysis of the surface hyphae; one of the conspicuous differences between the rind and medullary regions is due to the deposition and accumulation of dark brown, melanin-like pigments around and in the walls of the outer hyphae. If the rind is physically removed another quickly differentiates under most conditions, presumably because of the autolysis of the exposed hyphae associated with the accumulation of oxidized polyphenols in the hyphal walls. It has been found that the brown pigment in the rind of sclerotia of *Sclerotium rolfsii* has the properties of a typical melanin (Bloomfield & Alexander, 1967; Chet, Henis & Mitchell, 1967). Rich & Horsfall (1954) found that mycelial extracts from M. *fructicola* contained the polyphenoloxidase tyrosinase and that the germ tubes and mycelium of this fungus took on a dark colour when exposed to sub-lethal doses of certain polyphenols. During morphogenetic studies on the sclerotium of *Sclerotinia sclerotiorum*, Wong & Willetts (1974) reported that tyrosinase was moderately active in sclerotial initials and highly active during the enlargement phase; activity of the enzyme was not detected in aerial or submerged vegetative hyphae. There was no evidence of pigmentation at the time of initial formation or active sclerotium development, and it was suggested that tyrosinase might have a metabolic role during sclerotium initiation and development in addition to its involvement in the melanization of the rind.

In culture, a rind differentiates first on the surface of the stroma exposed to air to form an 'outer' rind; the lower rind develops only when the culture begins to dry out. This also applies to stromata of M. *fructicola* in host tissues; the Old World species often do not form an inner rind so that a fully differentiated stroma is not produced (Willetts, 1968*c*).

Medulla. This stromatal region consists mainly of closely interwoven hyphae which are similar in size and superficial appearance to vegetative hyphae. Usually the greatest hyphal density is towards the outer surface of the stroma;

this may be related to higher oxygen levels in tissues near the surface (Chapter 4). Most medullary hyphae (Fig. 3.1 (E & F)) are about 4-7 μm in dia and contain food reserves in large vacuoles and lipid bodies (Willetts & Calonge, 1969*b*). Interspersed amongst these hyphae is a network of smaller ones (1-2 μm in dia) with well-defined organelles (Fig. 3.1 (D)). Their structure suggests that they are metabolically active hyphae that are responsible for the initiation of new growth by and from the stroma. Probably the energy used by small hyphae is obtained from the reserves in the large ones with which they have close contact. Thick-walled cells, in which some cell contents remain, are found in the medulla and these probably serve a protective function.

A gelatinous matrix or slime fills the interhyphal spaces of the sclerotial medulla of many fungi and indeed has been used as a diagnostic feature in Whetzel's key (1945) to the genera of the Sclerotiniaceae. In the brown rot fungi this extracellular slime is a polysaccharide; its composition in *M. fructicola* (Feather & Malek, 1972) differs somewhat from that in *M. fructigena* (Archer, Clamp & Migliore, 1976) (see Chapter 5). The mucilaginous layer over the surfaces of hyphae probably holds hyphae loosely together and has a morphogenetic function (Willetts, 1972). Mucilage is produced in abundance in liquid cultures of the fruit-rotting Monilinias and also in the field where it accumulates on diseased tissues and cements mummies firmly together, particularly after the mucilage has dried out and become hard. The role of mucilage as a protective layer against mechanical and physical factors is discussed in Chapter 6. Also during rainy periods it may facilitate the absorption and retention of water by diseased parts of the plant, particularly by fruit mummies and wood cankers.

Development of stromata

In fruits. An important requirement for stromatal or sclerotial development is the formation of a mass of hyphae that can become interwoven to form a compact tissue. To achieve this an abundance of nutrient or available energy is needed for the growth of a dense mycelium; this is provided in the fleshy, nutrient-rich tissues of ripe fruits in which stromata develop. When a ripe fruit is infected there is rapid growth of the fungus through the host tissues. However, the growth of vegetative hyphae within the fruit will be affected by the accumulation of inhibitory substances and by competition between hyphae, particularly for nutrients and oxygen. There is a build-up of oxidized polyphenols in fruits following infection, but growth of mycelium of the brown rot fungi continues despite the accumulation of these substances although the activities of some enzymes are inhibited. If there are no mechanical or chemical barriers to the spread of mycelium through the tissues a mass of interweaving hyphae is produced; eventually a rind develops on exposed surfaces and the mycelial mass becomes a stroma. No specific morphogenetic factors have been shown to be involved in the initiation of stromata in fruits; if there is an active infection site and good growth conditions such as an abundance of readily degradable, susceptible host tissue, sufficient moisture, etc., then a stroma will develop by apparently haphazard mycelial growth throughout the fruit but with the greatest mycelial density towards the surface. Corner (1950) suggested that the sclerotium of *Typhula* spp., after a stimulus for concrescence, also develops in this aimless manner (Willetts, 1972).

Under experimental conditions *M. fructicola* produces well-developed stromata in pears and stone fruits but not in apples, although the latter are sometimes mummified by this species in the field (Willetts, 1968*c*). The outer cells of apples and pears are mummified by *M. laxa* and *M. fructigena* but often an inner

rind does not differentiate; this applies to naturally and artificially infected fruits. Fully-differentiated stromata are formed in stone fruits infected
by *M. laxa* but usually the thicknesses of the stromata produced by this species and *M. fructigena* are less than when *M. fructicola* is responsible for
mummification. On apples and pears *M. laxa* f. *mali* produces only small localized brown areas around the sites of infection but stromatization is more
extensive in stone fruits although an inner rind rarely develops.

In culture. Small stromatal initials of *M. fructicola* form *in vitro* by dichotomous branching and septation of hyphae (Willetts, 1968*b*). Permanent uni-
ons between hyphae are brought about by hyphal fusions while mucilage secreted
by hyphae probably serves as a loose adhesive between adjacent hyphae. Several
hyphae often grow together to form a strand and a network of such strands develops. Usually, after growing together for a short distance the hyphal units
of a strand separate and join other strands. This tends to promote hyphal
interweaving and the binding of the mycelium into a compact tissue. Many small
aggregates of closely interwoven hyphae are formed in an area of the culture,
and these coalesce to give a characteristic plate-like stroma that may extend
almost throughout the culture dish. Sometimes small discrete areas of plectenchyma are formed in culture to give discernible patterns, but the factors responsible for this uniform distribution are not well understood. Some conditions that produce patterning are physical or chemical barriers to growth,
changes in growth conditions such as temperature or light, and uneven nutrient
distribution in the substrate.

The scorpioid, geniculate type of hyphal growth of *M. laxa* affects the way in
which the stroma of this species develops. There is repeated branching of the
hyphae to give small, rounded and discrete aggregates of vegetative hyphae.
The small, ball-shaped, closely interwoven initials are formed on or just
beneath the surface of the agar and are joined together by short strands of 3
or 4 hyphae. The initials coalesce to form small, discrete plates of stromatic tissue. The stromata of *M. laxa* f. *mali* develop in a similar manner but
single hyphae, rather than strands, connect hyphal aggregates prior to coalescence of the initials.

Many interwoven strands that present a basket-work effect are produced *in vitro*
by *M. fructigena*. The hyphae branch infrequently and this tends to accentuate
the interwoven appearance when viewed under the microscope. Frequent branching takes place at the outer surface of the stroma giving a more compact
tissue in this region. Stroma formation and the rate of pigmentation is much
slower in *M. fructigena* than in the other brown rot species.

MACROCONIDIA

Macroconidia (conidia) are the main propagules of the brown rot fungi. Under
humid conditions, dense conidial tufts (sporodochia) develop on the surfaces
of fruits, blossoms and other infected tissues. The tufts or pustules are often arranged in concentric rings around the sites of infection. Wormald
(1920) observed that on plums *M. fructigena* produced pustules that were about
1 mm in dia with a maximum dia of 1.5 mm and 'light buff' on Ridgway's scheme
of colours (Ridgway, 1912); pustules of *M. laxa* were smaller, about 0.4 mm in
dia, with a maximum of 0.8 mm, and 'smoke grey' in colour. The sizes of pustules were affected by environmental conditions but relative sizes remained
the same. Coalescence of pustules is sometimes observed, particularly on old
mummies. Harrison (1928) described the pustules of *M. fructicola* as grey when

young but becoming light fawn as they mature and later a bright fawn colour.
The size of the pustules approximates to those of *M. laxa* (Wormald, 1954) and
Harrison (1928) described them as of the 'pinhead type'. Jenkins (1965*a*)
referred to the pustules of *M. fructicola* as 'greyish olive' on Ridgway's
colour scheme.

Microscopic examination shows that the tufts consist of numerous short conidiophores bearing long chains of conidia (Fig. 3.2 (E)). The conidiophores are
similar in appearance to vegetative hyphae and consist of 2 or 3 rectangular
cells, each about 13 µm long. The lengths of conidial chains are variable.
Often a chain of 20 conidia is seen, but the maximum number of conidia that
can be produced by one conidiophore is probably much greater than this provided growth conditions remain suitable for spore development. Branched chains
of conidia are commonly formed.

Formation of spore chains

Developmental studies on macroconidia of *M. fructicola* have been carried out
by Hall (1963), on all three species by Willetts & Calonge (1969*c*) and on *M.
laxa* by Hashmi, Morgan-Jones & Kendrick (1972). There are no apparent differences in macroconidial ontogeny amongst the species. Macroconidia are produced by a budding process; stages in their development are shown diagrammatically in Fig. 3.2 (A-E).

The sporodochia that form on the surfaces of fruits infected with brown rot
consist of varying numbers of conidiophores and spore chains. Electron microscope studies (Willetts & Calonge, 1969*a*) have shown that the first sign of
spore initiation is a slight thickening of the wall over the apex of the mother
cell. This is probably associated with the synthesis of material needed for
the wall of the new spore. The plasmalemma of the mother cell becomes wrinkled
owing, presumably, to an increase in its length and the normally close contact
between the membrane and the cell wall is lost. A bud is blown out by stret-
ching of the wall and plasmalemma (Fig. 3.2 (B)). The developing spore is
ovoid in shape and when it has grown to a length of about 10 µm, another bud
is produced at its tip. The first-formed conidium continues to enlarge until
it is the size of a mature spore. Budding continues until a long chain of
conidia is produced (Fig. 3.2 (D)) with the first-formed spore remaining attached to the conidiophore and with the latest bud at the distal end of the
chain. Sometimes a hypha that is of smaller diameter than buds and normal
vegetative hyphae grows out of the tip of the most distal bud of a chain.
This change in type of growth is often associated with variations in environmental conditions and can be compared with germination of conidia.

Several nuclei pass into each young bud. Usually more nuclei are found in
conidia near the base than in those at the terminal end of the conidial chain.
Nuclear division is very rapid and the nuclei become assorted throughout the
chain and its branches by continual nuclear movement in an apical direction
from one conidium to another.

Branching usually originates from a triangular-shaped segment that produces
two dorsi-lateral outgrowths (Fig. 3.2 (D)). Each outgrowth gives rise to a
chain of conidia, sometimes of equal length but usually one branch is dominant
and produces more spores than the other. Further branching may take place and
the arrangement of conidial branches is similar to the mycelial growth habit
of the brown rot fungi. Sometimes branches arise by budding at the side of an
intercalary spore in a conidial chain and this bud becomes the first spore in
a sub-apical branch.

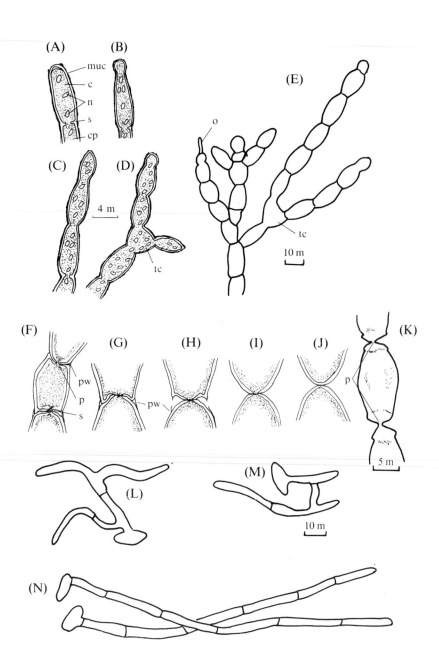

The delimitation of spores along the conidial chain does not follow a definite pattern. The budding process results in regular constrictions along the length of the chain and consequently the septa required to complete delimitation are shorter than those that develop in vegetative hyphae. Septum formation may begin soon after the bud is produced or a whole chain of young spores may be formed before the onset of septation. Occasionally fully differentiated septa are found at the most distal end of the chain while the older buds have no septa or ones that are only partly differentiated. High relative humidities appear to inhibit the formation of septa so that there is incomplete septation of chains that are formed under moist conditions. Harrison (1928) noted the occasional formation of two constricting walls instead of one. A small platform of tissue separating adjacent spores developed but this did not become a disjunctor of the type found in some members of the genus *Monilinia*.

Septa form by centripetal growth across the constrictions between spore initials. A nucleus, associated with one or more additional membranes, is often found in the region of septum development. The fully-formed septum has a simple central pore through which organelles, cytoplasm and nutrients move freely from the vegetative mycelium *via* the conidiophore to the youngest bud at the growing apex. Before spores are liberated, septal pores must be plugged.

Hall (1963) and Willetts & Calonge (1969*a*) described the macroconidium of the brown rot fungi as a blastospore and the development as acropetal. Hashmi *et al.* (1972) also used the term 'blastic' to describe the conidial development by *Monilinia laxa*. Turian (1966) referred to conidium formation by *M. fructigena* as arthrosporic. At low temperatures, *M. fructicola* produces intercalary spores which could be classed as arthrospores (H.J. Willetts, unpublished); these spores resemble chlamydospores. They have irregular shapes, dense contents, and are larger than blastosporic conidia.

Fig. 3.2.   Conidia of the brown rot fungi.

(A-D) Stages in development. (A) Conidiophore (cp) and young conidium (c) containing 3 nuclei (n); note septum (s) between the cells and mucilaginous layer (muc) that does not extend over the tip of the conidium from which a bud is about to develop. (B) A young bud (b) that will develop into a conidium. (C) Further development of a conidial chain. (D) A branched conidial chain showing a triangular-shaped cell (tc) from which branches have originated.

(E) A conidial chain; note the hyphal outgrowth (o).

(F-J) Stages in the separation of conidia (Woronin, 1900). (F) Adjacent cells in a spore chain with septum (s), pore (p) and primary wall (pw) on the outside of the chain. (G-J) Stages in separation of spores.

(K) Tracing of scanning electron micrograph of conidia with final contact only at pores (p) (Willetts & Calonge, 1969*a*).

(L & M) Germination of conidia of *M. laxa*.

(N) Germination of conidia of *M. fructigena* which is similar to *M. fructicola*.   (L-N from Wormald, 1954).

Liberation of spores

Often the last spore to be formed is the first to be liberated. Sometimes a conidial chain breaks some distance from the distal end and small segments, which consist of several spores, are liberated to give a multiple propagule. Each cell of the segment may produce a germ tube which is capable of developing into a mycelium when deposited on a suitable substratum. The triangular cells from which branches originate also function as spores.

The actual process of separation of conidia in a chain of spores of *M. fructigena* has been described by Woronin (1900) who illustrated his work with excellent drawings (Fig. 3.2 (F-J)). The young conidium has an outer primary cell wall and an inner secondary one. Each conidium in the chain grows independently and opposite pressures develop between adjacent spores so that mature conidia tend to pull away from their neighbours. These opposite forces eventually rupture the outer primary wall that is continuous along the conidial chain; the chain fragments and spores are liberated. Dry conditions promote shrinking followed by rupture of the primary wall. This partly explains why conidia of *M. fructigena* separate readily under conditions of low humidity.

Spore structure

The mature macroconidium is ellipsoid, ovoid or lemon-shaped, one-celled and colourless when viewed under the light microscope. The lateral walls of the spore are about 0.2 μm thick. Transmission electron microscope studies have shown a thin electron-dense outer layer (approx 0.02 μm thick) and an inner, electron-transparent layer (approx 0.18 μm thick). At each pole there is a flattened papilla which is more rigid than the lateral areas of the wall; the pore, which is plugged just before fragmentation of the conidial chain, is found in this part of the wall.

The conidium is multinucleate with an average of about seven nuclei per spore and a range from four to ten. Large centrally-placed nucleoli are present in the nuclei (D.C. Fry, unpublished). Other organelles that are seen under the electron microscope are numerous, globose mitochondria and irregular membrane systems. Sometimes there are glycogen granules and lipid bodies in mature spores, although they are usually few in number.

Conidial dimensions

Spore size has been used by many workers as a criterion for the identification of the **brown** rot fungi. Thus there are many records of size of spores of the three species and some of these, with the relevant references, are listed in Table 3.1.

Probably the main conclusion that can be arrived at is that conidia of *M. fructigena* are uniformly larger than those of *M. fructicola* and *M. laxa*. Conidial size is very variable and is influenced by environmental factors. Harrison (1928) noted that the range of size quoted by a number of workers for conidia of *M. fructicola* is so great as to span both summer and winter conidia of *S. cinerea* (= *M. laxa*). The formation of small winter conidia by *M. laxa* is itself an illustration of the effect of environment on the variability of spore size. Wormald (1920) observed that strains of *M. laxa* growing on sterilized potatoes in the laboratory produced conidia with dimensions that were $1\frac{1}{2}$ times as great as conidia of the same isolate growing on diseased material in the field.

TABLE 3.1. DIMENSIONS OF CONIDIA OF BROWN ROT FUNGI

Species	Host	Country of origin	Dimensions (av figures in μm)	Reference
M. fructicola	Variety of stone fruits	U.S.A.	14.7 x 9.9	Matheny (1913)
	Apricots	U.S.A.	14.9 x 10.6	Ezekiel (1924)
	Peaches	Australia	15.9 x 10.2	Harrison (1928)
	Quinces	Australia	15.9 x 9.7	Harrison (1928)
M. laxa	Ascospore culture from plum	England	12.9 x 9.0	Ezekiel (1924)
	Peaches	U.S.A.	14.1 x 11.0	Ezekiel (1924)
	Pears	U.S.A.	14.5 x 10.6	Ezekiel (1924)
	Plums	England	Summer 17.0 x 11.0 Winter 11.5 x 8.0	Wormald (1920)
M. fructigena	Apples	England	21.0 x 13.0	Wormald (1920)
	Apples	England	18.0 x 11.4	Ezekiel (1924)
	Pyrus malus	Holland	18.9 x 11.7	Ezekiel (1924)

Spore germination

The conidia of the brown rot fungi germinate on moist substrates but precise data, obtained under rigidly controlled conditions, are lacking. A very detailed study was carried out by Lin (1940) who found that under the conditions of his experiments conidia of *M. fructicola* did not germinate often in pure water; occasionally a small percentage of spores formed minute germ tubes. Mycelium of both *M. fructigena* (Carlile & Sellin, 1963) and *M. fructicola* (Van den Ende & Cools, 1967) inhibit germination of their own spores. Successful spore invasion by members of the Sclerotiniaceae appears to need nutrients or growth-promoting substances in the infection court (Chapter 4). These substances are obtained in nature from wound extrusions and secretions which accumulate in or on host plants. The apparent need for exogenous nutrients suggests that there are not sufficient reserves in the conidia to provide the energy required for infection. Naqvi & Good (1957) concluded that carbohydrate reserves in conidia of *M. fructicola* are negligible; this could be the reason for stimulation of germination by glucose and other carbohydrates.

Under suitable conditions, a germ tube is produced after 2 to 3 hr of incubation. Sometimes germination takes place while the spores are still attached in the chain. Hall (1963) described nuclear changes during the germination of conidia of *M. fructicola*. One of the nuclei in the conidium moves into the germ tube when the latter has grown to a length of about 10 µm and other nuclei then follow as the germ tube elongates. A septum often develops across the germ tube close to the conidium. The nuclei that move out of the spore divide synchronously and the newly-formed daughter nuclei become distributed through the new mycelium that develops from the sporeling. The type of growth of the germ tube has been used to distinguish between the brown rot species. Wormald (1920) reported that the germ tube of *M. fructigena* grows out on prune-juice agar as a single, almost straight hypha, 400-1200 µm long, before it branches (Fig. 3.2 (N)). The hypha eventually branches after 24 to 48 hr and a 'dendritic branching system' is formed. Often a second germ tube, about 10-30 µm in length, grows from the conidium. *M. fructicola* resembles *M. fructigena* in that an unbranched hypha, at least 200 µm long, but sometimes of length up to 750 µm, grows from a conidium after germination. The germ tubes of *M. laxa* usually become geniculate and branch close to the spore to give, initially, a very irregular branching system (Fig. 3.2 (L & M)). The differences in the growth patterns of germ tubes of *M. fructicola* and *M. laxa* have been confirmed by Ezekiel (1924) and Jenkins (1965a).

MICROCONIDIA

The microconidium of the brown rot fungi differs considerably in both form and function from the macroconidium. As long ago as 1851, Tulasne referred to the microspores of Discomycetes as either spermatia or conidiola. The classic work of Drayton (1934) produced conclusive experimental evidence that the microconidia of *Sclerotinia gladioli* function as spermatia. Subsequent work (Drayton, 1937; Gregory, 1938, 1941; Groves & Drayton, 1939) on several related species indicated that the development of mature apothecia by some members of the Sclerotiniaceae depends upon spermatization and that the microconidium is a functional spermatium. However, this has never been demonstrated for the brown rot fungi but analogy with related species suggests their originally spermatial nature, whether or not they are now functional. Humphrey (1893) and Jehle (1914) claimed that normal germination takes place, but later investigations were unable to verify this. However, more recently Terui & Harada (1971) observed germination of microconidia of *M. fructicola* taken from mucilaginous masses which had developed on fruit tissue media at 10-20°C. The germ tubes grew to a length of 5-15 µm and tended to swell just behind the tip. Some unpublished observations of H.J. Willetts and also of J. Tarran indicate that small germ tubes are produced infrequently by microconidia of *M. fructicola*. Obviously if microconidia are able to germinate, they do so only with difficulty. Dodge (1932) found that microconidia of *Neurospora tetrasperma* germinate when a few days old but as the spores age the ability is lost.

In the field and in the laboratory all the brown rot fungi produce microconidia in abundance on the surfaces of mummified fruits (Humphrey, 1893; Jehle, 1910; Heuberger, 1934). Also microspores sometimes develop in large numbers in cavities within mummies such as in depressions caused by uneven drying out of tissues, in spaces which remain between the outside of infected fruits and hyphal mats that develop over them, and in loosely interwoven areas of the medulla (Willetts, 1968c). In culture, small cream-coloured viscous drops are sometimes seen and microscopic examination shows them to be clusters of microconidia suspended in a fluid, probably of mucilaginous origin. Microconidial clusters become obvious macroscopically if they form black, pycnidium-like masses, and these are most frequently found at the sides of Petri dishes where mycelium has encountered a mechanical barrier. Similar, pycnidium-like masses are sometimes found dispersed through cultures or in areas where mycelial growth has been inhibited for some reason, for example in regions where contaminants are encountered or in areas where cultures have staled.

Development of microconidia

Developmental studies on the microconidia of the brown rot fungi have been described by Heuberger (1934) and Willetts & Calonge (1969a). The formation of microspores by *Botrytis cinerea* is very similar (Brierley, 1918).

Microconidia are borne on microconidiophores which are dichotomously branched hyphae of 2.5-3 µm diameter. The degree of branching depends on cultural conditions. The septate branches terminate in bottle-shaped, often asymmetric phialides, from the apices of which the microspores are cut off in succession (Fig. 3.3 (F & G)). The first spore appears to emerge by rupturing the primary wall of the phialide and the extrusion of the microspore as a bubble-like structure. Presumably the inner wall of the phialide is sufficiently plastic to be blown out and will form a thin wall over the young spore. The outer wall remains as a collar through which later-formed microconidia extrude. The stages in the formation of the second and subsequent spores are shown diagrammatically in Fig. 3.3 (A-E). Short chains of several microconidia develop in this way and the mucilaginous layer formed around the spores probably holds them together. Spores with this type of development agree with Tubaki's (1958) description of a phialospore.

Structure of the microconidium

The mature spore is round to slightly pear-shaped (approx 2.0 µm in dia) with a wall (approx 0.15 µm thick) which has an electron-transparent inner layer and an electron-dense outer one similar to the wall of vegetative hyphae and conidiophores of the brown rot fungi. The microspore has a relatively simple internal structure. The most prominent feature is a large central body which often fills half the volume of the spore (Fig. 3.3 (E)). This body contains lipid material and probably serves as a food reserve. A single nucleus, which is large in proportion to the size of the cell, is present in each spore. In mature spores the amount of cytoplasm is relatively restricted and only a few

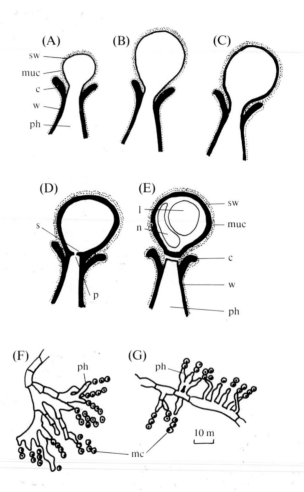

Fig. 3.3. Microconidia of the brown rot fungi.

(A-E) Development of second and subsequent microconidia of *M. laxa*
f. *mali* (Willetts & Calonge, 1969*a*). (A & B) Early stages in the
extrusion of the tip of the protoplast of a phialide (ph). Note
the wall of the phialide (w) which is continuous with the thin
spore wall (sw) and the collarette (c); also the layer of mucilage
(muc) over the surface of the phialide and spore walls. (C) The
spore wall has thickened. (D) Centripetal growth of a septum (s)
across the canal between spore and mother cell; a simple pore (p)
remains in septum. (E) Unequal splitting of septum between spore
and phialide. The newly formed spore is slightly pear-shaped and
has a large oil drop (l) and a comma-shaped nucleus (n).

(F & G) Phialides (ph) and chains of microconidia (mc) of *M. fructicola*.

membranes and small mitochondria are present. Obviously the microconidium has only limited metabolic activity which may partly account for its inability to produce a mycelium.

APOTHECIA AND ASCOSPORES

The apothecium is the perfect stage of the Discomycetes, the group of Ascomycetes in which the brown rot fungi are classified. Ascospores, which are sexual spores, are borne on the apothecium. Ascospores are irregularly produced by the brown rot fungi unlike some members of the Discomycetes that do not produce any other type of dispersive spore. Aderhold & Ruhland (1905) reported finding apothecia of both *M. fructigena* and *M. laxa* in Europe; other records of this species come from Italy by Manaresi (1920) and Russia by Solkina (1931) but ascocarps have not been seen in Britain. The perfect stage of what was probably *M. laxa* was found on cherries in Holland by Westerdijk (1912), and Wormald (1921) observed fructifications of *M. laxa* on naturally-infected plum mummies that had been left on the ground and in pots of soil in the open at Wye, Kent. The perfect stage of *M. laxa* f. *mali* has not been reported. There have been numerous records of apothecia of *M. fructicola* in America (Norton, 1902; Dandeno, 1908; Bartram, 1916, etc.) but fewer in Australia (Harrison, 1922, 1933) and New Zealand (Cunningham, 1922*b*). Apothecia of *M. mali* have been collected in Japan (Terui & Harada, 1966*b*).

Development of apothecia

In many Ascomycetes, ascocarp development takes place after the copulation of spermatia (microconidia) with physiologically specialized hyphae which in some species may be distinguished morphologically (trichogynes) (Drayton, 1932, 1934, 1937; Gregory, 1938; Groves & Elliott, 1961; Elliott, 1964). There are, however, several different patterns of spermatization in the Ascomycetes and these have been reviewed by Kamat & Pande-Chiplonkar (1971). Only one report of the production of apothecia by *M. fructicola* in culture has been found in the literature (Terui & Harada, 1966*d*). Mature stromata, which were cultured on both potato sucrose agar and steamed apple tissue, were incubated under carefully controlled conditions of light, temperature and moisture. Apothecia developed several months after the start of the experiment. There is no evidence from the field or laboratory to suggest that spermatization is a necessary preliminary to apothecial initiation by *M. fructicola*. Heuberger (1934) suggested that the dikaryotic phase of this species arises directly from a nuclear exchange between vegetative homokaryotic hyphae and that its microconidia are non-functional: he also concluded that morphologically distinguishable receptive hyphae are not produced. Similar conclusions have been arrived at for *Sclerotinia sclerotiorum*, in which the perfect stage is like that of the brown rot fungi (Björling, 1951; Kosasih & Willetts, 1975).

The most detailed morphological study of apothecial development by the brown rot fungi is that of Norton, Ezekiel & Jehle (1923). Presumably apothecial development is similar for all brown rot species, although details are only available for *M. fructicola*. A series of diagrams illustrating ascocarp development is shown in Fig. 3.4 (A - F).

Apothecial initials develop in the medulla of the stroma. They are first detectable as small nests of hyphae (centra) that increase in size by the active division and growth of the hyphae to give primordia. An initial becomes visible from the surface of the stroma as a small, raised, black, shiny protuberance (about ½ mm dia). Norton *et al* recorded 675 such protuberances on one

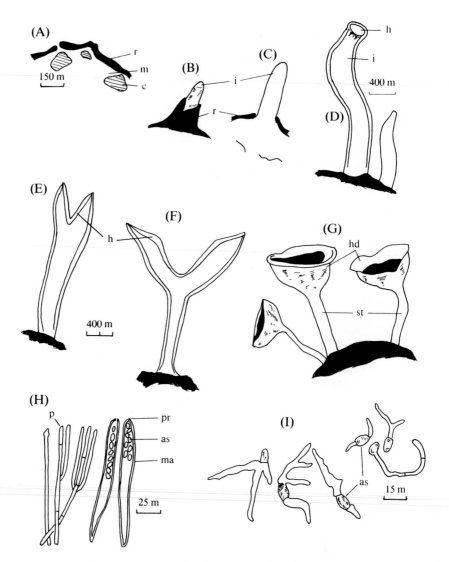

Fig. 3.4. The perfect stage of the brown rot fungi.

(A-F) Development of apothecia of *M. fructicola*. (A) Centra (c) or
nests of hyphae protected by rind (r) of mummy (m). (B) Initial
(i) after rupturing the rind (r). (C) Enlarging initial. (D) Two
young apothecia, with the hymenium (h) beginning to differentiate
in one. (E & F) Longitudinal sections of later stages showing
hymenium (h). (G) Mature apothecia showing head (hd) and stipe
(st). (H) Paraphyses (p) and asci (ma) containing ascospores (as)
with their arrangement monostichous (single row) in one and distichous in the other; spores are discharged through pore (pr).
(I & J) Ascospores of *M. laxa* which germinated on prune agar (I)
and in distilled water (J).   (H, I and J from Wormald, 1921).

peach mummy but rarely more than 25 fully-differentiated apothecia were observed on large mummies under natural conditions; even fewer developed on smaller
fruits such as plums and cherries. Continued growth of the initial leads to
rupture of the stromatal rind and the emergence of the young stipe that is
pointed at its tip. As further elongation of the initial takes place the tip
becomes rounded and a small depression develops on the upper surface provided
there is adequate illumination. The head becomes a campanulate (bell-shaped)
disc which is slightly broader below the top; it becomes cup-shaped and finally
flat (Fig. 3.4 (G)). On the upper surface a hymenium develops that consists
of asci, each containing 8 ascospores, and sterile paraphyses. When the apothecium is mature the hymenium is exposed.

Heuberger (1934) made a detailed cytological study of apothecial formation by
M. fructicola but only once found signs to suggest that hyphal structures,
similar to the ascogonial coils described by Drayton for *S. gladioli*, were
present before a centrum was initiated. On that single occasion, Heuberger
observed several large hyphae in which there were many small nuclei. In the
nest hyphae from which ascocarps developed, Heuberger distinguished two types
of nuclei: small ones (1 μm dia) with clear nucleoplasm and one central
nucleolus − this nuclear type was present in ascogenous hyphae, conidia, ascospores and mycelium; larger nuclei (2 μm dia) with denser nucleoplasm and two
or three nucleoli, found in the paraphyses of the hymenium. The asci develop
from croziers formed by the tip cells of the ascogenous hyphae in the manner
described in many mycological text books. The only nuclear fusion observed is
in the young ascus before ascospore formation. The haploid chromosome number
of 4 is obtained after the first division of the 3 that take place in the
young ascus.

Structure

Most morphological studies on apothecia have been concerned with gross characters and details, including many measurements, of fertile tissues. However,
Korf & Dumont (1968) emphasized the need for more information on the microanatomy of sterile elements.

The mature apothecium varies greatly in size depending upon environmental conditions and amount of available nutrient. Attachment to a mummy may usually
be traced, although on occasions the stroma that bears the apothecium is very
wrinkled, limited in area and thin. Probably such mummies have remained in
the soil for several years and have partly disintegrated due to weathering and
biological degradation.

The stipe. The stipe (stalk) serves to carry the fertile disc (head) above
ground thus enabling better dispersal of ascospores. The length of the stipe
is determined by the position of emergence of the initial from the stroma in
relation to the light source and to the depth at which the mummy is buried in
the soil or by litter. Apothecial stipes of *M. laxa* that measured from 0.4 to
2.8 cm were observed by Wormald (1921), while Cunningham (1922*b*) recorded one
of *M. fructicola* that was over 8 cm long. Stipe diameter (about 0.3 to 1.5
mm) is less variable than stipe length. The stipe is usually light brown and
smooth towards its tip while near the base it is dark brown, sometimes with
numerous, slender, septate, rhizoid-like hyphae about 1 mm in length. The
fully differentiated stipe consists of an ectal excipulum which encases the
medullary excipulum. The former is formed of closely compressed hyphae, which
are about 3 times as long as wide, while the latter is made up mainly of septate, sparingly-branched, elongated hyphae arranged in parallel rows.

The disc. When fully differentiated, the disc or head usually measures up to about 1.0 - 1.5 cm in diameter. At first the hymenium is light-brown to buff in colour but at maturity it is almost white. The disc consists of: an ectal excipulum, which is an outer layer, up to 100 μm thick, of light-brown to hyaline, closely fitting hyphae; a medullary excipulum, which forms the main part of the disc, made up of hyaline, branched, septate filamentous hyphae; a sub-hymenium of several layers of hyphae interwoven to give a pseudoparenchymatous tissue; and a hymenium on the upper surface of the disc. The hymenium consists of asci interspersed with paraphyses that are simple or with one to three branches (Fig. 3.4 (H)). The asci, before they have discharged their ascospores, and paraphyses are approximately the same length. Eight, single-celled, mainly ovoid ascospores are produced in each ascus and when first formed these are arranged in a single row (monostichous) but before discharge they become distichous and grouped near the pore at the apex of the ascus (Fig. 3.4 (H)). The approximate dimensions of asci and ascospores which were given by Wormald (1954) for the three brown rot species are shown in Table 3.2.

TABLE 3.2. MEASUREMENTS OF ASCI AND ASCOSPORES (Wormald, 1954)

	Asci (μm)	Ascospores (μm)
M. fructigena	112-180 x 9-12	9-12.5 x 5-6.8
M. laxa	121-188 x 7.5-11.8	7-19 x 4.5-8.5
M. fructicola	102-215 x 6-13	6-15 x 4-8.2

Ascospores are forcibly discharged through pores at the tip of the ascus. This is a common feature of the inoperculate Discomycetes (Ingold, 1971).

Factors affecting apothecial formation

Some of the factors affecting the development of apothecia are discussed briefly in Chapter 4. Climatic conditions are obviously of great importance and are probably responsible for the vernal development of apothecia. Norton et al. (1923) noted that when peaches bloomed early then apothecia were produced correspondingly early. This suggests that the environmental conditions that bring about the breaking of dormancy of fruit trees also influence apothecial formation. Some obvious factors are temperature, moisture content of the soil and of the mummies, humidity of the atmosphere, type and intensity of light.

Temperature. Apothecia are produced at lower temperatures than those at which best mycelial growth is obtained. Ezekiel (1924) concluded that a period of incubation at cold temperatures is required for the initiation of apothecia by M. fructicola. However, Harrison (1922) obtained the perfect stage of this fungus after a winter when there were only a few frosts, suggesting that an extended period of incubation at low temperatures is not essential for successful apothecial production. Data available from studies of other members of the Sclerotiniaceae indicate that the optimum temperature for apothecial initiation and then development is about 15°C (Elliott, 1965; Purdy, 1967). Apothecia of M. fructicola were obtained on well-developed stromata grown on potato sucrose agar and on apple tissues at 24°C for 3 months; the stromata were kept for a further period of 3 months at 8°C and then within several days of transference to 12°C apothecial initials were observed (Terui & Harada, 1966*d*).   Cultures of *M. mali*, one of the brown rot fungi of Japan, produced the perfect stage after incubation at 0°C for 3 months (Terui & Harada, 1966*c*). With respect to a period of incubation at low temperatures as a prerequisite for apothecial initiation it is probably significant that most members of the Sclerotiniaceae are low-temperature organisms. Their survival depends to a large extent on the resistance of the stroma to severe winter conditions. Presumably during the resting period there is greatly reduced metabolic activity and possibly metabolism along different pathways that, when growth conditions improve, could lead to the initiation of apothecia rather than conidial production or external vegetative growth. It seems likely that any factor that inhibits the two latter processes could, when other conditions are suitable, promote the formation of the perfect stage.

Moisture. Apothecia develop only on fruit mummies on the ground and they have never been reported on mummified fruits still hanging from trees. This is probably associated with the greater desiccation of the fruit in the tree compared with that in soils and the reduced ability of mummies to absorb moisture during periods of rain or from atmospheres with very high relative humidities and retain it long enough for apothecial initiation and differentiation. Probably a high and constant moisture content must be maintained for some time before initiation of apothecia and also throughout the period of development. Cunningham (1922*c*) noted that apothecia were more readily produced from mummies buried in hard and compacted soil than in loose soil. Apothecia are found in areas of orchards where the soil remains damp due to shading by trees or buildings; also litter often covers mummies on which ascocarps develop. All of these are factors related to the maintenance of high moisture levels in the soil, especially in the cool conditions of early spring when evaporation will be at a relatively low level. Also, showery weather often precedes the discovery of the perfect stage in the field. In the laboratory, moist sand (Terui & Harada, 1966*c*,*d*) and a complete cover of damp moss (Baxter, Zehr & Epps, 1974) have been used to maintain high moisture content of mummies on which apothecia of *M. fructicola* were produced.

Light. Controlled studies of the effect of light on ascocarp development by *M. fructicola* are very limited. The available evidence indicates that diffused light is needed for complete differentiation of the apothecium. Work carried out on *S. sclerotiorum* is probably generally relevant to the brown rot species. Laboratory experiments have shown that the apothecial stalks of *S. sclerotiorum* are distinctly photosensitive. In complete darkness the stalk elongates but a disc does not differentiate until a light stimulus is received. This may be either daylight or artificial light. Little is known of the effect of different types of light on apothecial initiation and development. Bedi (1962) concluded that a photoperiod of 12 hr is adequate for normal development of apothecia by *S. sclerotiorum* but a photoperiod of 1 to 2 hr is insufficient. The reason for the dependence of disc differentiation on light is not known. In a review of the photoresponses of fungi, Carlile (1970) suggested that light may indirectly affect the activity of respiratory enzymes. Considerable energy is needed for the differentiation of the disc and the subsequent development of the hymenium. Possibly light may indirectly influence the availability of energy for these processes.

Other physical conditions must also be involved in initiation, development and maturation of apothecia. Low pH of soils, the depth at which mummies are buried in soil and the position in which the mummy falls in the orchard are only a few of the other factors that may affect initiation and differentiation of ascocarps. The infrequency of formation of apothecia by *M. laxa* and *M. fructigena*, the sometimes erratic development of ascocarps by *M. fructicola* and the difficulties of producing the perfect stage in the laboratory suggest that a number of exacting and interacting conditions, both of the environment and of the fungus, must be fulfilled before sporocarps are produced.

Chapter 4

PHYSIOLOGY

The brown rot fungi grow well in culture and abundant sporulation takes place on a variety of media and on inoculated plant materials. Mycelia and conidia are also usually readily produced in the field or in storage. Thus the orga-nisms are convenient for general physiological studies on fungi. An extensive literature has accumulated on the physiology of this group, but the data tend to be very scattered. No attempt is made here at a comprehensive cover of the available literature, but only to give a background of the main aspects of the physiology of this group and to list relevant references, particularly those that have been published since Wormald's monograph in 1954.

NUTRITION

Germination requirements

It has been reported that conidia of the brown rot fungi do not germinate in distilled water (Lin, 1940; Wormald, 1954) but this requires further investi-gation as the methods used to harvest spores could have been responsible for considerable leaching of materials from them causing subsequent growth inhibi-tion in the absence of exogenous nutrients. Also in many experiments germina-tion has probably been stimulated by nutrients carried over from the medium on which the spores have been produced (McCallan & Wilcoxon, 1939). Support for this suggestion was given by Peterson (1941), who found that less than 10% of conidia of *M. fructicola* germinated when transferred to distilled water by means of a camel hair brush. Masri (1967) recommended the use of sterilized absorbent cotton wool swabs for the harvesting of spores of *M. laxa* from the surfaces of sporulating colonies. This is a useful technique for the collec-tion of conidia for nutritional studies on spore germination. Germination is markedly stimulated by the addition of exogenous plant extracts (Hall, 1971*b*), other nutrients, e.g. 0.1% orange juice (McCallan & Wilcoxon, 1939) or mix-tures of aqueous solutions of sucrose with potassium or sodium citrate (Miller, 1944). Conidia of *M. fructicola* contain limited amounts of glycogen and lip-ids (D.C. Fry & H.J. Willetts, unpublished), but presumably the reserves do not provide sufficient energy for the infection process.

Natural media

Whetzel (1945) described how most members of the Sclerotiniaceae depend upon a supply of exogenous nutrients for growth beyond the germ-tube stage. Under natural conditions wound extrusions or exudates from the host surface are a source of energy for initial growth, while nutrients needed for later mycelial development are obtained by the enzymatic breakdown of host tissue.

In the laboratory all species grow well on a variety of liquid and solid natu-ral media that may be either shaken or still. Better growth is obtained on rich organic media than on synthetic media. Potato dextrose agar is often used for culturing the brown rot fungi, but this medium must be acidified to obtain good sporulation by *M. fructigena*, *M. laxa* and *M. laxa* f. *mali*. The mixed vegetable juice referred to as V8 (Campbells Soups Ltd, King's Lynn,

Norfolk, U.K.) is useful as a liquid or agar medium to culture the Old World
species, especially for the production of conidia. On V8 agar cultures, and
under conditions of alternating light and darkness, abundant sporulation is
obtained in regular concentric rings around the inoculum. On malt agar, cultures sometimes tend to stale, but staling is reduced under continuous illumination. Prune juice agar is a highly suitable medium for growth and has been
used in many of the classical studies on the brown rot organisms (Harrison,
1928; Wormald, 1921). Archer (1973a) studied the dry weight and type of mycelial growth of *M. fructigena* on a variety of media and, after 48 hr, optimal
growth was obtained on a glucose-malt agar; *M. fructicola* also grows extremely
well on this medium (J. Tarran, unpublished). Phillips & Harvey (1975) described a medium selective for the brown rot fungi based on peach extract with
added pentachloronitrobenzene, neomycin and streptomycin.

The three species grow well on discs cut from most fruits, but potato discs
acidified with 7.5% malic acid (Wiltshire, 1920) constitute one of the best
substrates for mycelial growth and sporulation.

On suitable static liquid media, the brown rot species form a floating mycelial
mat. In submerged shake cultures mycelial pellets can be formed, and this
technique was used by McCallan & Miller (1957a) for studies on the action of
fungicides on growth of *M. fructicola*.

Synthetic media

Synthetic media have been extensively used in laboratory studies on the brown
rot fungi. In recent years, a medium containing sodium polypectate, ammonium
tartrate and magnesium sulphate has been used in enzyme studies of *M. fructigena* and, to a lesser extent, of *M. laxa*. In both still and shake liquid cultures extracellular pectolytic enzymes are induced and accumulate in the medium (Byrde & Fielding, 1968; Archer, 1973a,b; Willetts *et al.* 1976).

Carbon sources. Many carbohydrates, including glucose, fructose, sucrose
(but not starch) (Willetts, 1968a; Wilson, 1970; Terui & Harada, 1970), pectin
(Hall, 1967a; Byrde & Fielding, 1968), L-arabinose, galactose and mannose
(Archer, 1973a), sorbitol (Lacok, Stanova & Bacigalova, 1975), and galacturonic
and glucuronic acids (Rattigan & Ayres, 1975) are suitable sources of carbon.
An increase in the concentration of carbohydrates in the medium usually gives
better growth of aerial, vegetative hyphae and more abundant sporulation, provided an optimal amount of a suitable nitrogen source is available. Archer
(1973a) found that *M. fructigena* has the ability to utilize organic acids
which, as he pointed out, is to be expected because of the high levels of un-
dissociated free acids present in apple fruits. These organic acids act as
respiratory substrates but are not good sources of carbon for general mycelial
growth.

Nitrogen sources. Limited growth takes place on urea, nitrates and nitrites
but organic nitrogen sources such as peptone and asparagine give better mycelial growth (Cole, 1956; Hall, 1967a; Willetts, 1968a). Hall (1967a) was unable to detect significant differences in growth of *M. fructicola* on selected
sugars with potassium nitrate as the nitrogen source, but obvious growth differences were observed when glucose or arabinose provided the carbon source
with asparagine as the source of nitrogen.

C/N ratio. The C/N ratio must always be taken into consideration when stu-
dying the effects of nutrition on fungal growth. Hall (1933) found that there

was a drift downwards of pH of the medium during growth of the mycelium of *M. fructigena* in culture and that this was greatly influenced by the C/N ratio. Since pH affects the degree of zonation of colonies, the C/N ratio is also a factor involved in zonation.

Accessory substances. Thiamine hydrochloride can stimulate vegetative growth but suppresses sporulation by *M. fructicola*; the addition of biotin and riboflavin to the medium slightly increased mycelial dry weight, while inositol, calcium pantothenate, nicotinic, folic and ascorbic acids and pyridoxine hydrochloride had no apparent effects on growth (Terui & Harada, 1970).

TEMPERATURE

Wormald (1954) referred to the early studies *in vitro* on the temperature relationships of the brown rot fungi. Results have not always agreed as equipment for the maintenance of accurate temperatures has only become available in relatively recent times; also in most experiments only a limited number of temperature intervals can be studied at any one time because of the large number of incubation chambers required. Considerable variability in temperature requirements would be expected between isolates of the same species, particularly those collected from different habitats. Another important consideration is the interaction between temperature and other external and internal factors on the results obtained in temperature and most physiological studies.

There is general agreement that the optimum temperature for mycelial development and sporulation is about 25°C; conidia germinate and mycelia develop at 0°C but the rates are very slow; mycelial growth stops at 30-35°C, and the death point of mycelium is about 50°C (Ezekiel, 1924; Wormald, 1954; Willetts, 1968*a*). Stromata would be expected to have lower thermal death points than vegetative mycelium as they have become adapted to survive at sub-zero temperatures; probably their highest thermal death points are not significantly different from those of mycelia. Spores probably survive extremes of temperatures better than mycelia. Jerome (1958) found that conidia of *M. fructicola* were fully viable after storage at temperatures in the range 2-42°C for 8 weeks at relative humidities of 40-98%. Cold treatment was found to enhance the germination potential of conidia of *M. laxa* (Masri, 1967). The optimum temperature range for the germination of spores of *M. fructicola* has been recorded as 20-25°C (Weaver, 1950) and 21-27°C (McCallan, 1930; Wellman & McCallan, 1942). The latter workers found that at 27°C about 65%, and at 10°C about 20% of spores had germinated within 1 hr; after 50 hr, rates of germination were 98% or more over the range 10-30°C; at 35°C the highest germination rate was 90%. Over a range of about 0-30°C, temperatures above and below the optimum delay but do not inhibit germination.

Stromata of *M. fructicola* developed most abundantly and in the shortest time at 25°C, which is also the optimum for mycelial growth (Willetts, 1968*a*). Data are not available on the optimal temperature for apothecial formation by the brown rot fungi, partly because of the difficulty in obtaining the perfect stage in the laboratory. Comparison with related members of the Sclerotiniaceae suggests that temperatures best suited for initiation and differentiation of apothecia of the brown rot fungi are lower than those for mycelial growth and sporulation. Apothecia of *Sclerotinia sclerotiorum*, which form readily under experimental conditions, have an optimum temperature for development of about 15°C (Purdy, 1967). In orchards, apothecia of *M. fructicola* are produced in the spring when temperatures, in the regions where the fungus is endemic, probably fluctuate around a mean of about 14°C.

H-ION CONCENTRATION

Many workers have studied the effect of pH on growth of various stages of the
brown rot fungi, the classic investigation being the one made by Hall (1933).
Acidic conditions favour the growth of the three *Monilinia* species with optimal growth at pH from 4.0 to 5.0; mycelia grow over a range of initial pH from
1.5 to 9.0. However, there is considerable variability between isolates as
shown by Thind & Keitt (1949) who found marked variation even between mono-
ascosporic isolates from the same ascus. Studies on initial and final pH of
agar cultures upon which active brown rot colonies were developing have shown
that in alkaline media there is a downward drift of pH to about 4.0 - 4.5
(Willetts, 1968*a*; Archer, 1973*a*). When the initial pH value of the culture
medium was below 4.0 there were no significant pH changes during growth of cultures. Hall (1933) found that, in culture, zonation of *M. fructigena* developed
over an initial pH range of 1.8-7.0 with unstaled, uniform growth in the range
2.2-5.5. The mycelium staled and formed irregular zones if the initial pH was
higher than 5.5, and the rate of mycelial growth and sporulation decreased as
the pH of the medium became more acidic than 2.2. The best zonation was on
media with an initial pH of about 4.5 and buffered to maintain this H-ion concentration.

The optimum initial pH for stroma formation by *M. fructicola* was the same as
that which gave the most abundant mycelial growth, i.e. 4.0-4.8 (Willetts,
1968*a*). Microconidia of *M. fructicola* were produced over a pH range of 3.3 -
7.9 in studies carried out by Heuberger (1934), but their production was
sparse on media that were highly acidic. Norton, Ezekiel & Jehle (1923) determined that, under the conditions of their experiments, apothecial development
of *M. fructicola* was inhibited in soils with H-ion concentrations close to neu-
trality; the optimum pH for the formation of ascocarps was 2.5, but this is
much lower than the pH of agricultural soils. The mummies used in their experiments were collected from peach orchards and they were selected because apothecial initials were already protruding from the surfaces of the mummified
peaches; the design of their experiments was such that no indication of the
conditions required for the initiation of apothecia was given.

RELATIVE HUMIDITY AND MOISTURE

The restrictions imposed on fungi by their dependence upon water were emphasized by Raper (1968) in a review of the evolution of fungi. For normal development, vegetative mycelium must have intimate contact with water, and even
slight desiccation stops mycelial growth either permanently or until water is
again available in a liquid or vapour state. Growth *in vitro* of *M. fructicola*
was found to be uninterrupted at relative humidities above 96%; below 93%
growth was retarded (Weaver, 1950). In nature, moisture is available from infected host tissue and the type and condition of the infected tissue greatly
affect the amount of mycelium produced. At very high relative humidities, or
when tissue is water-soaked, infection of woody tissues such as twigs may become
severe, but under less humid conditions the activities of the fungus are
seriously curtailed or stopped (Weaver, 1950; Corbin & Cruickshank, 1963 - also
see Chapter 7). Normally the vegetative mycelium produced on the surface of
the host or above the culture medium is relatively sparse. A dense hyphal mat
develops over the surfaces of infected fruits that have been stored under warm,
humid conditions or on fruits that have become mummified on the tree or on the
ground when the weather was warm and wet (Woronin, 1900; Willetts, 1968*c*).
Apart from high moisture levels, an abundance of soluble nutrients associated
with softening of fruits is needed to support mat-growth. Conidiophores nor-

mally develop under drier conditions than vegetative mycelium and hence are found on the surfaces of fruits or in other aerial positions. An increase in relative humidity often suppresses conidiophore and conidial production and stimulates vegetative growth. The septa that separate conidia of the spore chains do not develop under moist conditions (Willetts & Calonge, 1969a) and relatively low relative humidities are needed for fragmentation of conidial chains (Byrde, 1954a). Conidia do not differentiate in submerged cultures.

The fruit mummies of the brown rot fungi become very dry and remain in this form for long periods. When the moisture content of mummies is restored, either by the uptake of free water or water vapour, conidia develop. A detailed study of the effect of moisture on the sporulation of *M. fructicola* on apricots was made by Corbin & Cruickshank (1963), who found that the water content of tissues greatly influenced the initiation and intensity of sporulation. Conidia were most readily produced on fruitlets and fruits, while on peduncles, laterals and mummified fruits sporulation depended upon the moisture levels of these tissues. Corbin & Cruickshank observed that alternation of high with low relative humidities produced greater intensity of sporulation than that produced when the atmospheric humidity was maintained at a continuously high level. Alternating conditions such as these occur in showery weather in the field, and as a result of repeated drying and remoistening fresh conidia are produced at intervals over a long period of time on the same areas of fruit mummies.

OXYGEN RELATIONSHIPS

Much of the literature on oxygen uptake and carbon dioxide liberation by the brown rot fungi is related to the use of these organisms for fungicide tests. Probably many of the conclusions made from studies on other fungi are directly relevant to the *Monilinia* spp. (see Cochrane & Cochrane, 1966).

Rates of respiration of fungi vary greatly with the age of the culture (Darby & Goddard, 1950); also it would be expected that different respiratory pathways such as the Embden-Meyerhof-Parnas (EMP), hexose monophosphate (HMP) and the Entner-Doudoroff (ED) reaction sequences will operate in different structures and stages of the life cycles. The available data on the brown rot fungi indicate that in spores, mycelia and stromata there are no apparent deficiencies in the enzymes involved in these respiratory pathways (see Chapter 5).

M. fructicola was one of the fungi used by McCallan, Miller & Weed (1954) in studies on both endogenous respiration (i.e. in the absence of an external substrate source) and exogenous respiration (when nutrients are added to the medium to supply energy — in the study under discussion, the source was 1% sucrose). In two of their tests on *M. fructicola* McCallan *et al.* obtained results of:

> endogenous oxygen uptake - 5.1 and 4.5)
> exogenous oxygen uptake -54.2 and 47.2)   µl in 5 hr/mg spores

They found that the mean initial rate of endogenous oxygen uptake of spores over the first hour was 9.9 ± 1.8 µl oxygen/mg fresh spores. There was a slight but steady drop in the rate to a minimum at $2\frac{1}{2}$ hr and then a rise so that the maximum uptake was during the fourth hour; subsequently there was a steady decline and by the sixth hour the rate of oxygen uptake was about the same as that at the end of the first hour. McCallan *et al.* suggested that the maximum oxygen uptake was associated with the initiation of germination. Frampton & Marsh (1941) failed to detect any increased oxygen uptake during growth of germ tubes of *M. fructicola*. The respiration of resting and germinating spores of *M. fructicola* is depressed by copper, zinc and calcium compounds, but the toxicities can be overcome by the use of some salts and sulphydryl-containing compounds (Marsh, 1945; Yoder, 1950; McCallan *et al.*, 1954).

McCallan & Miller (1957*a*) failed to detect significant changes in oxygen consumption of mycelial pellets of *M. fructicola* when 1% sucrose was added to the medium; this is contrary to the results for spores obtained by McCallan *et al.* (1954). Archer (1973*a*) recorded a high endogenous respiratory rate (about 7.0 µl/mg dry wt/hr) for mycelial pellets of *M. fructigena* after growth for 48 hr but he, also, was unable to detect an increase in oxygen uptake after the addition of glucose and sucrose to the medium. However, the addition of sodium fumarate (4×10^{-2}M final concentration) to the medium produced an increase in the rate of oxygen uptake, and Archer recorded a maximum of 13 µl/mg dry wt/hr after 8-10 hr; within 24 hr the oxygen consumption dropped to slightly below the initial amount and remained at this level until measurements were discontinued after 48 hr. After Archer had starved pellets in a minimal medium for 24 hr oxygen consumption was found to be 1.0 µl/mg dry wt/hr; when hexose sugars and also organic acids were subsequently added to the medium as exogenous carbon sources, there was a stimulation of oxygen uptake.

During the formation of compact fungal structures such as stromata, oxygen deficiencies may arise within the tissues (Willetts, 1968*b*,*c*) owing to slow diffusion of air into the medulla and also because of the competition for oxygen between the many interwoven hyphae which make up comparatively large fungal structures. Quantitative data are not available, but mathematical calculations (A.-L. Wong & H.J. Willetts, unpublished) suggest that oxygen is often deficient within sclerotia. Wong & Willetts (1974) found that induction of sclerotial initials of *Sclerotinia sclerotiorum* may be associated with a suppression of glycolysis and/or the Krebs cycle owing to reduced availability of oxygen and a corresponding enhancement of the pentose phosphate pathway. These findings may apply also to the development of stromata by the brown rot fungi (see Chapter 3).

Energy for spore germination and mycelial growth is obtained from aerobic respiration, and under most conditions the oxygen of the atmosphere is at a concentration greater than that required to provide energy for normal mycelial growth. When fruits infected with a brown rot fungus are incubated in a sealed container, oxygen must become rapidly depleted due to respiration, particularly of the fruit but also of the pathogen. Nevertheless, infection will continue to spread even though the oxygen concentrations are considerably lower and the carbon dioxide concentrations higher than those normally encountered. Quantitative data on the spread of *Phytophthora palmivora*, in cocoa pod tissue under low oxygen concentrations down to 2% (v/v) in the surrounding atmosphere, were published by Spence (1961) who showed that a normally weakly virulent isolate of the pathogen attacked more rapidly at 4% O_2 than at 21% O_2 at temperatures of 20-22°C or 29-31°C. These conditions are, however, far from anaerobic. Restricted growth of mycelia and germination of spores under anaerobic conditions has been demonstrated in only a few instances. The ability of stromatal and sclerotial hyphae to obtain a small amount of energy by fermentation could be an advantage during a resting period; unfortunately, respiratory studies of sclerotia are limited. In preliminary experiments (R.J.W.

Byrde, unpublished), pellets of M. *fructigena* in Warburg manometer vessels
were found to be capable of fermentation in that appreciable CO_2 output occurred on a glucose substrate, in the absence of oxygen.

LIGHT

Effect of light on cultural characteristics

One of the most significant studies on the effect of light on the brown rot
fungi was carried out by Hall (1933). She used mainly M. *fructigena*, although
M. *laxa* and M. *fructicola* were also included in her investigation. Hall found
that the linear growth rate of mycelium of M. *fructigena* was greater in inter-
mittent light and darkness than in continuous darkness; if acidic conditions
were maintained, the difference was not noted until after the eleventh day but
in alkaline media the difference was observed after the fourth day. Dickson
(1939) also found that colonies of M. *fructigena* grown on agar media in the
light had a much higher growth rate - measured by increase in colony diameter
- than similar cultures grown in complete darkness. Carlile (1965) observed
that any departure from optimal nutritional conditions caused staling of cultures of M. *fructigena* and that this was more marked in dark-grown cultures
than in illuminated ones. Thus Carlile's results were similar to those obtained by Hall and by Dickson. Carlile suggested that metabolism in the dark
and light is equally effective in supporting growth of the colony, provided
other conditions are optimal; variations from optimal conditions will affect
metabolism differently in the dark compared with under illumination. An
example of this is the greater linear growth rate of M. *fructigena* on malt
agar in the light than in darkness.

M. *fructigena*. Hall (1933) observed how in darkness M. *fructigena* produced
a dense, tough, skin-like plectenchyma of hyphae on the surface of the medium
with some sparse, aerial tuft-like growth bearing conidia; although the rate
of linear growth was slower than under illumination, the total dry weight of
the colonies was greater. Under alternating light and darkness the weight of
mycelium was less than in darkness, the plectenchyma relatively thin and aerial
tuft-like masses of mycelium bearing conidia were abundantly formed in zones.
In continuous light, there was very little plectenchyma development with only
diffuse aerial mycelium and spores.

A characteristic of the growth of many fungi, including the brown rot species,
is the development of zonation in culture or on host tissues (see Fig. 1.1, p.
7). The rhythmic growth which gives rise to zonation is influenced by environmental variables such as light and temperature, but is now thought to be controlled by a 'biological clock' (Sweeney, 1963). The most thoroughly studied
endogenous rhythms are those that have a natural period of approximately 24 hr
and these are referred to as circadian rhythms. There are many reports of exogenous rhythms in fungi, and Carlile (1965) in a review on the photobiology of
fungi, suggested that these should be re-examined to determine if endogenous
components are involved.

Zonation is produced by the formation of bands of abundant, fertile, aerial
hyphae (ridges) alternating with bands of sparse, sterile, surface hyphae
(hollows) across the diameter of the colony. Usually the growth of colonies
is unzoned for the first few days, even under conditions that are optimal for
the development of concentric ridges. Hall (1933) used M. *fructigena* cultures
to determine the relationship between the period of illumination and the posi-

tion of bands of spores. She found that there was a long period between the
beginning of the light period and onset of sporulation; growth of ridges was
mainly during the dark period, while hollows developed in the light. When
cultures were illuminated for a long period ridges were formed before the
period of illumination had ended, with shorter exposures, ridges developed
during the following period of darkness. Cultures incubated for a period
under conditions of alternating light and darkness and then in continuous
darkness developed zones of intense conidial production related to the last
period of illumination and one or more less clearly defined ridges formed
subsequently.

M. laxa. The response of *M. laxa* to light is similar to that of *M. fructigena.* Under conditions of alternating light and darkness, ridging is produced
by *M. laxa* but aerial mycelium is less floccose than in cultures of *M. fructigena* and there are no obvious differences between the densities of vegetative
mycelium in the light and darkness zones. In continuous darkness, a dense
plectenchyma develops, with occasional tuft-like hyphal masses; marginal lobing and staling take place during growth of the colony. The relationship between time of illumination and the development of ridges and hollows is similar
to that described for *M. fructigena.*

M. fructicola. When grown in continuous darkness and uniform temperature,
cultures of *M. fructicola* sporulate profusely to produce a continuous carpet
of spores. Under conditions of alternating light and darkness, concentric ridges and hollows are formed; ridges coincide with growth during the dark periods
and hollows with growth in the light. There is no overlapping of ridges into
the periods of light nor *vice versa* as in *M. fructigena.* Thus unlike *M. fructigena,* which requires light for the production of conidia, *M. fructicola* needs
darkness for sporulation. Van den Ende & Cornelis (1970) suggested that light
stimulates the development of conidiophores by *M. fructicola* but inhibits conidial formation. They referred to the production of a photoproduct ('P310')
which accumulated at higher levels in mycelium grown in light of short wavelength
and of high intensity. Circadian rhythm can be induced in cultures of *M.
fructicola* by the introduction of amino acids into the medium (Jerebzoff, 1965).

Wavelength and zonation

The brown rot fungi have been used on several occasions for the study of the
spectral regions that are active in the induction of circadian rhythm in fungi.
Jerebzoff (1961) suggested that only visible radiations with wavelengths shorter than 500 nm were active in the production of zonation in cultures of *M.
fructicola.* Blue light (440-490 nm) was found by Janitor (1970) to be the
most effective for sporulation and vegetative growth by *M. fructigena,* and
there was a decreasing stimulatory effect in the red, orange, yellow and green
regions. Jerebzoff & Jacques (1972), in a detailed study on the effects of
light of different wavelengths on cultures of *M. fructicola,* found that 5-day-
old cultures of this fungus that had been incubated in darkness absorbed
light from the shorter wavelengths, with the strongest peak at 400 nm, a sharp
one at 365 nm and the smallest peak (which was, however, clearly defined) at
455 nm. The most effective wavelengths for the stimulation of growth of fertile conidiophores were in the near ultraviolet at 390 and 370 nm and the blue
spectral region at about 420 and 470 nm; with increasing irradiance levels,
longer wavelengths extending from the green to the red became effective. The
equal quantal spectra for growth of conidiophores and for rhythm induction by
M.fructicola were qualitatively similar but higher irradiance levels were needed
for the latter. Jerebzoff & Jacques concluded that the same photoreceptor system is active in the induction of conidiophores and zonation.

Photoreceptors

Porphyrins, carotenoids and flavins have been suggested as photoreceptors in plants and fungi and were discussed by Carlile (1965). He favoured a flavin as the most widespread photoreceptor in fungi and referred to the results of experiments he had carried out on *M. fructigena* when dark-grown cultures were found to be less sensitive to the effects of an inhibitor of flavin biosynthesis than light-grown ones. Carlile suggested that light stimulates a flavoprotein electron-transfer pathway and depresses activity in an alternative pathway; to support this hypothesis, he quoted his findings that dark-grown cultures of *M. fructigena*, but not light-grown ones, gave a strong Nadi reaction which is indicative of the presence of cytochrome oxidase and hence could point to the nature of the alternate electron-transfer pathway. Jerebzoff & Jacques (1972) concluded that their results with *M. fructicola* could be explained if carotenoids and/or flavins act as photoreceptors. The activity of light of wavelengths up to 630 nm could support the participation of porphyrin as the photoreceptor but excluded a cytochrome effect. However, different photoreceptors may be involved in photoresponses by *M. fructicola* and *M. fructigena* since they do not react to light in the same way.

Brauner (1954) suggested that the riboflavin-catalysed photo-oxidation of indole-3-acetic acid might be the basis of photoresponses of fungi but there is little evidence of hormonal systems in fungi except in the co-ordination of sexual processes. Khan (1966), however, found that light and indole-3-acetic acid have the same effect on sporulation by *M. fructigena* and the one can be used to replace the other.

It is clear from the literature that the brown rot fungi provide good models for studies on the photoresponses of fungi, especially as two different reactions are found in the group. Detailed studies on the role of light are required and could contribute to our understanding of circadian rhythm in fungi and also in higher plants.

Chapter **5**

BIOCHEMISTRY

Comparatively few studies have been concerned with the biochemistry of
Monilinia spp.; however, there is little reason to expect this genus to differ
markedly from other Ascomycetes (e.g. *Neurospora*) which have received more comprehensive study. General reviews of biochemistry and physiology of fungi have
been published by Foster (1949), Hawker (1950), Cochrane (1958), Ainsworth &
Sussman (1965), Burnett (1968) and Turner (1971). An exception to the sparse-
ness of information on *Monilinia* spp. is the study of the pectolytic enzymes,
considered at length at the end of this Chapter.

CELLULAR CONSTITUENTS

The limited quantitative information on cell composition is summarised in
Table 5.1: unfortunately much of the data are preliminary and uncorroborated.
It is clear that there are large differences between the water content of
mycelium, either in the form of pellets or filaments, and that of conidia.

Jones, Farmer, Bacon & Wilson (1972) analysed the cell walls of *M. fructigena*
and reported that these contained 41.6% carbon and 1.7% nitrogen. By g.l.c.
analysis of alditol acetates, the sugar content was estimated as: glucose,
43%; mannose, 11%; fucose, 2%; rhamnose, 2%; total, 58%.

INTERMEDIARY (GENERAL) METABOLISM

Limited information is available on intermediary metabolism. Dowler, Shaw &
Gottlieb (1963), who included *M. fructicola* amongst the ten fungi that they
used for terminal oxidation studies, demonstrated the presence of an electron
transport system in cell-free extracts of mycelium; NADH cytochrome c reductase (optimum pH 7-8) and NADH oxidase (optimum pH 7.0) were involved. The
following dehydrogenases were found: glucose-6-phosphate dehydrogenase, triose
phosphate dehydrogenase, and, in the tricarboxylic acid cycle, isocitric,
malic and a trace of succinic dehydrogenases. Pyruvic and α-ketoglutaric dehydrogenase activities were not detected. NADP$^+$-specific glutamic dehydrogenase was present. On glucose-yeast extract medium, maximal NADH oxidase and
NADH cytochrome c reductase reached maximal activity per flask after 24 hr,
and per mg dry wt after 36 hr. The NADH oxidase activity of a purer preparation was markedly stimulated by the addition of exogenous cytochrome c. In
this respect *M. fructicola* differed from most of the other fungi examined.

Subsequently, Huber & Gottlieb (1969) demonstrated the presence of all enzymes
of the Embden-Meyerhof-Parnas glycolytic pathway in cell-free extracts of *M.
fructicola*; the hexokinase was fluoride-dependent. The presence of 6-phospho-
gluconate dehydrogenase in addition to glucose-6-phosphate dehydrogenase suggested an operative pentose phosphate pathway (hexose monophosphate shunt).
These results, coupled with those of Dowler *et al.* (1963), outline a complete
system for energy production from glucose by *M. fructicola*.

In a preliminary study of the effects of fungicides on fungus enzymes in buf-
fer extracts of mycelium of *M. laxa*, Byrde, Martin & Nicholas (1956) demonstrated the presence of the enzymes catalase; cytochrome c oxidase and reduc-

TABLE 5.1. ANALYSIS OF CELLS OF *MONILINIA* spp.

Constituent	Species	Growth form	Percentage of dry wt (w/w)	Method of analysis	Reference
Water*	Fc	Conidia	25.0	Drying at 95°C	Yarwood (1950)
		Pellets	92.0	Not stated	McCallan & Miller (1957*a*)
	Fg	Pellets (in suspension)	98.6 – 99.2 (w/v)	Drying at 80°C	Archer (1973*b*)
		Mycelium (4-days-old)	92.7	Drying at 80°C	
Phosphorus					
– total			0.52	Fiske & Subba Row (1925)	
– lipid+			0.09	"	
– nucleic acid+			0.29	"	
– inorganic+			0.15	"	Preliminary data of Byrde (1958)
Nitrogen					
– total			2.56	Micro-kjeldahl digestion and Markham distillation	
DNA			0.27	Diphenylamine (Burton, 1956)	
RNA			2.05	E_{260} of perchloric acid digest	
Total nucleic acid			2.78	"	
			3.22	Based on 9% P	
ADP	Fc	Conidia	0.69	E_{260} of specific eluate	Owens *et al.* (1958)
ATP			0.54	"	
Lipid	Fg	Mycelium	6.42	Dry wt of chloroform extract	Byrde (1958)

Fc = *M. fructicola*;   Fg = *M. fructigena*

* On fresh wt basis   + As P

tase; succinic, isocitric and glutamic dehydrogenases; hexokinase, aldolase, fumarase and alkaline phosphatase. The effects of sulphur on cytochrome c reduction by cell-free preparations from *M. fructicola* were studied by Tweedy & Turner (1966). The localization of acid phosphatase in organelles of *M. fructigena* was studied by Hislop, Barnaby, Shellis & Laborda (1974) (see below).

Cooley (1914) reported oxalic acid production in old cultures of *S. cinerea* (= *M. laxa*) on peach or plum juice.

Metabolism of phenolic and related compounds

Over 50 years ago, Wormald (1920) used oxidase reactions, with tannic, gallic and pyrogallic acids as substrates, as a useful taxonomic guide (see also Ezekiel, 1924). Polyphenol oxidase, of the tyrosinase (catecholase) form, was shown to be secreted by *M. fructicola* (Rich & Horsfall, 1954): the presence of a similar enzyme, and of peroxidase, in mycelial extracts of *M. laxa* has also been demonstrated (Byrde *et al.*, 1956).

M. fructigena can metabolise various organic acids, some of which occur naturally in apple fruit. Thus Fawcett & Spencer (1967) demonstrated the presence of phenolic acids, probably including 4-hydroxybenzoic and 4-hydroxy-3-methoxybenzoic acids, in a mixture of syrup from healthy apples and Hall's medium on which the fungus had grown for 10 days at 23°C. Subsequently they showed that chlorogenic, quinic, *p*-coumarylquinic and shikimic acids were rapidly converted (8 hr) to 4-hydroxybenzoic acid in culture (Fawcett & Spencer, 1968). The last-named acid was not detected when caffeic acid (or glucose) was used, indicating that it is the quinic acid moiety in chlorogenic acid that undergoes metabolism. 4-Hydroxybenzoic acid was itself slowly degraded. Fawcett and Spencer deduced that significant dehydratase pathways existed (see Fig. 5.1); by contrast, β-oxidation of *p*-coumaric acid to 4-hydroxybenzoic acid was slow (8 hr). Changes in phenol concentrations have also been demonstrated *in vivo* (Chapter 7).

Byrde & Woodcock (1958) had earlier demonstrated the slow β-oxidation by *M. laxa* of a series of ω-(2-naphthyloxy)-n-alkyl carboxylic acids, but found that hydroxylation of the aromatic nucleus occurred only slowly.

An acetylesterase capable of hydrolysing phenolic esters was detected in mycelial extracts of *M. laxa*, and was also shown to be secreted in agar medium. The lower esters (e.g. acetyl) were hydrolysed most rapidly, but the enzyme had little effect on alkyl acetates (Byrde & Fielding, 1955).

PROTEIN AND AMINO ACID METABOLISM

There is little information on general metabolic pathways. Hall (1971a) reported secretion of a protease by *M. fructicola* when this fungus was grown on media with gelatin or casein hydrolysate as nitrogen sources. By contrast, when grown on gelatin agar, *M. fructigena* was unable to hydrolyse gelatin (Swinburne, 1975), nor was gelatinase detected in filtrates from cultures in pectate-ammonium tartrate liquid medium (Byrde & Fielding, 1968). One would not expect this medium to induce synthesis.

In preliminary experiments (Byrde, 1958), mycelial pellets of *M. fructigena* neither decarboxylated arginine, aspartic acid, glutamic acid, histidine, lysine or tyrosine, nor did they deaminate α-alanine, arginine, aspartic acid, cystine, glutamic acid, lysine or serine. However, utilization of asparagine as a nitrogen source implies the presence of an active asparaginase.

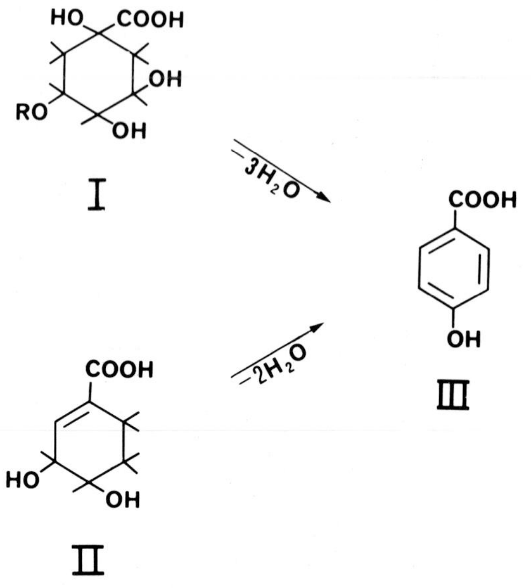

Fig. 5.1. Conversion of quinic acid (I ; R = H), chlorogenic acid
           (I ; R = caffeoyl) or shikimic acid (II) to 4-hydroxybenzoic
           acid (III) by dehydratase activity.

M. fructicola was shown to produce a sulphur-containing polypeptide, monilicolin A, that has about 64 amino acid residues and an approx mol. wt. of 8000
daltons (Cruickshank & Perrin, 1968). Its biological activity is discussed in
Chapter 7.

STEROLS AND THEIR METABOLISM

Some information on sterol biosynthesis has become available in the course of
fungicide studies by Kato, Tanaka, Ueda & Kawase (1974, 1975), who showed ergo-
sterol to be a major sterol in *M. fructigena*; lanosterol, obtusifoliol and 24-
methylene-dihydrolanosterol were also detected.

POLYSACCHARIDES AND THEIR METABOLISM

The presence of an extracellular polysaccharide slime, and its possible role in
survival, are mentioned in Chapter 6. The composition of this polysaccharide
has been studied in two species, with differing results. Thus Feather & Malek
(1972) isolated a highly-branched glucose polymer from *M. fructicola* which had
mainly 1,3- and smaller amounts of 1,4- linkages. No other sugars were detected. By contrast, Archer, Clamp & Migliore (1976) found that the slime of *M.
fructigena* was essentially a glucan, but contained traces of galactose and mannose. This polysaccharide was polydisperse and highly viscous, the viscous
fraction being that of highest mol. wt. Periodate oxidation studies again indicated a branched structure, but with a preponderance of 1,4- linkages. Utilisation of such polysaccharides may well be a factor in the high level of endogenous respiration (Chapter 4).

Secretion of polysaccharide-degrading enzymes has been much studied. In view of the fact that biosynthesis of such enzymes is often induced by the appropriate substrate, or related compounds, and repressed by high levels of readily utilisable sugars (e.g. glucose), it is important to take account of the composition of the culture medium when assessing reports of secretion or its absence.

Three reports have concerned polysaccharides not associated with plant cell walls: thus Lacok, Stanova & Niznanska (1972) gave circumstantial evidence for invertase activity in *M. fructigena,* in that it hydrolysed sucrose early in its growth in culture. Lacok, Stanova & Bacigalova (1975) reported chromatographic evidence for the conversion of dulcitol to fructose by *M. fructigena* and to galactose by *M. laxa.*

The presence of a β-acetylglucosaminidase (EC 3.2.1.30) in mycelial extracts and culture filtrates of *M. fructigena* grown in a glucose-based medium was demonstrated by Reyes & Byrde (1973): the enzyme was apparently present in a single molecular form, had an isoelectric point of 3.76, a molecular weight of 141,000 daltons, and a pH optimum for hydrolysis of the p-nitrophenyl glycoside of 5.4. Although it accumulated in autolysing cultures, there seemed to be no direct involvement in fungal wall lysis, as the enzyme was virtually unable to degrade chitin. By contrast, it readily attacked chitobiose, and may have a 'scavenging'role in autolysis. The presence of a β-1,3-glucanase was also demonstrated in old cultures.

Enzymes degrading plant cell walls

Because of their probable role in the pathogenicity of the brown rot fungi, extracellular enzymes degrading plant cell walls have been much studied, and recent progress in biochemical methods has enabled a detailed analysis to be carried out of the various molecular forms in which they frequently exist. For general reviews of wall-degrading enzymes, see Bateman & Millar (1966) and Wood (1967).

Recent advances in knowledge of the biochemistry of higher plant cell walls culminated in the model put forward by Albersheim and his co-workers (Talmadge, Keegstra, Bauer & Albersheim, 1973; Bauer, Talmadge, Keegstra & Albersheim, 1973; Keegstra, Talmadge, Bauer & Albersheim, 1973) for walls of cultured sycamore cells and subsequently shown to be probably relevant to a wide range of dicotyledonous plants. The main components of the complex structure are cellulose elementary fibrils composed of β-1,4-D-glucopyranose units, and rhamnogalacturonan chains which form the backbone of the pectic substances, with which polymers of neutral sugars (α-L-arabinofuranose and β-D-galactopyranose polymers) are associated. The link between the pectic and cellulosic components is thought to be *via* a xyloglucan held to the cellulose by hydrogen bonding, and covalently to the rhamnogalacturonan through arabinan and 4-linked galactan. Also present in the model is a structural protein, rich in hydroxyproline units, bearing tetra-arabinoside groups. The linkage to this protein from the rhamnogalacturonan appears to be *via* a 3,6-linked arabinogalactan to serine.

  Cellulase. Dealing with these polymers in sequence, cellulose degradation by *Monilinia* spp. has been recorded, but seems to be very restricted. Thus Ozawa (1952) reported secretion of cellulase by *S. cinerea (= M. laxa).* Calonge, Fielding, Byrde & Akinrefon (1969) detected a trace of activity (against carboxymethyl cellulose) in extracts of ripe pear fruits rotted by

M. fructigena but, as shown by Cole & Wood (1961*b*) not in infected apple fruitlet extracts. Hall (1971*a*), by means of a cup-plate assay with sodium carboxymethyl-cellulose, detected very weak cellulase activity when *M. fructicola* was
grown for five or more days on a medium with carboxymethyl-cellulose as carbon
source, but he stressed that only a sparse mycelium developed.

Xylanase secretion by *S. cinerea* was reported by Ozawa (1952); Byrde &
Fielding (1968) detected no β-xylosidase in culture filtrates of *M. fructigena*,
but the pectate medium used would not be expected to induce this enzyme.

Pectolytic enzymes

The main backbone of the amorphous pectic matrix comprises chains of D-galacto-
pyranosiduronic acid, linked α-(1,4)-, and with single 1,2- rhamnopyranose
units at intervals which alter the orientation of the chain. The acidic groups
may be esterified with methoxyl groups.

Although the linkages involving rhamnose seem to be stable, the polygalacturonic acid chain is attacked by two enzymes which are secreted by all three
Monilinia spp.

With the terminology of Demain & Phaff (1957), as amplified by Bateman & Millar
(1966), and the Enzyme Commission (EC) code numbers, these are (Fig. 5.2):

Polygalacturonase (EC 3.2.1.15) (PG), which hydrolytically attacks polygalacturonic acid.

Pectin lyase (= pectin methyl-*trans*-eliminase) (EC 4.2.2.10) (PL), which attacks a polygalacturonic acid of a high degree of esterification by a 'lytic'
or '*trans*-eliminative' mechanism which does not involve the addition of water,
but leaves an unsaturated bond between C-4 and C-5 on one of the two terminal
residues.

With either enzyme, when the chain is cleaved at random, the prefix *endo-* is
used; *exo-* denotes an enzyme that specifically attacks the terminal linkage,
liberating the monomer.

A third enzyme is involved in de-esterification of units in the chain:

Pectin esterase (= pectin methylesterase) (EC 3.1.1.11) (PE), which liberates
the methoxyl groups from the carboxyl groups of the galacturonic acid. All
three species can secrete this enzyme.

Work with *Monilinia* spp. prior to 1950 dating from that of Bruschi (1912) and
summarized by Wormald (1954) was greatly handicapped by the very incomplete
knowledge of the chemistry of the pectic substances, and the terms 'pectase'
(= PE), 'pectinase' (= PG or perhaps PL) and 'protopectinase' were used. The
latter implied the ability of a preparation to degrade 'native' pectin, although the precise chemical nature of the substrate has never been defined.
Sometimes the ability to macerate plant tissue has been equated with 'protopectinase', but Wood (1967, p. 140) pointed out that maceration, although probably including the action of protopectinase, could involve many other enzymes.
The effects of pectolytic enzymes on plant tissue are discussed in Chapter 7,
together with their role in the changes produced during infection of fruit by
Monilinia spp.

TABLE 5.2. MULTIPLE FORMS OF PECTOLYTIC AND RELATED ENZYMES SECRETED BY *MONILINIA* SPP.
(after Willetts *et al.*, 1976).

Species/sub-species	PG	Isoelectric points		PE	AF
		PL			
M. *fructicola*	9.7	8.3		5.0	3.0, 5.1, 7.1
M. *fructigena*	(2.8), 4.4, (5.5), 9.7	8.2		4.8	3.0 7.0
M. *laxa*	(3.0),(4.6) 10.1	8.5, 9.1		4.8	6.7, 7.2
M. *laxa* f. *mali*	5.1 9.7	9.1		4.7	7.2

Underlining indicates the activity of the form.

Brackets indicate trace quantities.

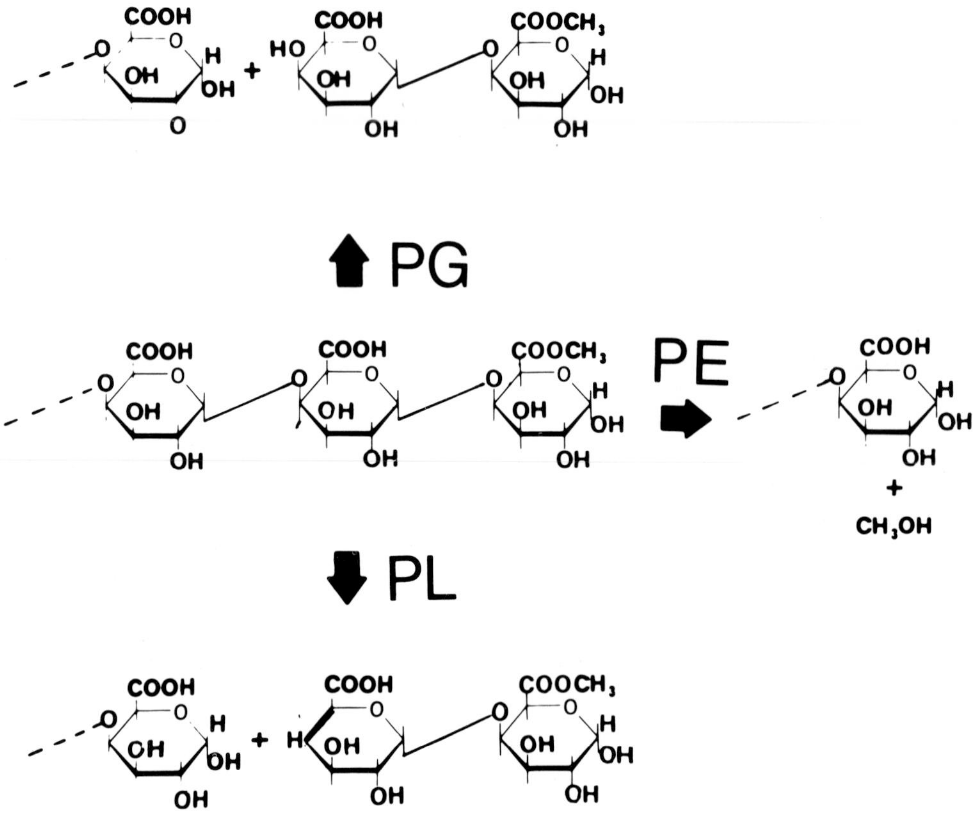

Fig. 5.2. Action of polygalacturonase (PG), pectin lyase (PL) and pectin
esterase (PE). The PG and PL are of endo-type. (Based on
Archer, 1973*b*)

In addition, understanding of the complexity of the enzymes involved has been
increased by the introduction of the techniques of gel filtration, separating
molecules on the basis of molecular size, and of isoelectric focusing, separating proteins on the basis of their isoelectric points (pI values) (see Fig.
5.3). These, together with electrophoresis, have demonstrated the existence
of multiple forms of some of the enzymes, which may well account for the apparent anomalies in the behaviour of crude culture filtrates containing a mixture of enzymic forms.

The overall pattern of secretion of pectolytic enzymes by *Monilinia* spp. in a
liquid medium based on sodium polypectate was described by Willetts, Byrde,
Fielding & Wong (1976) and is summarised in Table 5.2. Apart from the relevance to pathogenicity (Chapter 7), the patterns indicate possible inter-
relationships between the species and sub-species. Common to all four types
examined were a PG of pI 9.7 and a PE of pI 4.9.

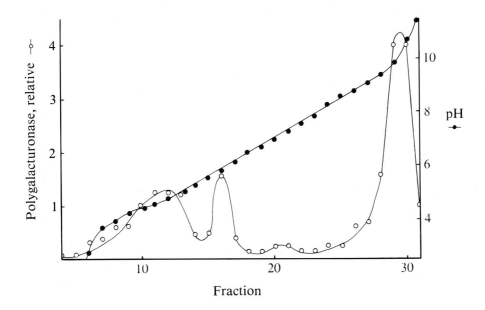

Fig. 5.3.   Isoelectric focusing pattern of endopolygalacturonase in a
            dialysed culture filtrate of *M. fructigena*. The pH gradient
            (3.5 - 10.0) is established by added carrier ampholytes, and
            the proteins in the filtrate migrate to their isoelectric
            points. The component of pI approx 3.0 (Table 5.3) is not
            resolved in this system. (Data of A.H. Fielding).

The individual enzymes will now be considered in more detail, taking the species in turn and describing predominantly work since 1954.

M. *fructigena* secretes PG, which exists in at least four molecular forms
(see Table 5.3 and Fig. 5.3). Earlier work with a crude culture filtrate had
shown the activity towards sodium polypectate to have a fairly broad pH optimum at about pH 5.5 - 6.0 (Cole, 1956; Fielding & Byrde, 1969). Cole found
lower pH values for hydrolysis of pectin and a laboratory-prepared sodium
pectate. Comparison of the rate of decrease in viscosity of a sodium pectate
solution with the release of reducing groups at first indicated that the poly-
galacturonate chain was attacked randomly, i.e. endo-PG activity was involved
(Fielding & Byrde, 1969). However, Archer (1973*b*) found that, at 50% decrease
in substrate viscosity, the proportion of linkages hydrolysed (as calculated
from reducing group liberation) was not identical in the four principal molecular forms examined. This suggests that hydrolysis is not in fact always
truly random, although none of the forms appears to be of the S-polygalacturon-

ase type described by McClendon (1975). In addition, hydrolysis of sodium
polypectate was faster than that of esterified pectin, indicating that the enzyme was a true PG (Cole, 1956; Fielding & Byrde, 1969). Activity was stable
during exposure over a wide pH range; an unusual bimodal thermal stability
pattern was found for the crude culture filtrate, but a purified preparation -
presumably one specific form - showed rapid inactivation at 80°C. Further
work (Archer & Fielding, 1975) has shown that the unusual thermal stability
was probably associated with the peak of pI 4.6, which even withstood auto-
claving with comparatively slow loss of activity.

At least one of the PG components is inducible (Archer, 1973b). Enzyme activity can be induced by pectin (Cole, 1956), D-galacturonic acid (Byrde, 1966),
and related compounds (Archer, 1973b). Such induction can be repressed by the
presence of readily-utilizable carbon sources such as glucose at 10^{-2}M, an
example of the widely-recognised phenomenon of 'catabolite repression' (Archer,
1973b). By contrast, the PG of pI 9.7 is constitutive (Archer, 1973b). Taken
together, these results confirm Cole's (1956) view that PG was 'at least partially adaptive'.

PL is secreted by $M.$ $fructigena$, and its properties were described by Byrde &
Fielding (1968). Although there was some evidence for the existence of two
distinct forms during purification by ion-exchange chromatography on CM-
Sephadex columns, isoelectric focusing has subsequently detected (in several
strains) only one peak, of pI approx 8.0 (Archer, 1973b; Willetts et $al.$, 1976).
Possibly two forms do exist, of identical pI values, but with different affinities for CM-Sephadex.

The PL components studied by Byrde & Fielding (1968) showed optimal activity at
pH 7 and 8 respectively; they were stable over a wide range of pH, but were
relatively thermolabile. Archer (1973b) showed that the PL was an endo-PL and
was inducible (see also Table 5.3).

$M.$ $fructigena$ also secretes PE (Cole, 1956; Cole & Wood, 1961b). Isoelectric
focusing over the pH range 3.5 - 10 indicates that the enzyme exists in a single form of pI about 4.9 (Byrde, Fielding, Archer & Davies, 1973), but examination by narrow-range isoelectric focusing detected the existence of multiple
forms within the main peak (Archer, 1973b). Its pH optimum is about 5.0
(Byrde et $al.$, 1973). PE is constitutive and is conveniently obtained by
using a sucrose carbon source (see also Table 5.3).

$M.$ $laxa$ (and $M.$ $laxa$ f. $mali$) by contrast, have been comparatively little
studied. Cole (1956) demonstrated secretion of PE and a little PG, and this
was confirmed by Slezarik & Rexova (1967). The secretion of PL was demonstrated by Willetts et $al.$ (1976), who examined the multiple forms of the pectolytic enzymes (Table 5.2). The pattern shown by $M.$ $laxa$ f. $mali$ was simpler than
that of the main species.

$M.$ $fructicola$. Earlier work on $M.$ $fructicola$ was summarised by Wormald
(1954). Reinganum (1964) demonstrated the secretion of PE and PG in culture
and showed that, while both were produced constitutively, the addition of a
pectic material to the medium enhanced secretion. Hall (1971a) confirmed the
secretion of PE and PG, the latter having maximal activity at pH 6.5 and see-
ming to diffuse from the hyphal tips. Some evidence for the existence of a
polymethylgalacturonase (PMG), as distinct from PG, was presented (see also
Paynter & Jen, 1975). Enzymes of the PMG type hydrolyse high-methoxyl pectin
in preference to low-methoxyl pectin, without prior de-esterification by PE.

TABLE 5.3. PROPERTIES OF MULTIPLE FORMS OF WALL-DEGRADING ENZYMES OF *M. FRUCTIGENA*. Based on Archer (1973*b*), Byrde *et al.* (1973), Laborda *et al.* (1973) and unpublished data.

Enzyme	pI value	Apparent mol. wt. (daltons)	Relative activity	Optimal pH	Remarks
AF	3.0	220,000	+	3.0 – 4.0	Tolerant of low pH
	4.5	350,000	++	5.7 – 6.0	Intracellular only
	6.5	40,000	++	5.0	Less tolerant of low pH
PE	4.5 – 4.9	40,000	++	5.0	4 to 15 units hexose/molecule
PG	3.0	37,000 – 58,000	+	–	Ill-defined
	4.6	75,000	++	4.8 – 6.2	See text; a glycoprotein
	5.5	38,000	+	5.3	Stable over wide pH range
	7.7	–	+	–	Intracellular only
	9.7	37,000	+++	5.3	Constitutive. Less than 4 units hexose/molecule
PL	8.2	25,700	++	8.0	Secreted only at neutral or alkaline pH. Less than 2 units hexose/molecule

– = not estimated

Paynter & Jen (1975) confirmed the secretion of PE and endo-PG, and demonstrated for the first time the secretion by *M. fructicola* of an endo-PL and of an exo-PG. The PG activity in a 2-day-old culture showed heat stability (cf. Archer & Fielding, 1975, working with *M. fructigena*).

Enzymes degrading neutral sugars

As already mentioned, neutral sugars (arabinans and galactans) are closely associated with the rhamnogalacturonan of the host cell wall, and arabinose oligomers with the structural protein. Apple fruit pectin is particularly rich in arabinogalactan (Barrett & Northcote, 1964).

Enzymes attacking arabinans have been demonstrated in a range of plant pathogenic fungi, including *M. fructigena* (Byrde & Fielding, 1965; Fuchs, Jobson & Wouts, 1965). The α-L-arabinofuranosidase (EC 3.2.1.55) (AF) of this species was found to hydrolyse the terminal bond, liberating monomeric arabinose from arabans, and the pH optimum was about 4.0 (Fielding & Byrde, 1969).

Subsequent work has demonstrated the existence of three forms (Table 5.3), two of which are found both intra- and extracellularly, and one of which, of high mol. wt., is only intracellular. The kinetic parameters of the three forms are distinct (Laborda, Fielding & Byrde, 1973; Laborda, Archer, Fielding & Byrde, 1974). More critical examination showed the presence of multiple components within the major activity peaks. The localization of the enzyme in hyphae of *M. fructigena* was examined by Hislop, Barnaby, Shellis & Laborda (1974), who showed that, like acid phosphatase, it was present in whorl-like structures in organelles which appeared to migrate to the plasmalemma, presumably enabling the enzyme to be secreted by a process of reverse pinocytosis (Fig. 5.4). Earlier work by Calonge, Fielding & Byrde (1969), with a less specific stain, had indicated that multi-vesicular bodies were involved in the secretion of AF, and also perhaps other extracellular enzymes. An antiserum to one of the forms (pI 3.0) has been obtained from sheep (Hislop, Shellis, Fielding, Bourne & Chidlow, 1974); this antiserum did not cross-react with the other forms of the enzyme. This seems to be the first report of an antiserum to a wall-degrading fungal enzyme.

The existence of multiple forms of AF in *M. fructicola, M. laxa* and *M. laxa* f. *mali* has also been demonstrated. The patterns are characteristic of the species, and may be useful for identification purposes. Thus, *M. fructicola* has a predominant form with pI 5.2, while *M. laxa* shows a characteristic double peak in the region 6.5 - 7.5 (Willetts *et al.*, 1976) (Table 5.2). The enzymes in these species have not been further characterized.

β-*galactosidase* has been detected in culture filtrates of *M. fructigena* (Byrde & Fielding, 1965), but has not been studied in detail. *S. cinerea* (= *M. laxa*) was shown to secrete a galactanase (Ozawa, 1952). In view of the galactan content of plant cell walls, further study of this group of enzymes in *Monilinia* spp. is needed.

Inhibition of the wall-degrading enzymes

The importance of the wall-degrading enzymes of *Monilinia* spp. in pathogenicity (Chapter 7), has led to the study of their inhibition by various chemical compounds, and Table 5.4 lists examples of compounds inhibiting activity by 50% or more. In general, the enzymes are remarkably resistant to conventional enzyme poisons and even to proteolytic enzymes (Fielding & Byrde, 1969).

TABLE 5.4. INHIBITION OF DEFINED PECTOLYTIC ENZYMES OF *M. FRUCTIGENA*.

Enzyme	Inhibitor	Concentration	Inhibition (%)	Reference
AF (pI 3.0)	L-Arabono-γ-lactone	10^{-2}M	93	Laborda *et al.* (1974)
AF (pI 4.5)	"	"	60	"
AF (pI 6.5)	"	"	97	"
"	Oxidized apple juice	17%	55	"
PG	Leucoanthocyanins	–	approx 75–90	Cole (1958); Cole & Wood (1961*b*)
	Catechol, *d*-catechin and *l*-epicatechin in oxidized state; leucocyanidin	10^{-2}M	63 – 95	Byrde *et al.* (1960)
	Gallotannins	10^{-2} G-equiv.	75 – 85	Williams (1963)
	Tea phenolics	0.7%	62 – 73	"
	Pentagallolyl glucose	10^{-2}M	96	"
	Mercuric chloride	10^{-3}M	50	Fielding & Byrde (1969)
	p-Chloromercuribenzoic acid	10^{-3}M	57	"
	Urea	8 M	80	"

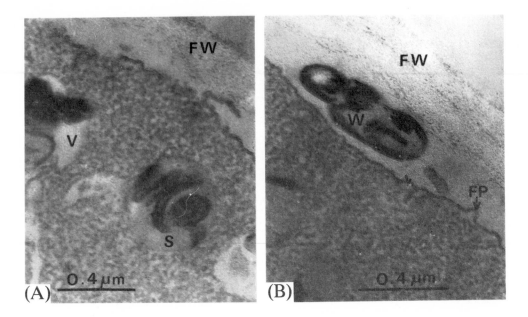

Fig. 5.4.   Histochemical localization of α-L-arabinofuranosidase, acting on
1-naphthyl-α-L-arabinofuranoside as substrate, in hyphae of *M.
fructigena*.   Enzyme product (dark) is:

(A) In intracellular whorled structures in a sphaerosome-like
body (S) or a vacuole (V).

(B) In whorl-like structures (W) in a similar body outside the
plasmalemma (FP), though still inside the fungal wall (FW).

(Photos: E.C. Hislop).

Oxidized polyphenols are the only group which are highly active against PG.
The mechanism of their action is probably a non-specific protein precipitation,
and tannic acid has indeed been used in the purification of AF from *M. fructigena* (Fielding & Byrde, 1969).   The inactive complex with tannic acid can be
reactivated by treatment with acetone (Shibata & Nisizawa, 1965).

As might be expected, a number of fungicides added to the medium reduced pectolytic enzyme secretion (Grover & Moore, 1962), but these are probably acting
on protein synthesis or general metabolism rather than in a specific manner.

Chapter **6**

SURVIVAL

Fungi must be able to survive under extreme conditions of the habitat, often
for long periods. Many different factors are involved and these interact very
closely so that it becomes difficult to distinguish between them. The stres-
ses caused by desiccation and extremes of temperature illustrate this well.
Consequently, the same structural and physical features of an organism may be
effective in giving resistance to several adverse conditions of the environment. A considerable literature has accumulated on this aspect of survival
and some relevant reviews have been published (Hawker, 1957; Park, 1965, 1968;
Mazur, 1968; Willetts, 1971; Coley-Smith & Cooke, 1971). Apart from the ability of an organism to retain viability when the habitat is unsuitable, other
inherited adaptations must also be considered. Some of these adaptations include 'competitive saprophytic ability' (Garrett, 1950, 1956, 1970), 'genetic
variability, disseminability and responsiveness' (Sussman, 1968).

The main purpose of this Chapter is to relate the morphology and metabolism of
the brown rot fungi to their survival under adverse environmental conditions of
the type referred to as 'deleterious agents' by Sussman (1968). These agents
include: desiccation, extremes of temperature, harmful solar radiations, toxic
substances and starvation. Only those toxic substances produced by the activities of other micro-organisms will be discussed in this Chapter, although
others which are naturally present in the soil and atmosphere or introduced by
man, particularly fungicides (Chapter 8), are also involved.

A detailed study on the viability of conidia of M. *fructicola* on fruit mummies
and peduncles under field conditions in Australia has been reported by Shepherd
(1968). Abundant sporulation was observed on infected fruits, and the viability of the conidia was very high (97-100%); within 2-4 weeks viability was
rapidly reduced to below 10%; after overwintering on mummies in the tree only
0.1 - 6.0% of spores were found to germinate. Very light showers of rain induced resporulation on mummies, and the conidia that developed were of very high
viability. Similar results were obtained from fruit peduncles; after several
months on the tree the viability of the conidia on peduncles was very low (0-
2%); when old infected peduncles were incubated in a saturated atmosphere abundant sporulation was observed and the viability of the spores ranged from 79
to 92%. Numerous spores were present on mummies that had fallen to the ground
but the spores, and also the mycelium in the fruits, were largely inviable
after a few months. It seems unlikely from this work that conidia which have
overwintered on fallen mummies are an important source of inoculum in the
spring, but it is unwise to generalize from results obtained in one locality.

The reasons for the loss of viability of conidia and mummies of the brown rot
fungi are often difficult to determine and there is great variability according
to the conditions under which the material is kept. This is illustrated by
studies carried out by Willetts (1971) on the viability of peach and nectarine
mummies of M. *fructicola*; in aseptic laboratory tests mummies retained their
viability for several years while similar mummies that were kept out-of-doors
in untreated, regularly-watered garden soil at temperatures ranging from 10 to
20°C had disintegrated within 5 months. The breakdown of the stromatized tissue was thought to be due to the activities of other micro-organisms in the

soil. However mummies often survive for long periods in soil. Pollock (1918) reported that stromatized plums produced apothecia of M. fructicola after 10 years in soil, and there are numerous records of survival of mummies for several years. Records of mummy longevity in the tree do not appear to be available. Mycelium in peach trees survived for 5-6 months when not subjected to the harsh, dry, hot conditions of mid-summer in inland New South Wales, but infections of apricot trees in the same area failed to survive for 8 months or more when part of this period was under summer conditions (Kable, 1969a).

Jenkins (1968a) studied the longevity of conidia of M. fructicola under field conditions and found that less than 1% of conidia remained viable after exposure for 8 days in the tree canopy; conidia in contact with unsterilized soil had lost their viability within 24 hr. Conidia prepared in a suspension of sterile water lost viability more quickly on exposure to conditions in the orchard than spores that remained dry prior to exposure. However, Kable (1965b) found that conidia of M. fructicola survived for up to 4 months on peach leaf surfaces in orchards. Jenkins (1968a) considered biotic rather than physical factors to be the major cause of loss of viability in his investigation, although he recognized desiccation as one factor which will affect conidium longevity.

DESICCATION

Most fungi have a large surface:volume ratio that gives great surface contact with the environment. This high ratio may be advantageous when the fungus is growing in a suitable substratum under favourable physical conditions, but it is a great disadvantage in a hostile environment. Certain stages in the life cycles of fungi, such as resting spores, sclerotia and rhizomorphs, are able to survive under dry conditions but mycelia are usually confined to moist habitats where desiccation is not a major problem.

The brown rot fungi infect woody tissues, blossoms and fruits, but their mycelial growth is greatly influenced by the moisture content of the infected parts or the relative humidity of the atmosphere (Chapters 3 and 7). In the field extensive hyphal growth is observed only in ripe fruit tissue; the cells of the host become embedded within the fungal mycelium so that some of the environment is virtually contained within the fungus. However, once the stroma has differentiated the enclosed cells are not a source of nutrients during resting periods.

The conidia of the brown rot fungi do not serve as resting spores. Conidia of M. fructigena have high resistance to uniform conditions of desiccation in vitro, even when these are more extreme than would be encountered in nature (Naqvi & Good, 1957). These workers concluded that dehydration is not a significant factor in the inactivation of spores, and suggested that very moist conditions are more harmful than dry ones. However, results from in vitro studies could be misleading, and survival under fluctuating conditions must also be considered. Germinating spores of M. fructicola retain their viability after at least one prolonged period of drying (Grindle & Good, 1961; Good & Zathureczky, 1967).

The ability to retain viability at low moisture levels of the cell is of great ecological significance for the survival of the individual and thus of the species. Infected twigs, fruit peduncles and mummies may remain in the tree canopy for several months and on occasions are subjected to extreme drying from sun, wind and possibly frost; yet since new crops of conidia are produced on these tissues after a period of rain (Fig. 6.1) it is clear that the fungus is able to survive long periods of dehydration.

Fig. 6.1. Production of conidial pustules of the brown rot fungi on overwintered infected host tissues previously subjected to extreme drying and marked temperature variations.

(A) *M. fructigena* on mummified apple.

(B) *M. laxa* f. *mali* on infected apple spur.

Seeds of higher plants are normally stored by man in an air-dried state, sometimes for several years. However, it is essential that excessive water is not removed or, conversely, that the moisture level is not too high, as both conditions will cause reduction or complete loss of viability. Generally, resistant fungal vegetative structures also survive longer after they have been air-dried (Sussman & Halvorsen, 1966). Water is actively extruded from fungal tissues (Wilson, 1948) and this is often associated with the secretion of sugars (Kybal, 1964; Cooke, 1969). In culture plates, large moisture drops accumulate on exposed surfaces of sclerotia or stromata but in the field these are not seen, except under humid conditions, because of evaporation from their surfaces. Active exudation of water lowers the moisture content of the tissues and even small changes in the hydration of tissues may have a significant effect on survival. Cooke (1969) found that sclerotia of *Sclerotinia sclerotiorum* and *S. trifoliorum* contained about 60% water after 13-16 days; in the field, dehydration of brown rot mummies is often greater than this, especially when the mummified fruits remain hanging in the tree canopy.

When hyphae are arranged to form plectenchymatous structures as in stromata there is a great reduction in water loss, particularly from those hyphae in the

centre of the structure. Nevertheless, on occasions the amount of interhyphal moisture must be low and then resistance to further desiccation becomes
the property of individual cells. The walls of medullary hyphae of brown rot
stromata are as thick or thicker than those of macroconidia of these fungi and
are able to survive limited desiccation. Also the mucilage layer on the surface of stromatal hyphae may be of some significance in resistance to drying.
Feather & Malek (1972) and Archer, Clamp & Migliore (1976) found that the sli-
mes which are produced in abundance by M. fructicola and M. fructigena are
polysaccharides composed largely of glucose units (see Chapter 5); Webb (1965)
suggested that mucopolysaccharides may have a protective role against dehydration. Different degrees of agglutination of sclerotia of Typhula spp. were
observed by Corner (1950), who interpreted these differences as evidence of an
evolutionary process giving better adaptation to xerophytic and low-temperature
conditions.

Within hyphae some water is relatively loosely held in the 3-dimensional network of peptide chains. This water of hydration is the first to be lost from
the cell by slow air-drying. It becomes increasingly more difficult to with-
draw water as, with dehydration, the concentrations of substances dissolved in
the aqueous phase increase. Osmotically-bound water is lost from the cell only
under extreme conditions; permanent damage may take place when this bound water
is removed and consequently there is a reduction or loss in viability. Soluble
sugars have been found to accumulate during sclerotial development of several
fungi (Le Tourneau, 1966; Cooke, 1969) and probably, by analogy, in stromata of
the brown rot fungi. Lewis & Smith (1967) suggested that mannitol, apart from
serving as a reserve of nutrient, is important also in the maintenance of high
osmotic pressures in mycelium during periods of environmental water stress.

The close arrangement of the hyphae of the stromatic rind results in the formation of a mechanical barrier that reduces the loss of water from interhyphal
spaces of the medulla. Sometimes crusts of dried-up, deeply pigmented hyphae
remain over stromatal and sclerotial rinds and, in nature, the skins of fruits
mummified by the brown rot fungi often remain intact (Willetts, 1968c). These
provide extra, possibly protective coverings over the outer surfaces of stromata. The thickening of rind cells and the deposition of melanin and mucilage
in and over hyphal walls of the rind may also impede desiccation. The rinds of
sclerotia of Sclerotium cepivorum and Sclerotium rolfsii, which are very similar to the stromatal rinds of the brown rot fungi, have been shown to serve as
effective barriers to water absorption (Coley-Smith, 1959; Chet, 1969) and presumably also to water loss.

Most of these considerations are concerned with survival under moderate or extreme conditions of desiccation of the type encountered by mummies and fruit
receptacles that remain hanging from trees in orchards. Survival of these is
of great importance, and conidia produced on them when conditions are favourable provide the main sources of primary infections in the spring. Probably
the mucilaginous matrix, in which the medullary hyphae of the stroma are embedded, facilitates rapid uptake of water during rain showers and the retention of
moisture for sporulation. Pectic substances may also retain water (Chapter 7).
However, in the soil or on the surface of the ground where mummies are frequently found, conditions of severe desiccation are seldom experienced (Garrett,
1956), although occasionally stromata may become dehydrated during periods of
drought or frost.

EXTREMES OF TEMPERATURE

Resistance to desiccation and extremes of temperature have much in common; tissues may dry out as a result of both low and high temperatures. Data from the field tend to be incomplete and often contradictory, while in the laboratory it is difficult to reproduce the effects of fluctuations of factors that interact under natural conditions.

Perennial plants must be able to survive the rigours of the climate in the areas where they are grown; pathogens of these crops will not normally encounter physical conditions that will kill the hosts. Maximum temperatures in regions where fruit trees are grown probably rarely exceed 40-50°C, and these high temperatures would prevail for only a few hours during each day for variable periods during a growing season; temperatures may be at sub-zero levels for a few days to a few months each winter - usually the host and its pathogens will be dormant during these cold periods.

To some extent mycelia formed within host tissue will be protected against low and high temperatures by the plant. If the host and thus the fungus survive, further mycelial development and sporulation will take place when the environment becomes more favourable (Fig. 6.1).

Jerome (1958) demonstrated that conidia of *M. fructicola* retained their viability when kept in the laboratory at temperatures from 2 to 42°C for 8 weeks with relative humidities in the range 40-98%. Dormant and germinating spores of *M. fructicola* also survive sub-zero temperatures for at least several days (Smith, Miller & Bassett, 1965). Temperatures of about 50°C for intervals as short as 30 sec significantly reduced percentage germination and hot broth killed the spores more quickly than hot air; at relative humidity of 50%, hot air was less lethal than at r.h. of 80% or 90% (Smith *et al.*, 1965; Smith & Blomquist, 1970). Ultrastructural changes were observed in spores of *M. fructicola* after heat treatment (Baker & Smith, 1970). Anoxia appears to increase the resistance of spores to subsequent heating while the respiratory inhibitors sodium azide and sodium arsenite resemble anoxia in their effect on survival of conidia of this species (Bussel, Miranda & Sommer, 1971). Stromata are better adapted to survive extremes of temperatures than are conidia or vegetative mycelium although stromata, as sclerotia in general, resist cold conditions more effectively than hot ones.

The basic mechanisms of cold resistance are probably alike in many different organisms and similar adaptations are found in a range of plants. Mazur (1968) concluded that the resistance of fungi to low temperatures depends upon the prevention of intracellular ice formation and their ability to resist dehydration. Slow air-drying results in the removal of water of hydration and most of the water that remains will be bound water that will not be available for the formation of intracellular ice. Mummies remaining for some time on trees and on the surface of soils become air-dried and should be in a suitable state to survive extremes of temperature. Mummies that become buried in soil may be subjected to some air-drying before they are covered with earth or litter; also the active extrusion of water will reduce moisture content to some extent. The rind, if it is complete, effectively seals the medulla from the outside and should help to maintain stromata in a dry state provided the soil does not become water-soaked.

Other mechanisms apart from slow air-drying must operate in resistance to sub-zero temperatures as, on occasions, mummies with high moisture contents survive very low temperatures (Willetts, 1971). High concentrations of solutes within the cell depress the freezing point and reduce the formation of intracellular ice crystals to some extent; medullary hyphae are generally rich in nutrient reserves, some of which increase the osmotic concentration of the cells. Roberts (1969) suggested that, in cold-hardened plants, there is a substitution of modified forms of proteins for the proteins that carry out essential functions at normal temperatures. Consequently metabolism is changed at the low temperatures and the changes could increase the chances of survival by achieving better water-holding capacity of essential proteins, reduced sensitivity to cold and the formation of protective substances. Mazur (1970) emphasized the importance of protection of the cell surface in survival against freezing. Several substances, including sugars and proteins, have been found to protect cells against cold. Soluble sugars are secreted by sclerotia during their development (Cooke, 1969) and accumulate in interhyphal spaces and over the surfaces of the whole structure. This deposit of sugary substances may be of great significance in survival under several environmental conditions.

In general, the principles involved in resistance to high temperatures appear to be similar to those which apply to survival against cold. Heat resistance of microbial cells increases with decreasing humidity. Even small changes in water content may have considerable influence on survival owing to the greater stability of proteins in a dry state (Hansen & Riemann, 1963). As in resistance to low temperatures, some chemicals will protect against high temperatures. These substances replace bound water by forming hydrogen bonds with proteins and thereby retain the integrity of macromolecules.

Much work is required before survival at high and low temperatures is well understood.

RADIATIONS

In nature, fungi on the aerial parts of plants are exposed for long periods to varying levels of ionizing, u.v. and i.r. radiations. Fungi in the soil are protected from injury by irradiation; on the surface of the ground, protection is given by shading from vegetation and plant debris. Thus brown rot conidia formed on infected parts of the host, and to a lesser extent mycelium in fruit mummies that remain hanging on the tree, are exposed to high levels of solar radiation while mycelium within the host tissues and mummies that fall to the ground are protected from the harmful effects of such radiation.

Most of the data available on the effect of radiation on fungi have been obtained from laboratory studies and little is known of the chronic effects of solar radiations that reach the surface of the earth. Thanos (1951) showed that there was a significant reduction in viability of spores of M. *fructicola* after short exposures to u.v. radiations in the laboratory. Shepherd (1968) concluded that in exposed situations conidia of M. *fructicola* were killed relatively quickly but, when they were protected from short wavelength solar radiation, survival was for longer periods. Considerably higher dosages of radiation were necessary to kill spores at low r.h. than at saturation.

The most effective dispersal of brown rot conidia is by water splash (Chapter 7) and, presumably, spores that are disseminated in this way escape some of the drastic effects of u.v. light. When transmission is by wind spores are subjected to considerable irradiation during their transport through the atmosphere. Another factor that must be considered in survival of spores during transport is the screening effect of cloud cover. Abundant production of conidia of the brown rot fungi is during wet, cloudy weather and these are the conditions when epiphytotics occur. The buff/grey pigmentation of conidia could also give some protection against harmful light waves.

Many of the features already discussed as of importance in resistance to other environmental factors will also reduce inactivation by solar radiations. Melanized structures are more resistant to u.v. light than are hyaline ones (Sussman, 1968); the structure and composition of the rind provide a protective barrier for the more loosely interwoven medullary hyphae; possibly mucilage on hyphae and over the exposed surfaces of mummies gives some protection, and the low moisture contents of air-dried tissue may prevent damage to essential proteins and other macromolecules by solar radiations.

COMPETITION FROM OTHER MICRO-ORGANISMS

Apart from the effects of physical factors of the environment such as temperature, humidity, moisture and solar radiations on survival of the brown rot fungi, biological factors must also be considered. This was well demonstrated by Lockwood (1960) who obtained varying degrees of lysis of living and dead mycelia of *M. fructicola* by microbial extracts. Some fungi are particularly susceptible to lysis by other micro-organisms while others are resistant to microbial degradation. Considerable evidence indicates that melanin or related substances may have great ecological significance in reducing damage by the lytic action of micro-organisms (Potgieter & Alexander, 1966; Bloomfield & Alexander, 1967; Kuo & Alexander, 1967; Chet, Henis & Mitchell, 1967). The means by which melanin gives protection against biological degradation is not known. Two mechanisms have been suggested: the hyphal wall is protected by a deposit on the outer surface of the hyphae and/or by the formation of a complex with the components of the wall, particularly with chitin; melanin inhibits the enzymes, mainly chitinases and glucanases, associated with biological degradation. Examples of both mechanisms are available from higher plants. Bull (1970a), in a study on the degradation of hyaline and melanized cell walls of *Aspergillus nidulans* by glucanase and chitinase from a soil streptomycete, found that there was a non-specific binding between melanin and enzymes associated with wall degradation and therefore non-competitive inhibition; he concluded that there is electrostatic attraction between the enzymes and melanin. A detailed investigation of a cellulase-melanin model system gave further support for this (Bull, 1970b).

Chlamydospores and sclerotia were described by Potgieter & Alexander (1966) as particularly resistant to biological degradation in soils. However, there must be degrees of resistance according to soil type and other environmental factors. This is well illustrated by the rapid and complete degradation of fruits mummified by brown rot fungi in some soils and positions but their excellent preservation in others. Obviously the types of micro-organisms present in a particular soil are of considerable importance together with physical factors such as temperature and moisture of the soil. The claim that a period of chilling is necessary for apothecial formation may be related to the lack of activity of antagonistic micro-organisms at low temperatures and consequently better preservation of stromatic tissue in which ascocarps can be more readily initiated and then develop. Dry and acid soils also restrict microbial degradation of mummies, and this could explain why stromatic hyphae retain their viability for long periods under these conditions.

Michener & Snell (1949) found that *Bacillus subtilis* secreted substances that were antibiotic to several fungi, including *M. fructicola*. Jenkins (1968a) studied the longevity of conidia of *M. fructicola* that were introduced into sterilized and untreated soils on glass-fibre tapes; spores in sterile soil were still viable after 20 days but in unsterile soil conidia failed to germinate and showed evidence of lysis after one day - no conidia were detected after five days. Bacteria were present on the slides from untreated soils, and these were identified as a *Bacillus* species, probably *B. cereus* Frankland & Frankland. Colonies of this bacterium inhibited growth of *M. fructicola* in culture. This organism is a common contaminant of buds and fruits in orchards in Victoria, Australia where the work was carried out. Jenkins suggested that inactivation of conidia of *M. fructicola* in orchards is largely due to the antagonistic effects of bacteria and probably u.v. radiations, while other factors are of lesser importance. *Sporobacterium fungostaticum* and *Bacillus antimycoides*, which were isolated from air, were found by Keil (1950) to be strongly inhibitory to growth of *Monilia cinerea* (= *M. laxa*) on molasses agar cultures.

The survival of fruit mummies both in the soil and the tree canopy is more important in the life cycles of the brown rot fungi than survival of asexual spores as the latter are readily and abundantly produced on viable stromata and infected tissues when conditions become favourable. Probably much of the available data on the survival of sclerotia in soils is applicable to fruit mummies which have dropped to the ground and become buried. Halkilahti (1962) observed that sclerotia of *Sclerotinia sclerotiorum* were sometimes degraded in soils within several months by the activities of micro-organisms while others survived for $4\frac{1}{2}$ years; different strains of the fungus varied in their susceptibility to the antagonists. Severe infection of sclerotia by both fungal and bacterial pathogens is normally favoured by high temperatures. *Trichoderma* sp. is a common contaminant of brown rot mummies in Britain (A.T.K. Corke, priv. comm.) and in Australia (H.J. Willetts, unpublished). Harrison (1935) isolated *Ciboria aestivalis* from mummified apples, pears, stone fruits and quinces in New South Wales; this species appears to be parasitic on the stroma of *M. fructicola*. The sugars that are secreted by stromatic hyphae during their development are probably attractive to some micro-organisms and provide nutrient for infection of the stroma. A search for other microbial antagonists of fruit mummies could possibly provide information that may be useful for studies on the control of brown rot by biological methods (Chapter 9; see also Baker & Cook, 1974). The role of insects in the destruction of fruit mummies also requires thorough investigation.

STARVATION

Fruits stromatized by the brown rot fungi form a persistent resting stage that has a high level of endogenous reserves and hyphae capable of active metabolism when growth conditions are favourable. The mummy is partially sealed off from the physical environment by the rind. Thus the brown rot fungi are able to survive adverse conditions in a balanced and efficient manner in the absence of exogenous nutrients. Presumably the metabolism of the fungus is greatly reduced during resting periods and the stroma provides an example of 'inactive survival' (Park, 1968). Compared with many fungal structures, the nutrient reserves and inoculum potential of a well-formed mummy are enormous. When conditions are suitable many crops of conidia can be produced over an extended period and reserves are available to support the development of numerous apothecia. Usually conditions that are favourable for apothecium production are also those that result in rapid degradation of mummies, and in practice resistance of the latter to adverse conditions is greatly reduced following development of ascocarps. Thus it is unlikely that more than one crop of apothecia are produced in successive years on the same mummy except under unusual conditions.

Chapter 7

INFECTION

The term *infection* implies the entry of an organism or virus into a host and the subsequent establishment of a parasitic relationship with it. This may be a permanent or temporary association. Brown (1936) divided the process of fungal infection into three consecutive phases: prepenetration, which is concerned with the pathogen before penetration of the host surface; penetration itself, when entry into the host takes place; and post-penetration, when the pathogen is attempting to establish a nutritional relationship with the host. These three phases are interdependent and no clear demarcation can be made between them. However, for convenience, infection has been discussed in this Chapter under the three phases described by Brown, with further sub-divisions when necessary. Resistance to infection is considered in a later section.

PRE-PENETRATION

Types of Inoculum

Asexual spores (conidia) provide the main inoculum of the brown rot fungi. The spores develop abundantly on infected host tissues in the spring and initiate primary infections of healthy tissues, and, with *M. laxa*, particularly of blossoms. Under favourable conditions, sporulation takes place on the newly infected tissues and conidia may be produced throughout the growing season although the spores are usually most abundant just before and at the time of fruit-ripening.

In North America, ascocarps of *M. fructicola* are reported to be produced in spring and ascospores provide inoculum for infection of fruit tree blossoms that emerge at the same time as the sexual spores are liberated. However, ascospores are not considered to be a regular source of inoculum in areas where *M. fructicola* is a pathogen. The infrequent production of the perfect stage by *M. fructigena* and *M. laxa* suggests that ascospores are of only minor importance as a source of inoculum in the life cycles of these species.

Mycelium serves as inoculum when healthy tissues come into physical contact with diseased parts of plants. In the field, whole clusters of fruits may become infected by growth of mycelium from one diseased fruit and often mycelium grows into the peduncle; subsequently spurs or laterals are also penetrated and cankers may be formed in woody tissues, although cankers usually heal up or are invaded by secondary organisms.

Sources of Inoculum

The brown rot fungi survive the adverse conditions of winter as mycelium in fruit mummies, fruit peduncles, cankers on twigs and branches, leaf scars and buds. Under favourable conditions in the spring, the fungi sporulate on the infected tissues. There is only limited quantitative information on the importance of the different spring sources of spores, but it is generally accepted that peduncles and mummies provide the major primary inoculum sources. In many orchards, mummies are removed at pruning time (Chapter 9) but peduncles usually remain on the tree and have tended to be overlooked as sources of inoculum until comparatively recent times (Kable, 1965b; Sutton & Clayton, 1972). The sporulation capacity of infected peduncles decreases from the time the mummies are removed and is partly dependent upon sugar content of the tissues. Nevertheless, abundant sporulation takes place on peduncles in the early growing season and the spores provide inoculum for infections of blossoms, small fruits, immature shoots and leaves. Kable (1965b) concluded that, in the Murrumbidgee Irrigation Areas (M.I.A.) of New South Wales, infections in woody tissues must also be important sources of spores early in the season. Mycelia in buds, leaf scars and leaves do not appear to contribute significant numbers of conidia for primary infections. In areas where *M. fructicola* is found, ascospores may also cause primary infection.

Any infected tissue in which the moisture content is sufficient for sporulation may serve as a source of inoculum for secondary infection. Blighted blossoms sometimes produce spores throughout the growing season; green fruits that become diseased early in the growing season after injury by insects or other agencies can serve as sources of conidia for periods of several months. Wild plants growing in the vicinity of cultivated crops may also serve as sources of inoculum.

Kable (1969b) found that apricot and peach orchards located in the same neighbourhood in the M.I.A. of New South Wales were involved in a single infection chain. The mycelium of *M. fructicola* does not overwinter well in apricot trees growing in the region, and primary infection of apricot blossom was found to arise mainly from conidia produced on peach trees in neighbouring plantations. After the apricot flowers became infected there was a continuous infection chain in the apricot trees, unlike peaches, from flowering until harvest. Inoculum for infection of peach fruits probably came from the apricots and bridged a gap in the peach infection chain.

There are several records of the numbers of conidia of *Monilinia* spp. produced on infected tissues. Byrde (1952) estimated that plum and apple fruits mummified by *M. fructigena* produced approx 41 and 64 pustules per mummy respectively and that each mummy could produce up to 4×10^6 spores. Shepherd (1968) estimated that each average peach mummy has a potential for the production of 10^6 viable spores of *M. fructicola* during the spring period. Subsequent conidial crops are produced during wet or humid periods throughout the season. Shepherd suggested that mummies that fall to the ground during the winter months do not make a substantial contribution to conidial inoculum in the spring because of their decomposition. Presumably the spore loads from fallen mummies are very variable and would be greatly influenced by the climatic conditions of the season and the region. P.F. Kable (priv. comm.) found mummies that fall late in the winter are important sources of conidia and also of dried fruit beetles. The latter help disperse the inoculum in the spring. Estimates were also made of the conidia produced on peduncles that were incubated in moist atmospheres (Shepherd, 1968). The numbers produced in the first crop ranged from 1.9×10^4 to 9.8×10^5 with viabilities of the spores varying from 79 to 92%; in three subsequent crops, more than 10^3 spores per peduncle were obtained. Thus in an orchard or plantation an enormous spore load can be produced at a time when young blossoms and shoots are unfolding; further showers of spores will be liberated after rain or periods of high humidity.

Conditions affecting production of inoculum

Many different factors, including the physical environment, moisture content and nutrient status of the substratum interact to influence the production of

fungal fruiting bodies, asexual spores, mycelium and vegetative structures.
Corbin & Cruickshank (1963) emphasized the over-riding importance of water content of spore-bearing tissues as a factor affecting the production of conidia
of *M. fructicola*. They found that water-soaked fruitlets produced conidia
more quickly than did tissues that contained less moisture. Conidia continued
to be produced provided there was only minimal moisture loss from the sporulating tissue, a condition that was achieved in atmospheric relative humidities
of 94-100%. When there was a significant water loss, which was found at relative humidities of less than 94%, sporulation intensity was reduced. Spores
were produced in dry atmospheres on tissues, such as fruitlets and ripe fruit,
having high moisture contents but sporulation of peduncles, laterals and mummified fruits was observed only in wet weather. In the field, periods of high
and low relative humidities usually alternate, and these combine conditions
suitable for spore production with those favouring maturation and dispersal.
Thus a supply of fresh conidia is available for long periods of time. However,
the maximum numbers of conidia are not necessarily produced on these occasions.
At 20°C, a period of about 12 hr after water soaking is required for sporulation to take place; maximum sporulation was obtained between 36 and 48 hr. The
minimum moisture content of mummies for sporulation to take place at 26°C was
found by Jenkins & Reinganum (1968) to be 21%.

Dispersal of inoculum

Ingold (1966) recognised three phases in the dispersal of fungi: liberation of
spores from sporogenous tissues, transport to a suitable substratum for growth,
and deposition on the host or substratum. However, in studies on the *Monilinia*
species there have not usually been any attempts to distinguish between take-
off and transport, and almost nothing is known of landing. Spores of the brown
rot fungi are transported (and indeed may also be liberated) by wind and air
currents, water splash or a variety of vectors.

Conidia

The conidia of the brown rot fungi are dry air spores (Hirst, 1953; Zoberi,
1961). The spores are not violently discharged but are set free by air currents and wind. The conidiophores, although short and unspecialized, elevate
the spore chains above the infected tissues on which the sporogenous hyphae develop and give better exposure to air currents. Also, except when mummies have
fallen to the ground, infected fruits and peduncles are in positions that are
well placed for efficient take-off and aerial dispersal of the spores they bear.

Rain splashes are important as a means of liberating fungal spores (Gregory,
Guthrie & Bunce, 1959). Jenkins (1965*b*) used a trap designed by Corke (1958)
for collection of water-borne conidia of *M. fructicola*. It was found that considerable numbers of conidia were washed by rain from sporodochia, produced on
blossoms, and an association was observed between blighted blossoms and rotting
of fruits beneath them. Apart from providing a method of dislodging conidia,
rain droplets supply the moisture essential for germination of the spores and
subsequent mycelial development. Shock waves produced ahead of the drops will
also lead to the liberation of dry spores (Hirst, 1961; Hirst & Stedman, 1962;
Jarvis, 1962).

The development of automatic spore traps, of which Hirst's (1952) is the best-
known, has enabled precise studies to be made of air-borne fungal spores in the
atmosphere. Kable (1965*a*) used the Hirst spore trap to study conidial dispersal of *M. fructicola* in a peach orchard in the semi-arid M.I.A. of Australia.

He found that there was one major dispersal period each year which started
about one month before the fruit was harvested and reached a maximum at harvest time. Dispersal continued beyond the harvest time for about 2 months,
but during the remainder of the year only small numbers of conidia were recorded. Dispersal was favoured by low relative humidities and high wind speeds,
which are the conditions most frequently experienced during the early afternoon. Inoculum became depleted after a period when conditions favoured optimal dispersal, but renewed conidial production took place after rain showers
had fallen on spore-bearing tissues.

Jenkins (1965b) also used the Hirst spore trap to study the dispersal of $M.$
$fructicola$ in a peach orchard in Victoria, Australia where conditions are more
humid than in the area where Kable's observations were made. Jenkins found
that there was maximum dispersal of spores at the hottest time of the day which
coincided with the lowest relative humidity; at night, when air turbulence was
at a minimum, there was minimum dispersal. Corbin, Ogawa & Schultz (1968) obtained similar results when they used the Hirst spore trap to study the epide-
miology of $M.$ $laxa$ in an apricot orchard in California. During the spring only
small numbers of conidia were collected and the occurrence of the spores was
erratic. The maximum number of spores coincided with the period when fruits
were ripening and there was a decrease in spore numbers after the fruit had
been harvested. A correlation was observed between the number of air-borne
conidia collected per day and the number of infected ripening fruits bearing
sporodochia. Climatic conditions in the test area were such that wind veloci-
ties were highest in the late afternoon when air temperatures were becoming
cooler and the relative humidities increasing. Under these conditions, Corbin
et al found that there was a gradual increase in spores collected from sunrise
to 1 p.m. and then a rapid increase through the afternoon and early evening
with a maximum at sunset.

Roberts & Dunegan (1932) considered that transport by air was the most important way that spores of the brown rot fungi reach their hosts. From a study
on the dissemination of conidia of $M.$ $laxa$ and their transport to apricot blossoms, Wilson & Baker (1948) calculated that spores released from a height of 6
ft were carried a distance of 3,770 ft when the wind velocity was 5 m.p.h.
They concluded that spores are dispersed from a point source to give a spread
the shape of a cone with the apex at the source of the inoculum and orientated
in the direction of the wind; the largest number of spores will be found in the
centre with progressive reduction as the distance increases vertically from the
central axis and horizontally from the point source. The effect of wind velo-
cities on dispersal was also studied by them, and they gave an equation for
determining the density of conidial dissemination at a known horizontal distance from the nearest source. The incidence of plant disease in the field
agrees with this type of spread from a point source (Gregory, 1966). However,
there is only limited information on the distances brown rot conidia are
transported by wind.

Thus, conidia of the brown rot fungi are disseminated by wind when temperatures
are high, relative humidities low and often at high ultraviolet light intensi-
ties. These are some of the conditions that could adversely affect viability
of spores, particularly when they are carried long distances in the atmosphere.
Unfortunately data on the viability of spores collected in Hirst spore traps
are lacking, and such information is needed to determine the real effectiveness, in respect to infection, of aerial dispersal of conidia. Even if a relatively high percentage of spores remain viable after aerial dispersal, the lack

of precision at landing reduces the incidence of infection by spores transported in this manner and enormous numbers of spores are required to ensure that some alight on susceptible hosts.

Jenkins (1965*b*) concluded that in Victoria, Australia, where his studies were carried out, splash dispersal of conidia of *M. fructicola* is more important than aerial dispersal. Kable (1965*a*) also found that water splashes readily dispersed conidia of *M. fructicola* and could be responsible for the build-up of brown rot epiphytotics. Pauvert, Fournet & Rapilly (1969) included *M. fructigena* in their investigations on dispersal of conidia by water drops in relation to the spore-bearing structures and found that dispersal was most rapid from sporodochia.

Unlike aerial dispersal that results in the spread of spores over a wide area, water splash dispersal brings about only short-range dissemination, mainly to other parts of the same tree or, in some instances, between adjacent trees. This is a disadvantage sometimes, but spores transported by water escape the extreme environmental conditions to which wind-borne inoculum is often subjected.

Animals, particularly insects, are important vectors of fungi, either incidentally or because of complex adaptations. Some of the known insect vectors of the brown rot fungi are included in the list of wound agents in Table 9.1. This list is far from complete, since almost any insect has the potential to pick up and carry spores from sporulating mycelium to healthy, susceptible tissues.

The plum curculio (*Conetrachelus nenuphar* Hbst) is closely associated with peach rot in the United States and it was thought at one time that brown rot infections were entirely caused by this insect. Roberts & Dunegan (1932) estimated that about 90% of brown rot infections of peaches take place through curculio punctures. However, although the surface of the plum curculio is well suited to pick up spores, the insect normally feeds only on firm tissues which are unlikely to have brown rot spores developing on them.

In California, Ogawa (1957) found that 'dried fruit' ('nitidulid') beetles (*Carpophilus* spp.) which were contaminated with spores of *M. fructicola* were attracted to damaged areas of fruit and spores were deposited at the feeding sites. Spores germinate readily in wounded tissue and initiate infection of the fruits. Dried fruit beetles are widely distributed in Australia and there, also, they have been shown to disseminate conidia of *M. fructicola* (Kable, 1969*a*). These insects appear to be of greater importance in the early stages of the pre-harvest build-up of the disease.

Kable (1969*a*) found that, during the 1-2 months before harvest, almost all infected fruits in the semi-arid M.I.A. of New South Wales were those which had been damaged by the oriental fruit moth (*Cydia molesta* Busck) and he suggested that the combined activity of the moth as a wounding agent and the dried fruit beetle as vector enable the fungus to be a troublesome pathogen in an area which should be comparatively free from the disease because of low atmospheric moisture and infrequent rain showers. This example illustrates how several factors may interact to produce a brown rot epiphytotic although some of the environmental conditions are unfavourable for growth of the fungi. Probably there are other similar interactions that have not been determined.

Man is a vector of many pathogens, including the fruit-rotting *Monilinia* species, and he can, inadvertently, bring about both long and short distance
transport. Birds have also been cited as vectors of brown rot fungi (Wormald,
1954).

Ascospores

Details on ascospore discharge by *M. fructicola* have been given by Roberts &
Dunegan (1932). The infrequent production of the perfect stage by *M. laxa* and
M. fructigena has prevented detailed studies on dispersal of ascospores of the
Old World species. Considerable information is available on the discharge of
ascospores by Discomycetes (reviewed by Ingold, 1960, 1966) and most of these
findings also apply to the brown rot fungi. Apothecia of *Monilinia* spp. are
stalked and consequently raised above the mummies on which they develop.
Also, ascocarp initials are phototropic (Norton, Ezekiel & Jehle, 1923) and
mature discs are orientated at right angles to the light source. The ascospores are discharged in the general direction of light and they are picked up
by air currents. Ascospores are normally produced on mummies lying beneath host
plants and this close spatial relationship greatly increases the chances of the
spores landing on susceptible tissues. Large numbers of ascospores are discharged from the ascocarp at the same time and, under certain conditions, spore
clouds can be seen rising from fruit bodies. The phenomenon of 'puffing' is
preceded by a build-up of turgor pressure within the asci. Usually the active
shooting off of spores is associated with increased air turbulence caused by
blasts of dry air or increases in atmospheric temperature. Also sudden exposure to light or an intensification of light may induce puffing. The greatest
height of discharge of ascospores from apothecia of *M. fructicola* recorded by
Roberts & Dunegan (1932) was 4.3 cm with 0.3 and 0.7 cm the lowest and average
heights respectively. Individual apothecia have been observed to produce
clouds of spores for periods of as long as 7 days.

PENETRATION

As described in the previous section, inocula of the brown rot fungi can be
deposited either directly into the host by insect vectors or on the surfaces
of susceptible plants by water splash or aerial dispersal. Initial entry into
fruit trees by the brown rot fungi is normally *via* blossoms or fruits, although
sometimes there is direct penetration of leaf surfaces. Conidia and ascospores,
which provide the inocula for most primary infections, require free moisture for
germination; this is obtained from films or droplets of water and from plant
exudates that accumulate on the surface of the host or in damaged tissues (Lin,
1942; Clayton, 1942; Weaver, 1950; Corbin, 1963). Germination of conidia takes
place in about an hour under optimal conditions, while ascospores require 4-6
hr. If the spores are not newly formed, they usually take longer to germinate.
Naqvi & Good (1957) found that germination of dried spores of *M. fructicola* was
delayed as long as 60 hr. They suggested that the delay was due to the time
needed to rehydrate and reactivate the protoplast. Nutrients in infection
drops stimulate the rate and percentage of germination (McCallan & Wilcoxon,
1939; Miller, 1944; Hall, 1971*b*).

Early workers thought that a wound was essential for effective penetration of
the brown rot fungi, but Cooley (1914) and Valleau (1915) showed that spores
placed on undamaged fruit surfaces could bring about rotting. However, the
incidence of brown rot diseases is greatly increased when fruits are damaged
since wounds provide more abundant moisture and nutrients for spore germination
and mycelial growth (Wormald, 1954; Jerome, 1958; Corbin, 1963; Biris, 1968;

Ogawa, Bose, Manji & Schreader (1972). Esam (1917) found that infection of
undamaged green fruits was achieved only at high inoculum densities but much
smaller amounts of inoculum brought about infection of ripe or injured fruit.
Since then many workers have arrived at the same conclusions.

Hair sockets have been reported as the sites of penetration of ripe peach
fruits by *M. fructicola* but stomata may also be the sites of entry and on infrequent occasions there may be direct penetration of the cuticle; stomata
have been described as infection sites of unripe peaches (Curtis, 1928; Smith,
1936). Hall (1971*b*) concluded that penetration of peaches may be through
either hair sockets or stomata and the infection court depends largely on
which site is most frequently encountered by germ tubes, i.e. stomata in unripe peaches and hair sockets in ripe ones. Hall showed that single spores
will initiate fruit infection. Curtis (1928) found that apricots were penetrated through both the cuticle and stomata, plums *via* stomata, and nectarines
through the cuticle. Moore (1951) described the penetration of apple by *M.*
fructigena through lenticels.

Mycelia generally have a greater potential than spores for infection, since
they have at their disposal greater reserves of food material. Thus the usual
method of inoculating fruits in the laboratory is by means of mycelium on
plugs of agar from which nutrients are derived. As described earlier, peduncles, twigs and other woody tissues are normally infected by mycelium that
grows and derives nutrients from mummies or diseased blossoms. Healthy fruits
are often infected by the growth of mycelium from diseased fruits with which
they are in contact. The available evidence suggests that conidia of the
brown rot fungi are not rich in food reserves.

Infection of blossoms by *M. fructicola* or *M. laxa* may be through any part of
the flower, although entry takes place more frequently through the stamens
(Calavan & Keitt, 1948; Weaver, 1950; Ogawa, Manji & Schreader, 1975) or the
stigma (Ogawa & English, 1960; Zwygart, 1970; Ogawa *et al.*, 1975) than any
other floral parts. By contrast, Jung (1956) maintained that *M. laxa* did not
penetrate more than 4 mm into the stigma of cherries. The greater susceptibility of stamens and stigmas presumably arises from the abundance of moisture,
pollen and exudates there: Ogawa & English (1960) noted the stimulatory effect
of pollen and leachates from floral parts on spore germination of *M. fructicola*
and *M. laxa*. Also, the lack of cuticularized tissue in these reproductive
structures is probably significant.

The process of infection of cherry flowers through the stigma was studied microscopically and histologically by Willer (1970), who traced infection through
the stigma, the ovary chamber and the pedicel to the woody tissue beyond.
Mycelium grew especially vigorously in the phloem tissue.

Of the environmental factors influencing blossom infection, Weaver (1950) found
that penetration of peach blossom by *M. fructicola* was greatly influenced by
atmospheric relative humidity. In a saturated atmosphere, entry was through
any of the floral parts, except the sepals, but at relative humidities of 80%
or lower, infection was only through stigmas. Because of the greater susceptibility of stamens and stigmas, open flowers were more readily infected than un-
opened ones (cf. Ogawa & English, 1960). Germination of *M. fructicola* spores
was recorded on peach petals at 5°C and low temperatures do not prevent infection in the orchard provided abundant inoculum and moisture are available. The
optimum temperature for penetration of blossoms was 25°C (Weaver, 1950).

Negligible blossom blight and losses of young peach fruits were recorded when inoculation was carried out 5 days after pollination; when the calyx had abscissed, uninjured peach fruits were not liable to become infected. Sutton & Clayton (1972) suggested that the presence of mycelium of M. *fructicola* in flowers prevents the formation of an abscission layer so that infected blossoms and fruits remain attached to the tree.

Compared with the losses caused when flowers and fruits are infected, crop losses resulting from direct injury of other parts of the plants are not important; consequently, these phases of the diseases have been less well studied. Leaves are infected through the uninjured epidermis or *via* wounds. Drummond (1934) suggested that plum leaves may be penetrated through leaf glands. Moore (1952) and Peterson & McGlohon (1967) reported direct penetration of peach leaf blades by M. *fructigena* and M. *fructicola* respectively. Sometimes shoots are invaded from the leaves and wither tip and spur blights develop; if the infection spreads cankers may be produced. Entry into spurs and branches also takes place *via* infected fruits.

Although there have been numerous studies to determine the actual site where the brown rot fungi penetrate their hosts, there is a lack of precise information, despite modern techniques, on how hyphae from mycelia or germ tubes from germinating spores enter undamaged tissues. Presumably this is because these fungi are mainly wound pathogens and it is only in a minority of instances (e.g. Willer, 1970) that direct penetration takes place. The establishment of the fungi within wounded tissues is probably similar to their growth inside the host, which is discussed in detail in the next section.

POST-PENETRATION

Once infection is established, the hyphae of the pathogen spread through the host tissues and bring about the symptoms already described in detail in Chapter 1. Briefly, in fruits these are the browning and softening of the tissue, although the resultant rot is firm by comparison with those caused by the 'soft rot' pathogens such as *Penicillium expansum* on apple (Cole & Wood, 1961a) or *Rhizopus arrhizus* on peach (Reinganum, 1964). The rate of increase in rot diameter has been recorded for several combinations of fruit host and pathogen species, including that of M. *fructicola* in peach (e.g. 0.59 - 0.92 mm/hr; Hall, 1972) and M. *fructigena* in apple (e.g. 0.64 mm/hr; Howell, 1975). The rate varies considerably at different stages in fruit maturity (Hall, 1972; S.A. Archer & M.E. Holgate, unpublished).

After a few days, conidial pustules of the fungus burst through the fruit epidermis and cuticle. Apart from enabling the fungus to perpetuate itself, this bursting leads to the desiccation of the host tissues and often, ultimately, to the formation of a mummified fruit. In the meantime, the pathogen develops a stroma of dense mycelium within the host, described in detail in Chapter 3.

In blossom and twig infection, necrosis is again the most obvious symptom; some of this may be due to the girdling of shoots or spurs leading to failure of the transpiration stream.

The cellular and biochemical processes responsible for these changes have been much studied, at least in fruit infection, but are still not fully understood.

Changes in the cell wall

At the cell level. Early studies with the light microscope (e.g. Behrens, 1898; Schellenberg, 1908; Valleau, 1915; Willaman, 1920) indicated that spread of the brown rot pathogens was generally intercellular, although Cooley (1914) considered that M. cinerea (= M. laxa) had no particular affinity for the middle lamella region, and could penetrate and permeate any part of the host. Reinganum (1964) cited unpublished work by R. Hall that demonstrated intra-cellular hyphae of M. fructicola in peach fruit.

Earlier findings have been confirmed by means of transmission electron micro-scopy (TEM), which indicated, at least for M. fructigena attacking pear fruit-lets, that the hyphae were generally intercellular. Occasionally however, particularly in older infections, hyphae became intracellular and the dead protoplasts were pushed across the cell lumen (Calonge, Fielding, Byrde & Akinrefon, 1969; Plate 1(A)). The wall was generally much less dense around the mycelium, but this effect was spatially limited to a distance of about 1 µm around each hypha.

In subsequent work by R.J. Pring (unpublished) pear tissue was again chosen for study because it is less acid than many fruits, and so can be more easily fixed. Material was examined by means of scanning electron microscopy (SEM), coupled with etching with sodium ethoxide solution (Pring & Richmond, 1975), and TEM. The etching method revealed the presence of 'ribs' within the wall tissue (Fig. 7.1(A)), that probably represented the outlines of tunnels made by the pathogen, M. fructigena. Fig. 7.1(B) shows such a tunnel in infected tissue of mature pear, with the hypha lying in it, and Fig. 7.1(C) a similar oblique section of highly vacuolated mycelium in an infected fruitlet. The presence of hyphae in tunnels was confirmed by TEM of the tissue, which showed that hyphae often grew in intercellular spaces (Fig. 7.2(A)) or else directly in the wall, distorting it to form a tunnel (Fig. 7.2(B)). These tunnels did not always seem to be centrally placed in the wall, i.e. they were not always along the line of the middle lamella. The marked distortion of the wall mar-gin (Fig. 7.1(C); Fig. 7.2(B)) suggests that mechanical pressure is involved in this tunnel formation, and supports the view of Behrens (1898). However, there was also evidence of localized enzymic wall degradation in Fig. 7.2(A) and (B), in that the density of the wall was much less in the region of the hypha. Another significant feature (Fig. 7.2(E)) was the marked convolution in the fungal plasmalemma, including lomasome-like bodies (cf. Calonge, Fielding & Byrde, 1969), reminiscent of those involved in extracellular enzyme secre-tion in the histochemical studies of Hislop, Barnaby, Shellis & Laborda (1974) (see Chapter 5). This Figure also shows a change in the staining characteris-tics of the fibrils in the host cell wall.

The etching technique strikingly confirmed the presence of intracellular hyp-hae, that seemed to grow directly out of the cell wall into the cavity formerly occupied by the protoplast (Fig. 7.2(D)); see also a transverse section of one such hypha in Fig. 7.1(C). There was no clear indication of wall degradation around the penetration site, and mechanical force seemed to be involved. How-ever, such clean-cut penetration holes of pathogens, with no visible remnants of torn wall, have been ascribed to the presence of insolubilized enzymes on the hyphal surface (Stahmann, 1973).

At the molecular level. Although mechanical pressure thus seems to be in-volved in both the intercellular and intracellular spread of the brown rot pathogens, biochemical evidence of several kinds supports the light and elec-

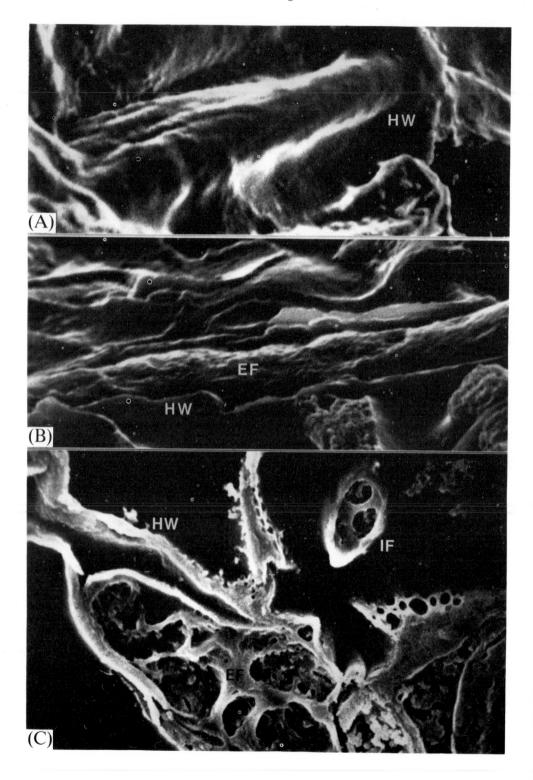

tron microscopic observations that enzymic attack also occurs. Significantly, the first studies on cytolytic enzymes in fungal parasitism were carried out on the related fungus *S. libertiana* (de Bary, 1886).

Firstly, extraction of infected host tissue by various methods has demonstrated the presence *in vivo* of a number of characterised enzymes of which biochemical details are given in Chapter 5. These include polygalacturonase (PG) (Cole, 1956; Cole & Wood, 1961*b*; Reinganum, 1964; Calonge, Fielding, Byrde & Akinrefon, 1969; Hall, 1972; Paynter & Jen, 1974), thus confirming earlier reports of 'pectinase' activity (Wormald, 1954); polymethylgalacturonase (Paynter & Jen, 1974); pectinesterase (PE) (Cole, 1956; Cole & Wood, 1961*b*; Reinganum, 1964; Calonge, Fielding, Byrde & Akinrefon, 1969; Paynter & Jen, 1974), confirming earlier reports of 'pectase' activity (Wormald, 1954); α-L-arabinofuranosidase (AF) (Calonge, Fielding, Byrde & Akinrefon, 1969; Laborda, Archer, Fielding & Byrde, 1974); and β-D-galactopyranosidase (Calonge, Fielding, Byrde & Akinrefon, 1969). In some of these reports activity seemed very low, but the use of extractants, such as strong solutions of salts to 'desorb' the enzymes from the walls, is now known to have a marked effect on the amount of enzyme obtained. Enzymes not detected include pectin lyase (Byrde & Fielding, 1968; Paynter & Jen, 1974) and, other than at a very low level, cellulase (e.g. Behrens, 1898; Schellenberg, 1908; Bruschi, 1912; Cole & Wood, 1961*b*; Calonge, Fielding, Byrde & Akinrefon, 1969). Pectin lyase has however been detected in extracts of hazel nut (*Corylus avellana*) infected by *M. fructigena* (S.A. Archer, priv. comm.).

The spatial distribution of enzymes within an infected fruit has also been studied (e.g. Byrde, Fielding, Archer & Davies, 1973; Paynter & Jen, 1974). Some were detected in increased amount, both in infected and adjacent healthy tissue.

Secondly, evidence has emerged, particularly from the detailed analytical data of Cole & Wood (1961*a*) and Reinganum (1964), that the enzymes are not only present, but also active. Thus Cole & Wood demonstrated a total loss of about 20% of pectic substances (based on carbazole estimation of extracts) following infection of apples by *M. fructigena*. There was an increase in monomeric D-galacturonic acid, indicating some form of PG attack. The pectic substances that remained were much more soluble in dilute alkali, suggesting that extensive demethylation by PE had occurred and that pectic acid (and its salts) had been formed. Willaman (1920) had earlier suggested that a hydrophilic gel of calcium pectate was formed in pectin degraded by *M. fructicola*, and that this gel was responsible for the firmness of invaded tissue. He also suggested that

---

Fig. 7.1.   Scanning electron micrographs of embedded and etched pear fruitlet tissues infected by *M. fructigena*.

(A)   Rib-like structure in host wall (HW) (x 2,800).

(B)   Longitudinal section of such a structure, showing intercellular fungus (EF) (x 7,000). (Mature pear).

(C)   Section showing intercellular hypha in host wall and cross-section of intracellular fungus (IF) (x 3,500).

All magnifications are approximate.

(Photos: R.J. Pring)

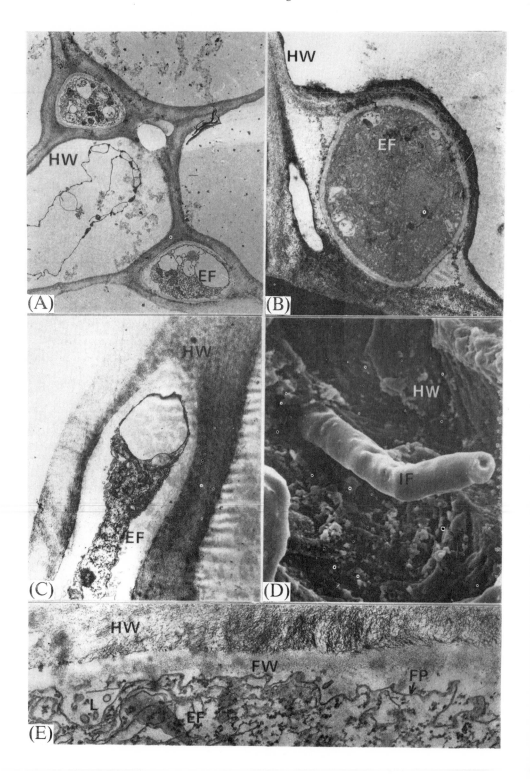

the hydrophilic nature of this gel helped the fungus in the fruit mummy. The virtual absence of cellulase secretion by the pathogen is presumably also significant, in that it permits part of the fruit tissue to survive intact. Reinganum (1964) stressed the difference between solubilization and breakdown of pectic substances, based on contrasting effects in green and ripe peach tissue infected by *M. fructicola*. He referred to the solubilization that occurs in the ripening of healthy peaches, and the favourable conditions provided for the advance of the pathogen if the fruit became infected at this stage.

Other evidence suggesting extensive PE activity (Byrde *et al.*, 1973) is based on the liberation of free methanol from rotting apples, and on staining with iron/hydroxylamine reagent (Reeve, 1957), which detects pectic substances in an esterified form. Demethylation seems to occur generally in infected tissue, and is not localized. The presence of increased levels of arabinose in infected apples has also been recorded (R.J.W. Byrde and A.H. Fielding, unpublished) indicating the presence of active AF.

As mentioned in Chapter 5, the advent of modern methods of protein separation has called for a re-examination of the extracellular enzymes. Table 7.1 summarises the effects of multiple forms of wall-degrading enzymes of *M. fructigena* on apple tissue, and shows those that have been detected in recently-infected fruit; it demonstrates the need to take the molecular form into account before ascribing effects to an enzyme activity in general. The PG is a particularly good example: this enzyme exists in at least four forms when the fungus is grown on a pectate medium, of which only those with pI values 4.6 and 5.5, although not detected *in vivo*, seem capable of macerating apple fruit tissue. The patterns of cell-separating and PG activities following different drastic heat treatments of this component were so similar, and unique, as to suggest that the PG itself was responsible for the cell separation (Archer & Fielding, 1975). By contrast, the PG of pI 9.7, which is the predominant form

---

Fig. 7.2.   Electron micrographs of pear fruitlet tissue infected by
            M. fructigena.

(A) Thin section showing host wall (HW) and intercellular
    fungus (EF). Note partly collapsed host protoplast and
    intact plasmalemma (x 5,000).

(B) Thin section showing intercellular hypha distorting the
    host wall (x 14,000).

(C) Oblique thin section of fungal hypha within the host
    wall (x 12,000).

(D) Scanning electron micrograph showing intracellular fungus
    (IF) penetrating the host wall (etched resin section)
    (x 1,400).

(E) Thin section of host-pathogen interface showing convoluted
    fungal plasmalemma (FP), a lomasome (L) and fungal wall
    (FW); the fibrillar host wall (HW) shows variable intensity of staining (x 46,000).

All magnifications are approximate.

(Photos: R.J. Pring)

TABLE 7.1. EFFECTS OF EXTRACELLULAR WALL-DEGRADING ENZYMES OF *M. FRUCTIGENA* ON APPLE FRUITS

Enzyme	pI value	Release of sugar residues from walls *	Tissue 'maceration' ‡	Tissue leakage ‡ ∅	Detected *in vivo* ∅
AF	3.0	+/-	- **	-	Yes
	6.8	++	- **	-	Yes
PE	4.5 - 4.9	not tested	not tested	?	Yes
PG	4.6	+	+++	++	No
	5.5	not tested	+++	+++	No
	9.7	++	-	-	Yes
PL	8.2	(++)	+	+	No

References   * Knee *et al.* (1975);   ‡ Archer (1973*b*, p. 293); Archer *et al.* (1972);   ∅ Byrde *et al.* (1973); Laborda *et al.* (1974);   ** Byrde & Fielding (1968).

Intensity of effect shown by no. of 'plus' signs.

in tissue extracts, is virtually unable to bring about cell separation (Archer, Byrde & Fielding, 1972) although it can liberate uronides from de-esterified apple cell walls (Knee, Fielding, Archer & Laborda, 1975). As PL is also absent, this may explain why extracts of infected tissue, although containing PG, often fail to bring about breakdown of healthy tissue, confirming reports by several earlier workers (e.g. Valleau, 1915; Davison & Willaman, 1927) who were unable to detect cell-separating activity in extracts of infected fruit. Lin (1948) claimed that extracts of apple tissue infected by *M. fructicola* brought about cell separation (but not death) of healthy apple tissue, while Reinganum (1964) extracted from peach fruits infected by *M. fructicola* an enzyme that could macerate potato tissue. Thus differences may exist between *M. fructicola* and *M. fructigena* in this respect. Alternatively, the higher phenolic content of apple and pear tissue may have resulted in enzyme inhibition in extracts of those hosts (Archer, 1973*b*) (see below).

The significance of multiple forms of these enzymes deserves brief comment. Vessell (1972) has suggested that it is advantageous for several forms of the same intracellular enzyme to exist, each having a different charge to permit easier attachment on differently-charged subcellular particles. By analogy, if a pathogen's extracellular enzymes exist in several forms, different parts of the host tissue could be acted upon by the chemically most appropriate enzymic form. Thus, pathogens with the greatest number of multiple enzymic forms should tend to cause the greatest cellular disorganisation and subsequent death of host tissue.

Isoelectric focusing patterns from extracts of infected tissue, when taken in conjunction with results from similar extracts of healthy tissue and from culture filtrates of the pathogen, are also useful in determining the likely origin of enzymes found there. PG and PL in fungal infections are usually accepted as being of fungal origin (Wood, 1967, pp. 171-172), but increases in PE activity often reflect activation of host enzyme (e.g. Langcake, Bratt & Drysdale, 1973). In brown rot infection of fruit, the origin is not always clear (e.g. Paynter & Jen, 1974), but in apples infected with *M. fructigena* isoelectric focusing patterns have implicated fungal PE (Byrde *et al.*, 1973). On the basis of a firm binding to host tissue, Paynter & Jen, however, favoured a host origin for PE in peaches rotted by *M. fructicola*.

Assessment of the relative importance of the wall-degrading enzymes of *Monilinia* spp., as in many other host-pathogen systems, is not easy. The enzymes may well act synergistically or sequentially. In general, PG, perhaps in association with PE, has come to be regarded as of particular importance, partly because it degrades one of the main 'backbone' polymer chains in the wall and also because there is some evidence that it is often the first enzyme to be secreted by a pathogen in contact with wall tissue (Albersheim & Anderson-Prouty, 1975). However, in the *M. fructigena*-apple system, Howell (1975) reached a different conclusion. She examined 119 isolates obtained by treatment of conidia of *M. fructigena* with a mutagen (mostly *N*-methyl-*N*'-nitro-*N*-nitrosoguanidine), in an attempt to correlate virulence (rate of pathogen advance *in vivo*) with secretion *in vitro* of PG, AF and PE. Multiple regression analysis of the data showed that up to 37% of the variability in virulence could be accounted for in terms of the parameters for pectolytic enzyme secretion and, of these enzymes, AF was significantly ($P = 0.01$) correlated with virulence. The reason for this result is not clear, but three possibilities were put forward (Howell, 1975): (1) arabinose (the end product of AF action) is a good carbon source for growth of *M. fructigena* (Archer, 1973*b*) and better than D-galacturonic acid; (2) arabinose is present in some phyto-haemagglutinins present in plant cell walls (Allen & Neuberger, 1973) that may act as enzyme inhibitors (Albersheim & Anderson, 1971), and AF may degrade these, as it can hydrolyse an apple wall glycoprotein (Knee, 1975); (3) AF may not itself be important, but its biosynthesis may be under the same control system as another, more important enzyme. It is perhaps significant that AF is the enzyme showing most variability between the different species (Willetts, Byrde, Fielding & Wong, 1976). The relative importance *in vivo* of the two extracellular forms of AF of *M.fructigena* was discussed by Laborda *et al.* (1974) who considered that the form of pI 3.0 was better suited to conditions of low pH or high polyphenol concentration. Knee *et al.* (1975) showed that the AF of pI 6.5 - 7.0 had the greater effect in liberating arabinose from apple wall preparations. By contrast, Howell found PE of little importance; nor was PG significantly implicated when some correlation with AF secretion had been eliminated, confirming the results of Hall (1972) with the PG of *M. fructicola*. Hall had also shown significant correlations between virulence towards peach and growth rate of *M. fructicola in vitro* on pectin, pectate, malt and (sometimes) glucose - asparagine agars. Howell found no correlation between virulence and growth on potato-dextrose agar. Koval' (1969) reported a correlation between hyphal diameter and virulence of *M. fructigena* to apple.

Changes in the host plasmalemma

At the cellular level. In the course of TEM studies it was soon obvious that the plasmalemma (protoplast membrane) of a pear fruit cell, even after it had been displaced by an intracellular hypha, did not lose its physical cohe-rence (Calonge, Fielding, Byrde & Akinrefon, 1969) (see also Fig. 7.2(A)). Physiological studies, however, had earlier shown that, even if the membrane was intact, its function was drastically impaired.

The method frequently used in physiological studies is that of Tribe (1955) which is based on the ability of the host plasmalemma to function as a semi-permeable membrane, so enabling it to release water to an ambient solution of higher osmotic pressure. As a result, the protoplast shrinks away from the cell wall and the cell becomes plasmolysed. Tribe included a neutral red stain in his reagent, which is taken up only by viable protoplasts (Stadelmann & Kinzel, 1972). Cole (1956) used Tribe's method to examine thin hand-sections of apple, pear and unripe plum fruit tissue infected by *M. fructigena* or *M. laxa*. Whereas stained plasmolysed protoplasts could be seen in uninvaded tis-sue, host cells in the region of the advancing hyphae and behind them were nei-ther plasmolysed nor stained.

Further confirmation of membrane dysfunction in infected tissue came from the demonstration by conductivity measurements that electrolytes leaked more rapidly from apple tissues infected by *M. fructigena* than from healthy tissues, even from those within 1-3 mm from the edge of the advancing rot (Byrde *et al.*, 1973).

The effects of membrane leakage are likely to be considerable: sugars and amino acids would leak out of the cells, and should be valuable to the pathogen in supplying it with readily-utilisable carbon and nitrogen sources, such as sugars and asparagine. Both Cole & Wood (1961*a*) and Lacok, Stanova & Niznanska (1972) reported a depletion of sucrose in tissue of apple and apricot respectively infected by *M. fructigena*. Secondly, if membranes of vacuoles, mitochondria, chloroplasts or other organelles are damaged, their contents will become mixed, a process sometimes described as 'decompartmentalization'.

Amongst the reactions that may then occur is the oxidation of phenols by poly-phenol oxidase enzymes, leading to tissue browning. Some apple pathogens, e.g. *Penicillium expansum* (but not *M. fructigena*) are able to inhibit the host phenolase system (Cole & Wood, 1961*b*; Walker, 1969). In addition, increased permeability of the membranes of host lysosomes, which contain autolytic enzymes, may be of importance in tissue disorganisation (Pitt & Coombes, 1969). Membrane damage has been widely used in physiological plant pathology as a criterion of host cell death and accounts for many of the symptoms of 'brown rot'. Other criteria, such as staining with tetrazolium salts to assay functional dehydrogenase, have been little used in studies of the brown rot diseases.

At the biochemical level. Three broad classes of pathogen-produced toxins that can affect membrane function have been recognised in plant disease (Wood, Ballio & Graniti, 1972): (a) enzymes; (b) host-specific, non-enzymic toxins; (c) other toxins, mostly of low molecular weight.

Considering enzymes first, a likely cause of membrane dysfunction might seem to be the secretion of phospholipases or sterol-degrading enzymes by the pathogen. From ultrastructural evidence this does not lead to complete lysis. Sterol-degrading enzymes have not been studied in the brown rot fungi, but a phospholipase present in culture filtrates of *M. fructigena* failed to bring about membrane leakage in apple tissue (Byrde *et al.*, 1973), a result parallel with those obtained by other workers from studies on phospholipase (phosphatidase) in other host-pathogen systems (e.g. Stephens & Wood, 1975).

Despite the fact that the primary site of action of pectolytic enzymes is the cell wall, there are many reports in the literature that membrane damage can occur as a direct consequence of the action of these enzymes, including those secreted by the brown rot fungi. Table 7.1 lists those enzyme components capable of causing cell separation, and of causing membrane damage. The two effects appear to be correlated, as they are in many host-parasite systems. This and many other considerations led Basham & Bateman (1975) to put forward the view that membrane dysfunction is a secondary but inevitable consequence of wall damage. However, it is still possible that enzymes like pectin lyase may be capable of some direct effect on the plasmalemma, or that they can penetrate it and cause intracellular disturbance.

As already mentioned, extracts of apples (and pears) infected with *M. fructigena* do not cause membrane dysfunction in healthy tissue, and this may reflect rapid inactivation of the enzymes by oxidized polyphenols in the extract or even before extraction (Cole & Wood, 1961*b*). Even incorporation of thiol reagents in the extractant, to prevent tissue oxidation, or the use of acetone powders, has not led to the extraction of an enzyme form, e.g. the PG of pI 4.6, able to bring about cell separation or membrane dysfunction in healthy apple tissue. Membrane dysfunction in the brown rot diseases may thus not be due to pectolytic enzymes.

Turning to non-enzymic toxins, specific or otherwise, little evidence is available on the involvement of such compounds in fruit rotting. Cooley (1914) demonstrated the presence of oxalic acid, a known phytotoxin (Wood, 1967), at a concentration of 17.4 mg/kg tissue in peaches that had been infected by *M. fructicola* until fully rotted. However, F. Reyes (unpublished) detected none in apples rotted by *M. fructigena*. Davison & Willaman (1927) reported that oxalates did not macerate apple tissue. Hawkins (1915) suggested that an acidic toxin produced by host or pathogen might be involved in rotting peaches.

Methanol, which is produced by PE action *in vivo*, proved non-toxic to apple tissue at concentrations in excess of those to be expected even locally (Byrde *et al.*, 1973).

In infection of woody parts of fruit trees, there is no strong evidence for toxin involvement *in vivo*. Valenta (1950) showed that *M. laxa* could produce an acidic heat-stable compound *in vitro* that was toxic to apricot shoots. Hiroe & Matsuo (1957) postulated toxin production in *Monilia* disease of cherry, and Willer (1967) considered that a fungal toxin might be involved in blossom infection. Sutton & Clayton (1972), on the basis of xylem discoloration, considered that a toxin was present in peach branches blighted by *M. fructicola*. Clearly, more study is required of the way host cells are killed by the *Monilinia* spp.

Gas changes

Ethylene liberation and its possible role in host-pathogen relationships was reviewed by Hislop, Hoad & Archer (1973) and by Archer & Hislop (1975), with particular reference to infection of apple fruits by *M. fructigena*.

Infection is followed by evolution of ethylene; most of the gas arises from the zone where host cells are undergoing necrotic changes. The system is also heat-labile, e.g. after treatment at 50°C for 20 min – which did not kill the cells by Tribe's (1955) criteria (unpublished data) – the tissue no longer gave off ethylene when infected with *M. fructigena* (Hislop, Hoad & Archer, 1973). The fungus in culture produces little or no ethylene, strengthening evidence for a host role in biosynthesis. However, the antibiotic rhizobitoxine had a sharply differential effect as between ethylene production by healthy tissue and that by infected tissue, suggesting that the pathways are not the same (Hislop, Archer & Hoad, 1973). Also, unlike the results found in some host-pathogen systems (e.g. Lund & Mapson, 1970), ethylene is not evolved when isolated tissue is damaged by partially purified pectic enzyme preparations.

Ethylene is known to trigger defence mechanisms in some host-parasite systems, and to be an important plant growth substance (Hislop, Hoad & Archer, 1973), so it may well have a role, yet to be elucidated, in the *Monilinia*-host interaction.

Oxygen uptake increased when infection occurred, both in peaches infected by *M. fructicola* (Hall, 1967*b*) and in apples infected by *M. fructigena* (A.H. Fielding, unpublished). Presumably these effects are connected with phenolic oxidation.

Other gases evolved include methanol and ethanol (Byrde *et al.*, 1973) and also acetaldehyde (Hrdlicka, Curda & Bauer, 1971), which can be fungitoxic to the pathogen (Aharoni & Stadelbacher, 1973).

Other changes

Other changes resulting from infection include: increased transpiration, due to stomatal disturbance (Majernik & Niznansky, 1962), and reduction in chlorophyll and other pigments during die-back infection of apricot trees by *M. laxa* (Haspel-Horvatovic, 1965, 1972) (but see Vizarova, 1975, for report on cytokinin secretion *in vitro*); a lowering of the content of various sugars in fruit tissues infected by *M. fructigena* (Cole & Wood, 1961*a*; Lacok *et al.*, 1972), presumably as a result of utilisation by the pathogen; and changes in ascorbic acid, total acids, carbohydrates and minerals in apples infected by *M. fructigena* (Glodeanu, Marinescu & Glodeanu, 1973).

Gumming of xylem vessels in infection of woody tissues has been described (e.g. Zwintzscher, 1955; Ogawa & English, 1960; Erdelska, 1965; Sutton & Clayton, 1972). Erdelska, working with *M. laxa* attacking apricot, distinguished between the formation of wound gum, developing in living cells in the wood and entering the xylem, and of lacuna gum, produced from all cells, but only during the growing period. The gums appeared to be polysaccharides with a varying degree of impregnation by oxidised polyphenols. Rosik, Kubala, Lacok & Stanova (1969) showed that *M. laxa* induced gum formation in peach; the polysaccharides contained D-glucuronic acid and its *O*-methyl derivative, D-galactose, L-arabinose and D-xylose. Zwintzscher (1955) associated gumming in infected woody tissues with resistance, but Ogawa & English (1960) regarded it as indicative only of cambial activity.

RESISTANCE TO INFECTION

In host plants

A number of factors have been suggested to be of significance in the resistance of fruits to brown rot, and some of these are listed in Table 7.2; see also Chapter 9 for an account of breeding for resistance and lists of resistant cultivars. Caution is needed in interpreting statements that a factor is important in resistance, when evidence is based on only a few cultivars. Of these factors, explanations of two active (as distinct from passive) mechanisms have been put forward in biochemical terms, and another in terms of cellular changes.

Firstly, in the apple cultivar Edward VII, relatively resistant to *M. fructigena*, the conversion by the pathogen of various host phenolic acids to 4-hydroxybenzoic acid and related compounds has been described. The transformation is effected by the fungus (see Chapter 5), and was first observed *in vivo*; it represents a mild form of 'lethal synthesis', since the end-products are somewhat toxic to the pathogen, though much more toxic to other fungi (Fawcett & Spencer, 1967, 1968). Hall (1972), however, failed to establish a role for methanol-soluble phenolic compounds in the lower growth rate of *M. fructicola* in immmature peaches.

Secondly, the failure of conidia of *M. fructigena* to infect wounds in fruits of some cultivars of cider apple has been ascribed to the oxidation of host phenolics by host polyphenol oxidase, followed by polymerisation to brown oxidation products capable of precipitating extracellular enzymes important in pathogenicity (Byrde, 1957; Byrde, Fielding & Williams, 1960). Cole & Wood (1961*b*) considered that the incomplete destruction of apple pectic substances by *M. fructigena* probably reflected the inhibition of its pectolytic enzymes by oxidized phenolic substances (see Chapter 5), and demonstrated that *Penicillium expansum*, which is able to prevent phenolic oxidation taking place (see Walker, 1969), destroys the pectic substances to a much greater degree. This polyphenol effect has also been implicated in another host-pathogen system (*Rhizoctonia solani* attacking cotton; Hunter, 1974), although its role in host resistance in general is not yet proven (see Wood, 1967, pp. 455-461; also Valleau, 1915).

Thirdly, there is some evidence that the laying down of wound tissue by the host may limit the spread of the brown rot fungi. Thus Zwygart (1970) des-

TABLE 7.2.   FACTORS ASSOCIATED WITH HOST RESISTANCE*

Host‡	Factor	Remarks	References
Apple	Acidity of juice	Conflicting views	Wahl (1926); Katser (1933)
	Hydroxybenzoic acids	See text	Fawcett & Spencer (1967, 1968)
	Phenolic content	In cider apples; see text	Byrde (1957)
	Respiration rate	High for resistance	Sokolov (1962)
	Sugar content	Low for resistance	Wahl (1926)
Apricot	Duration of flowering	Long for susceptibility	Stoyanov (1975)
Cherry	Flowering date	In relation to weather	Köck (1910)
	Fruiting habit	Less clustering for resistance	Tehrani & Dickson (1973)
	Gumming of wounds	Conflicting views; see text	Ellsmann (1939); Mittmann-Maier (1940a); Ogawa & English (1960); Zwygart (1970)
Pear	Catalase, peroxidase	High for resistance	Rekhviashvili (1973)[ø]
Plum	Cork in lenticels	For resistance	Valleau (1915)
	Fibre and pentosan content	High for resistance	Willaman et al. (1925); Curtis (1928)
	Parenchyma plugs in stomata	For resistance	Valleau (1915)
	Skin thickness	Injury less likely	Valleau (1915); Willaman (1926)
	Texture on ripening	Firm for resistance	Valleau (1915)

* See also the Section on Latency.
‡ The factors cited may well apply to a wider range of fruit hosts.
ø But see also Glodeanu, Glodeanu & Marinescu (1973), working with apples.

cribed the formation of phellogen at the margin of twig lesions in stone and pome fruit trees, but not until eleven days after the fungus had stopped advancing. He therefore regarded this process as a means of preventing further lesion spread rather than as the cause of the halting of a progressive invasion.

Of possible relevance to resistance is the report by Koval' (1969) that mycelium of *M. fructigena* in fruit of resistant cultivars of apple underwent degeneration, hypoplasia and lysis. Although autolysis might be responsible, the effects are reminiscent of those observed by Pegg & Vessey (1973) in tomatoes resistant to *Verticillium albo-atrum*, and shown to be due to a host lytic system (see also Albersheim & Anderson-Prouty, 1975).

In addition, some of the explanations put forward for latency (see below) may be relevant to resistance in general.

Latency

There have been many reports of a particular form of resistance to infection by *M. fructicola* of young, green stone fruits at the pre-pithardened stage (Valleau, 1915; Collard, 1918; Curtis, 1928; Wade, 1956*a*; Jerome, 1958; Corbin, 1963; Jenkins & Reinganum, 1965). The reason for this resistance has not been determined, but suggestions have been made by several workers and are discussed below.

Wade (1956*a*) found that apricot fruits were infected by *M. fructicola* at an early stage of fruit development. Histological studies suggested that infection was through stomata and in several instances conidia, some of which had germinated, were found within the stomatal cavities. Further differentiation of the fungus did not take place until the fruit began to ripen, but then the fungus caused a fruit rot which became apparent at harvest or in stored fruits. The early infection of apricots did not produce symptoms of disease and is therefore an example of *latent infection*. Initial penetration probably takes place between full bloom and petal fall (Morschel, 1955; Wade, 1956*a*). It was tentatively suggested by Wade that an inhibitory substance, postulated to be present in green apricot tissues, prevents differentiation of *M. fructicola*.

Jerome (1958) concluded from a study of the infection of peaches by *M. fructicola* that conidia are deposited among the hairs on the surface of the fruits and the propagules accumulate during the season but remain dormant while the fruits are unripe. The low incidence of disease in the immature fruits was attributed by her to the effects of a high mechanical resistance of the epidermis to penetration by the spores. Curtis (1928) found that after the fungus had penetrated the fruits, both ripe and unripe fruit tissues were susceptible and that entry through the epidermis was the limiting factor. Thus damage to the host tissues by mechanical means such as bruising or physiological factors, which cause splitting of the fruit or similar effects, will increase the chances of successful penetration and subsequent rotting of adjacent tissues. Jerome suggested that the resistance of fruits to penetration is reduced as they ripen, and spores on the surfaces of the fruits are then able to become established within the tissues, thus *latent contamination* and not latent infection was claimed to be responsible for rotting of ripe fruits. The studies of Dunegan (1950), Powell (1951) and Phillips & Harvey (1975) also support Jerome's conclusions that epidemics arise owing to the conidia which are present on the surfaces of fruits and which germinate when the fruits begin to ripen; Phillips & Harvey reported the presence of up to 170,000 propagules on a healthy fruit. Jenkins & Reinganum (1965) questioned the ability of conidia to survive for long periods on fruits in the orchard, and also to remain dormant during wet periods when the fruits are still immature.

Jenkins & Reinganum (1965) observed small lesions on immature apricots following infection by M. *fructicola*, and these lesions were more frequently observed in a season when blossom wilt was severe. The response of the host to infection was variable, but usually lesions could be seen macroscopically; this is an example of *quiescent infection* if Gaümann's (1950) description of a latent infection as one which produces no symptoms is accepted. Only a few cells may be affected by penetration of apricot fruitlets by M. *fructicola*, or a more extensive diseased area with the formation of a periderm could develop. Periderm formation is probably a histological defence mechanism resulting in the localization of the fungus. Jenkins & Reinganum (1965) suggested that isolated infections may initiate a limited chemical response by the host whereby symptoms were not easily discernible, while several penetrations within a small area would produce a greater and more obvious reaction by the host. The results obtained suggest that sometimes the response of the host to penetration permanently inactivates the fungus. Data collected from trials with eradicant sprays indicated that some quiescent infections were established during the blossoming period, probably between petal fall and shuck fall, but that probably infection could take place for several weeks after blossoming.

Both latent and quiescent infections, which were initiated in spring, were reported by Kable on peaches and apricots in the semi-arid regions of the M.I.A., Australia (Kable, 1969*a*,*b*). He regarded these as unimportant in the aetiology of the disease. From a later study Kable (1971*b*) reported that protectant fungicides applied to peach trees at the time of fruit ripening failed to control 'short-term' latent infections of fruits by M. *fructicola*, but that the penetrative action of benomyl was effective under similar conditions. Kable (1969*a*) found also that latent infections of peaches developed during the ripening period. Jenkins & Reinganum (1965) suggested that quiescent infections are responsible for considerable losses of fruit on the tree and in storage, particularly in seasons when conditions are not favourable for fruit infection just before and at harvest time. They emphasized the importance of effective spraying routines during and for a period after blossoming, as these are the times when quiescent infections are initiated.

Possible explanations for latency/quiescence. During the time that elapses between the initial infection and the stage at which the fungus breaks out into active colonisation, many changes occur in the host. Of these, few may be involved in the maintenance, and finally loss, of latency. Thus Wade (1956*a*) tentatively suggested that an inhibitory substance was present in green apricot tissue that kept the fungus in a latent condition, but subsequently declined in amount; he thought that the inhibitor might be an antibiotic or an organic acid. Ogawa (1958) reported that 'gaseous emanations' from green peach fruits were toxic to germinating conidia of M. *fructicola*; those from ripe fruits of peach, apricot and cherry were stimulatory. Wade & Cruickshank (1973) demonstrated that the addition of extracts from ripe or unripe fruit to the spore inoculum resulted in the development of a progressive infection, and postulated that the availability of host stimulatory substances to the latent pathogen was the main factor involved. The stimulatory substance was able to overcome the inhibitory effect of host polyphenols on the pathogen's pectolytic enzymes.

Jenkins & Reinganum (1965) considered some form of chemical defence to be a prerequisite for quiescent infection. They mentioned the possibility of inhibition of pectolytic enzymes by phenolic compounds, but also described the formation of a periderm, which they suggested constituted a second line of defence when the chemical resistance mechanism was overcome.

A completely different explanation for latency, at least in apple fruits, has been put forward by Swinburne (1975), who demonstrated that microbial proteases could act as 'elicitors', i.e. substances stimulating biosynthesis, of benzoic acid accumulation (a resistance reaction) in apples. Thus latent infections, typical of *Nectria galligena* and other pathogens, resulted from protease secretion by the fungus that triggered off a host system leading to benzoic acid accumulation. Older fruits would have lost the capacity to accumulate benzoic acid. *M. fructigena*, by contrast, secretes little or no protease, and is not held back as a latent infection. This hypothesis seems worthy of examination in stone fruits, and it may be significant that *M. fructicola*, unlike *M. fructigena*, can secrete protease (see Chapter 5).

In non-host plants

Presumably because of its ease of culture and its comparatively narrow host range, *M. fructicola* was used in the classic studies of host resistance by Müller (1956, 1958) and Cruickshank & Perrin (1961). When drops of water containing a spore suspension of the fungus were placed in seed cavities of detached pods of bean (*Phaseolus vulgaris*) – not a host of *M. fructicola* – a substance toxic to the fungus diffused out of the host tissue into the drops. In the absence of spores, no such toxic material accumulated. The compound, phaseollin, which was later chemically identified and shown to be of host origin, was termed a *phytoalexin*, and its production was regarded as a host defence mechanism. Similar results, involving another phytoalexin (pisatin), were obtained when endocarp tissue of detached pea pods was inoculated with spores of *M. fructicola*. For reviews of the phytoalexin concept, see Cruickshank (1966) and Kuć (1972).

M. fructicola has since been shown to elicit the formation of various phytoalexins or phytoalexin-like substances in a range of plant tissues: potato tuber slices (van den Ende, 1964); soybean seedlings (Biehn, Kuć & Williams, 1968); white clover leaflets (Cruickshank, Veeraraghavan & Perrin, 1974); fruits of egg plant (*Solanum melongena*) (Ward, Unwin, Hill & Stoessl, 1975); immature roots of carrot and green fruits of *Capsicum annuum* (van den Ende, 1969). Inoculation with *M. fructicola* was used as a routine method to induce the formation of the phytoalexin capsidiol in fruits of sweet pepper (*C. frutescens*) (Stoessl, Unwin & Ward, 1972; Baker, Brookes & Hutchinson, 1975). Leaves of this species, by contrast, scarcely reacted (Ward, 1976). As with some other phytoalexin systems, capsidiol is more toxic to *M. fructicola*, which is not a pathogen of sweet pepper, than to fungi that are pathogenic to this host (Ward, Unwin & Stoessl, 1973). Electron microscopy of inoculated fruits showed that *M. fructicola* was arrested in the third cell layer, but not before it had caused damage to the cell walls (Jones, Graham & Ward, 1975).

Inoculation with *M. fructigena* and *M. laxa* has also been claimed to induce the synthesis of phytoalexin-like substances in a non-host plant; thus, Ksendzova & Nilova (1975) reported that formation of such compounds in leaves of two wheat cultivars led to the suppression of sporing pustules on subsequent infection by the rust fungus *Puccinia triticina* (= *P. recondita*). However, no phytoalexin has yet been isolated and characterized from a monocotyledonous plant.

Cruickshank (1966) postulated that the non-host response to *M. fructicola* was triggered by a substance (now termed an *elicitor*) secreted by the invading fungus, and subsequently Cruickshank & Perrin (1968) demonstrated the presence, in the mycelium of *M. fructicola*, of the peptide 'monilicolin A' (see Chapter 5), capable of inducing the formation of phaseollin in *Phaseolus vulgaris* (but not of pisatin in *Pisum sativum*) at concentrations as low as 10^{-9}M. Subsequent work (Paxton, Goodchild & Cruickshank, 1974) has shown that triggering of phytoalexin formation by monilicolin A was not accompanied by the death of host cells, although necrobiosis occurred in a few isolated cells when tissue was inoculated with spores of *M. fructicola* (cf. Jones, Graham & Ward, 1975).

At first sight this work might seem of little relevance to the pathogenicity of the *Monilinia* spp. to fruits, especially as the initial choice of *M. fructicola* was more or less fortuitous. However, in subsequent comparisons of the ability of different fungi to elicit phytoalexin formation *M. fructicola* has often proved the most effective (e.g. van den Ende, 1964; Stoessl, Unwin & Ward, 1972; Ward, Unwin & Stoessl, 1975; Jones, Unwin & Ward, 1975).

Thus it would seem that some plants that are not hosts of *M. fructicola* recognise the fungus quickly and efficiently. Recognition is possibly mediated by some extracellular product. In a stimulating review which put forward new hypotheses to explain host-pathogen specificity at the biochemical level, Albersheim & Anderson-Prouty (1975) suggested that some elicitors, at least in fungi that show gene-for-gene relationships with their hosts, are similar in structure to some pathogen-produced phytotoxins; and that the biological role of elicitors in inducing phytoalexin formation may thus have evolved from the development of mechanisms in plants which result in the 'recognition' of pathogen-secreted molecules. The intensity of the response in non-host plants makes it tempting to speculate, therefore, that *M. fructicola* is 'recognised' as a potential pathogen of high virulence.

Albersheim & Anderson-Prouty also pointed out that the effect of monilicolin A on the natural hosts of *M. fructicola* has never been examined. It seems likely that, except in latent infections, the brown rot fungi possess some means of preventing their hosts from recognising their initial presence, and hence from mobilising resistance mechanisms in a sufficiently short time. Alternatively, the fungi may possess an efficient detoxication system for any phytoalexins produced by their hosts.

Chapter **8**

CHEMICAL CONTROL

The need to control the brown rot diseases arises from the serious economic losses that they can cause, and this Chapter starts with an assessment of these losses, before considering ways in which chemicals may be used to reduce them. The next Chapter describes other ways in which the diseases can be controlled.

There are several reasons why control is difficult: thus, as described in detail in earlier Chapters, the brown rot fungi frequently overwinter within the host tree and produce, close to susceptible tissue, large numbers of spores in the following season during conditions suitable for fresh infection. Furthermore, although but a single generation of the pathogen is involved in blossom infection, fruit can be infected over a fairly long period, during which successive generations of these freely-sporing pathogens enable them to build up rapidly even from a small overwintering inoculum. Latent infections and, in particular, the susceptibility of injuries in the fruit skin made by a variety of wound agents also pose special problems (see below, and the next Chapter). For a review of fungicidal control of the brown rot diseases, see also Kable (1971a); for a review of fungicides in general, see Torgeson (1969).

ECONOMIC IMPORTANCE

The economic importance of the fruit-rotting phase of the brown rot diseases is not difficult to quantify in a given orchard in a given season, as infected fruits are easily recorded in a sample, and are valueless. Alternatively the orchard as a whole can be examined (e.g. Croxall, Gwynne & Jenkins, 1953). However, it is not so easy to assess the overall losses in a country, or on a world-wide scale, because of several factors. For example, there are marked variations in disease incidence from one year to another, largely the result of seasonal differences in weather. Again, the monetary value of the crop per unit weight fluctuates markedly. Another important factor is the adoption and success of control measures. Thus the introduction in 1968 of benomyl, and later of other related fungicides, which are generally highly effective, has so greatly transformed the situation that in some countries the diseases now frequently cause only trivial losses. However, should the widespread development of strains of the pathogen insensitive to these fungicides occur (see below), it would be reflected in a resurgence of the losses unless equally effective compounds were found.

It is therefore important to be aware of the potential damage that these fungi can cause, and did cause in years prior to the use of these compounds. An account of losses prior to 1954 was given by Wormald (1954).

M. fructicola is still the most important of the three species, and has caused severe losses of stone fruits, particularly peaches, in the U.S.A., Canada and Australia, both before and after harvest. Thus McCallan (1946), not mentioned by Wormald (1954), estimated that the fungus caused a mean loss of 4.6% in peach and cherry over the decade 1930-39 in the U.S.A. Conners (1967) referred to great damage on plums, and the loss of tons of peaches in parts of Canada. Fig. 8.1(A) shows in diagrammatic form the frequency of brown rot

infection of fruit at harvest from unsprayed stone fruit trees in fungicide
trials in the U.S.A. and New Zealand reported by Zehr (1972-74) and MacNab
(1975). As such trials are normally conducted in orchards where the disease
is severe, the figures probably tend to represent the highest level likely to
be encountered rather than a typical commercial loss.

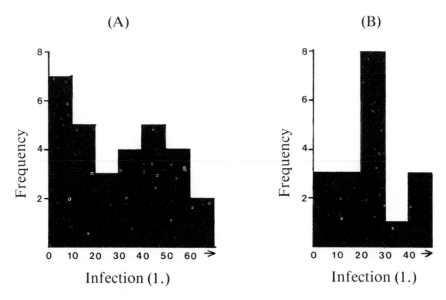

Fig. 8.1.   Frequency of occurrence of various infection levels on
            untreated stone fruit trees. (A), fruit rotting by
            M. fructicola; (B), blossom blighting by *M. laxa* (and
            occasionally *M. fructicola*).

In Eastern Australia, *M. fructicola* caused such severe losses (listed in Kable,
1969*a*) to peaches and other stone fruits in the period 1946-56 that a co-
ordinated Research Programme - the largest in the World against the brown rot
diseases - was mounted from 1957 to 1962 (Kable, 1971*b*). Losses worth 1 million
Australian dollars were reported by Kable in another severe epidemic in 1969 on
canning peaches in the Murrumbidgee Irrigation Areas alone, where such epidemics
occurred on average every four years, and lesser outbreaks in almost every other
year. In addition, *M. fructicola* caused a substantial reduction in the apricot
crop in six seasons between 1945 and 1968 through blossom infections (Kable,
1969*b*), and Wade (1960) reported that a decline in the Tasmanian apricot indus-
try was partly due to recurrent losses through *M. fructicola*.

By contrast, *M. fructigena* is much less damaging, although it occasionally causes economically important losses of apple and plum fruits in Europe, particularly in hot summers. For example, Burchill & Edney (1972) reported a fungicide experiment in a badly infected English apple orchard where trees sprayed
with captan suffered 35.8% fruit infection by *M. fructigena*. The disease is
frequently mentioned as an important pathogen in plant disease surveys (e.g.
Masurat, Peschel & Stephan, 1966). Ciferri (1953) reported 7.3% infection of
apples on unsprayed trees of Rome Beauty in Italy. In store it is not often
very serious: thus Preece (1967) mentioned mean losses of 0.2 - 1.5% in samples

of Cox's Orange Pippin apples taken from refrigerated stores in England from 1961 to 1965, with a range of 0.1 - 4.5% for individual orchards. Evans (1969) stated that brown rot and other rots (due to *Botrytis cinerea* and *Penicillium* spp.) usually accounted for less than 5% loss in storage, in a survey carried out in a typical English commercial store.

Little information is available on fruit losses caused by *M. laxa*, which is primarily a pathogen of blossom spurs and twigs. The economic importance of this phase of the disease is much more difficult to estimate than with fruit infection but can be extremely serious. Blossom damage can be reflected in two ways: through the loss of bloom - though, as with frost injury, the short-fall in yield is not necessarily proportional to the amount of blossom lost, as compensatory factors may be involved. Secondly, the amount of blossom in sub-sequent years may be reduced, following the spread of the pathogen into spurs and branches. The disease is particularly severe in Eastern Europe. Thus Youganova (1946) reported the incidence of twig infections by *M. laxa* to be as severe as 55% in an orchard in the Crimea. Sarejanni, Demetriades & Zachos (1953) reported severe damage to almond, and the destruction of the entire apricot crop around Athens. Vitanov (1961) recorded 45-50% incidence on one cultivar of apricot. Khokhryakova (1964) reported losses of 60-97% of apple blossom in the Khabarovsk area of the Far East of the U.S.S.R. by the related species *M. mali.* Fig. 8.1(B) gives the frequency of blossom blighting by *M. laxa* (and, in a few trials, by *M. fructicola* also) on unsprayed stone fruit trees in recent trials in the U.S.A. and New Zealand listed by Zehr (1972-74) and MacNab (1975); as with Fig. 8.1(A), the data are probably largely from orchards with a history of blossom infection.

As mentioned above, well-timed and thorough applications of benomyl and related fungicides generally reduce infection drastically, both of fruits and of blos-som and woody tissues. One exception was reported by Kable (1975), where even a full programme of benomyl did not reduce infection of peaches below 24%.

VULNERABLE STAGES IN THE PATHOGEN'S LIFE CYCLE

Plant pathogens are particularly vulnerable to chemicals at two stages in their life cycle: (a) when the spore of the pathogen is exposed on the host surface for at least several hours before it can penetrate the host and initiate an infection, and (b) in the dormant season, when the host can better tolerate chemicals with powerful biological effects. The advent of fungicides which affect nuclear division as their primary action has led to the possibility of inhibition at a third stage: (c) the onset of sporulation. These are consi-dered in turn in more detail below.

PROTECTION OF THE HEALTHY HOST AGAINST INFECTION BY SPORES

The classical concept of protective action by a fungicide was the inhibition of germination of the pathogen's spore by means of a film of fungicide deposit (Horsfall, 1956, pp. 31-44). Unlike many pathogens, however, spores of the brown rot fungi, when attacking fruit, generally penetrate through an injury in the fruit surface (this does not apply to the floral parts). The success of a conventional 'protectant' fungicide, applied to the healthy fruit, is thus of greatly reduced value if the wound agent, in removing the fruit skin, also re-moves the fungitoxic deposit. Should this happen, fungistatic action may be expected only if one of several conditions is met: (i) the fungicide is re-distributed by water (e.g. Hislop, 1967*a*) or in the vapour phase (Bent, 1967;

Hislop, 1967*b*); (ii) its application is made just after the spore alights; or (iii) the fungicide is sufficiently systemic to have penetrated the host tissue such that it is present at a fungitoxic concentration at the deepest point of injury.

The times at which the host is most susceptible have long been recognised to be at blossom time (for blossom infection) and the last few weeks before harvest. The timing of sprays with protective fungicides has been planned accordingly, with a tendency for fewer applications in some countries than in others, and on some fruits than on others.

Kable (1975) recently evaluated spray timing on canning peaches in the light of the introduction of modern systemic fungicides such as benomyl. In one season he demonstrated the value of a spray one month before picking for controlling fruit rot at harvest; by contrast, a spray applied nine days before harvest gave better disease control in stored fruit. The problem of controlling latent infection was also discussed, as in an earlier paper (Kable, 1971*b*).

To inhibit spore germination, a compound must possess fungistatic or fungicidal activity. Although commercial tests of fungicides now rely primarily on greenhouse or field tests, an estimate of toxicity can be obtained by means of a spore germination test *in vitro*, and the ease of culture and economic importance of *M. fructicola* led to its frequent adoption in the past as a test organism in fungicide screening, dating from the work by McCallan and his associates at the Boyce Thompson Institute, U.S.A. (e.g. McCallan & Wilcoxon, 1939) and culminating in the recommendations for spore germination test procedures of the American Phytopathological Society (1943). Masri (1967) published a method for use with *M. laxa*.

Methods of application of fungicides

In the field. Fungicides may be applied in many ways. The most usual is by ground spraying, with a power machine, and air or hydraulic pressure to propel the spray to the target. The volume of liquid applied can vary from spraying 'to run-off' (e.g. 200 Imp. gal/acre; 2240 1/ha) with hand lances ('guns') or automatic nozzles, down to ultra-low volume (e.g. 3 Imp. gal/acre; 34 1/ha) by means of an atomizer, with appropriate adjustment of the fungicide concentration. Overhead spraying has also been used successfully (Ogawa, Manji & Schreader, 1975).

Spraying from aircraft has been tried (Vasev, 1973; Zehr, 1974, Report 74), and the systemic properties and high fungicidal activity of thiophanate-methyl led Ogawa, Yates, Manji & Cowden (1972) to use it in this way against *M. laxa* blossom blight on apricot, applying it in 9.2 U.S. gal water/acre. Disease incidence was reduced significantly, from 31% to 9.5% of blighted blossoms.

In past years dusting was also extensively used and is still sometimes recommended (e.g. MacSwan & Koepsell, 1974), although the deposit is rarely as uniform as that achieved by spraying.

Post-harvest treatment. For fruit infection, fungicides may also be applied post-harvest as a dip. This method is widely used and has several features to commend it: economy of material, much less likelihood of insensitive strains of the pathogen developing in the field, and no contamination of the environment with consequent risk of side-effects. On the other hand, where

appreciable fruit infection occurs in the orchard before harvest, the method
is clearly less useful; it involves the use of expensive equipment, and can be
used only with non-toxic compounds. For a general review of post-harvest dips,
see Eckert & Sommer (1967); the specific problem of dipping against brown rot
of stone fruit was discussed by Kable (1974), who advocated the addition of a
wetting agent to the benomyl-dicloran dip used. He considered that the dip
should remain effective for at least 3 weeks without replacement. It would
require stirring well before each set of fruit was dipped, and could be 'top-
ped up' if necessary.

Sometimes formulations of the fungicides in an oil or wax emulsion have proved
particularly effective dips (e.g. Wells, 1972; Phillips, 1975; Koffman & Kable,
1975; Zehr *et al.*, 1975), and the use of hot water/fungicide dips has proved
advantageous (see the next Chapter). Wax formulations can also be applied to
the harvested fruit by spray or mechanical brush.

Fungicides in use as protectants

Table 8.1 gives details of the chemical composition, trade names and mammalian
toxicity of compounds in current use, and Table 8.2 lists data on antifungal
activity *in vitro* to *M. fructicola*. Other groups of important compounds sys-
tematically studied *in vitro* against *Monilinia* spp. include s-triazines (Wolf,
Schuldt & Baldwin, 1955), organic sulphur derivatives (Rich & Horsfall, 1961;
Carter, Garraway, Spencer & Wain, 1963, 1964; Owens, 1969; Richardson & Thorn,
1969), griseofulvin and related compounds (Crosse, McWilliam & Rhodes, 1964),
and 2-alkyl imidazolines (Wellman & McCallan, 1946).

The introduction of the *benzimidazole* group of fungicides revolutionised control of many plant diseases, including those caused by the brown rot fungi.
What may be regarded as the 'central' member of the group, *carbendazim* ('MBC'),
has been comparatively little tested for brown rot control, but both *benomyl*
(for which extensive data are available) and *thiophanate-methyl* break down to
carbendazim, which is generally regarded as the principal active molecule.
(For details of these inter-conversions see Kaars Sijpesteijn, 1972).

The primary mode of action of the group appears to be against fungal nuclear
division (Davidse, 1973; Hammerschlag & Sisler, 1973), and the compounds thus
generally exert a fungistatic rather than a fungicidal effect - i.e. the
pathogen is prevented from growing rather than being killed outright. However,
an equally important consequence of their fungistatic action may be the marked
suppression of sporulation of many pathogens, including, to varying degrees,
that of *Monilinia* spp. (e.g. Zehr, 1972, p. 41; Zehr, 1974, p. 31). In addition, the compounds have systemic properties, although translocation following
foliar application to woody plants is not extensive. Benomyl, at least, is
however capable of penetrating fruit tissue to a limited depth (Kable,
1971*a,b*; Ravetto & Ogawa, 1972; Phillips, 1975), which is probably of great
value against the brown rot pathogens. Ramsdell & Ogawa (1973*b*) demonstrated
the systemic activity of carbendazim in almond blossoms following pre-bloom
sprays of benomyl or carbendazim. Upham & Delp (1973) claimed that the addition of two surfactants to benomyl sprays increased penetration of herbaceous
plants. Kable (1975) reported that benomyl also had eradicant properties.

Of somewhat different chemical structure, and not subject to breakdown to
carbendazim, is *thiabendazole*. Its physiological mode of action is nevertheless probably similar to that of the other members of the group (Kaars

TABLE 8.1.   PRINCIPAL FUNGICIDES USED AGAINST THE BROWN ROT FUNGI

Common name	Chemical name*	Some trade names	Acute LD50 (oral, rats)+ (mg/kg)
Benzimidazole group:			
Benomyl	Methyl-N-(1-butylcarbamoyl)-benzimidazol-2-yl carbamate	Benlate	> 10,000
Carbendazim	Methyl benzimidazol-2-yl carbamate	Bavistin, Derosal	> 6 400 ‡
Thiabendazole	2-(4-Thiazolyl) benzimidazole	Mertect, Tecto	3 330
Thiophanate-methyl	1,2-Di-(3-methoxycarbonyl-2-thioureido) benzene	Mildothane, Topsin M	7 500
Captan	N-(Trichloromethylthio)-3a,4,7,7a-tetrahydrophthalimide	Orthocide	9 000
Chlorothalonil	Tetrachloroisophthalonitrile	Bravo, Daconil	> 10,000 ø
Dichlone	2,3-Dichloro-1,4-naphthaquinone	Phygon	1 300
Dicloran	2,6-Dichloro-4-nitroaniline	Allisan, Botran	1500 – 4 000
Dithianon	2,3-Dicyano-1,4-dihydro-1,4-dithia-anthraquinone	Delan, Thynon	1 015
Dodine	n-Dodecylguanidine acetate	Cyprex, Melprex	1 000
Triforine	1,4-Di-(2,2,2-trichloro-1-formamidoethyl) piperazine	Cela W.524, Saprol	> 6 000
Vinclozolin	3-(3,4-Dichlorophenyl)-5-methyl-5-vinyl-1,3-oxazolidine-2,4-dione	BAS 352F	10,000 ++
—	1-Isopropylcarbamoyl-3-(3,5-dichlorophenyl) hydantoin	26,019 RP, Rovral	> 2 000 **

* Names according to British Standards Institution, where available. + Values from Martin (1972), except as indicated. ‡ Woodcock (1972). ø Turner et al. (1964). ** Lacroix et al. (1974). ++ Hess & Löcher (1975).

TABLE 8.2. TOXICITY TO *M. FRUCTICOLA IN VITRO*

Fungicide	ED$_{50}$*	Other compounds tested	Reference
Benomyl	0.5 ppm [+]	Thiabendazole	Edgington *et al.* (1971)
Captan; folpet	10 μM; 1.7 μM	Other NSCCl$_3$ compounds	Lien *et al.* (1974)
Chlorothalonil	2.0 μM [‡]	Other isophthalonitriles	Turner & Battershell (1969)
Dichlone	0.1 μM	Other quinones	Owens (1953)
Dodine	6 μM	Other n-alkylguanidine acetates	Brown & Sisler (1960)

* Against spore germination, unless otherwise stated.

[+] Against mycelial growth.

[‡] Median lethal dose.

Sijpesteijn, 1972); for example, most strains of fungi that are tolerant to benomyl also show cross-tolerance to thiabendazole.

The group has generally given very good control of the brown rot diseases, both against blossom infection, and against fruit rot either as a pre-harvest spray or as a post-harvest dip, sometimes in hot water (see next Chapter). Common rates of application, in terms of active ingredient, are 0.025% for carbendazim and benomyl, 0.05% for thiophanate-methyl, and 0.03% for thiabendazole. In general, the last-named has given rather less effective control of the diseases; in a few trials, benomyl has proved less effective than usual (e.g. Kable, 1975). Tables 8.3 and 8.4 summarise reports on the performance of these fungicides against the brown rot pathogens in the field and by post-harvest dips respectively. For the latter, Koffman (1973) has shown an advantage in preparing benomyl and thiophanate-methyl dips several days before use; presumably this allows their conversion to carbendazim.

However, problems have arisen in the use of this group of compounds.

(1) They are toxic to earthworms and their use as sprays can result in drastic reductions in soil populations, especially of the surface-feeding species, *Lumbricus terrestris* (Stringer & Lyons, 1974).

(2) Fruit of certain apple cultivars, e.g. Cox's Orange Pippin and Golden Delicious, may have a higher proportion of their area affected by russet following such sprays (Byrde, 1972).

(3) Another complication arises from the selectivity of benomyl and related fungicides as between groups and even genera of fungi. Thus, as described in detail by Bollen & Fuchs (1970), the Phycomycetes are not affected, and it is primarily the Ascomycetes and Deuteromycetes (including *Monilinia* and *Sclerotinia*, but excluding some such as *Alternaria* spp.) that are controlled. Use of this group of fungicides has thus led to increasing severity of infection by Phycomycetes as, for example, by *Rhizopus* attacking peach fruits (Koffman & Kable, 1975). To obviate this effect, a second fungicide is sometimes added to benomyl (e.g. dicloran, that controls *Rhizopus* on peach).

(4) The widespread use of benomyl and related fungicides for disease control has frequently been followed by the appearance of pathogen isolates insensitive to these compounds (Evans, 1971; Dekker, 1972). Some isolates are frequently cross-tolerant to other fungicides in the group. A strain of the related fungus *S. homeocarpa* insensitive to benomyl has also been reported (Goldenberg & Cole, 1973). Abelentsev (1973), using three transfers in a 290-day period on benomyl-containing agar, induced *M. fructigena* and *M. laxa* to tolerate concentrations 3.6 and 2.8 times respectively higher than before. The acquired resistance was highly specific; it was not transmitted to progeny, and disappeared on using other fungicides. A recent development of particular interest is the appearance of a benomyl-insensitive isolate of *M. fructicola* in the field in Australia (Whan, 1976). Earlier, Tate, Ogawa, Manji & Bose (1974) had failed to detect insensitivity in 37 isolates of *M. fructicola* and 26 of *M. laxa* from California, despite the use of benomyl since 1972 (see also Ogawa, Manji & Schreader, 1975), and Kundert (1975) had reported no tolerance in *M. laxa* in Germany. Careful watch should therefore be kept for the appearance of similar isolates of this and the related species elsewhere in the world.

TABLE 8.3. CONTROL OF BROWN ROT DISEASES BY FIELD APPLICATIO   E BENZIMIDAZOLE GROUP OF FUNGICIDES (see also individual trial reports listed by Zen⊥, 1972-1974 and MacNab, 1975).

Host	Type of disease+	Pathogen*	Compound	References
Almond	B.B.	L	Benomyl, carbendazim	Ramsdell & Ogawa (1973b)
Apple	B.B.	M	Benomyl	Byrde & Melville (1971); Catling (1971)
	F.R.	Fg	Benomyl	Cole et al. (1971, 1973); Burchill & Edney (1972)
			Thiophanate-methyl	Cole et al. (1971, 1973)
Apricot	B.B.	Monilinia spp.	Benomyl	Waffelaert (1969); Heaton (1974); see also Bolay et al. (1972)
		L	Thiophanate-methyl	Ogawa, Yates, Manji & Cowden (1972); see also Bolay et al. (1972)
	F.R.	Fc	Benomyl	Ogawa et al. (1968); Heaton (1974)
Cherry	B.B.	Fc, L	Benomyl	Ogawa et al. (1968); see also Kundert (1972)
	B.B.& F.R.	Fc	Benomyl, thiophanate-methyl	Jones (1975)
Nectarine	B.B.& F.R.	Fc, L	Benomyl	Wells & Gerdts (1971); Heaton (1974)
Peach	B.B.	Fc	Benomyl	Ogawa et al. (1968); Northover (1972); Heaton (1974)
		Fc, L	Thiophanate-methyl	Ogawa, Yates, Manji & Cowden (1972); see also Kundert (1972)
	F.R.	Fc	Benomyl	Chandler (1968, 1974a,b); Delp & Klöpping (1968); Ogawa et al. (1968); Rohrbach (1973); Heaton (1974); Kable (1975)
			Carbendazim	Heaton (1974)
			Thiabendazole	Chandler (1974b)
		Monilinia spp.	Thiophanate-methyl	Ishii (1970); Rohrbach (1973); Heaton (1974)
Plum (prune)	B.B.& F.R.	Fg, L	Benomyl, thiophanate-methyl	Renaud (1970)
			Thiabendazole	Renaud (1968, 1970).

* Fc = *M. fructicola*; Fg = *M. fructigena*; L = *M. laxa*; M = *M. laxa* f. *mali*
+ B.B. = Blossom blight; F.R. = Fruit rot

TABLE 8.4.   POST-HARVEST CONTROL OF BROWN ROT (DUE TO *M. FRUITICOLA*) WITH
THE BENZIMIDAZOLE GROUP OF FUNGICIDES

Fruit	Fungicide	References
Apricot	Benomyl	Ogawa *et al.* (1968)*; Beattie & Outbred (1970); Jones *et al.* (1973).
	Thiabendazole	Beattie & Outbred (1970).
Cherry	Benomyl	Ogawa *et al.* (1968)*; Beattie & Outbred (1970); Jones & Burton (1973); Jones *et al.* (1973); Jones (1975); Koffman & Kable (1975).
	Carbendazim	Koffman & Kable (1975).
	Thiabendazole	Beattie & Outbred (1970); Jones & Burton (1973); Jones *et al.* (1973).
	Thiophanate-methyl	Jones & Burton (1973); Jones *et al.* (1973); Jones (1975).
Nectarine	Benomyl	Wells & Gerdts (1971); Smith & Anderson (1972, 1975); Wells (1972); Jones & Burton (1973).
Peach	Benomyl	Delp & Klöpping (1968); Ogawa *et al.* (1968)*; Daines (1970)*; Smith (1971); Stone *et al.* (1971); Smith & Anderson (1972, 1975); Smith & Keil (1972); Wells (1972)*; Jones & Burton (1973); Jones *et al.* (1973); Koffman (1973); Rohrbach (1973); Wade & Gipps (1973)*; Kable (1974); Wells & Bennett (1975)*; Zehr *et al.* (1975)*.
	Thiabendazole	Fripp & Dettman (1969); Daines (1970)*; Stone *et al.* (1971); Jones & Burton (1973); Jones *et al.* (1973); Wade & Gipps (1973).
	Thiophanate-methyl	Jones & Burton (1973); Jones *et al.* (1973); Wade & Gipps (1973).
Prune	Benomyl, thiabendazole, thiophanate-methyl	Jones & Burton (1973)*; Jones *et al.* (1973)*.

* includes mixtures with dicloran.

Benomyl and thiophanate-methyl dips also controlled
Monilinia sp. (*M. fructigena*?) on apple (Cole *et al.*,
1973).

The development of induced tolerance in the laboratory has also been reported
with polyram (Good & MacNeill, 1972), with copper sulphate (Mader & Schneider,
1948; Partridge & Rich, 1962), and with captan, glyodin, sulphur and mercuric
chloride (Partridge & Rich, 1962). Grover & Moore (1961) were able to induce

tolerance to cycloheximide (Acti-dione), dodine and folpet (Phaltan) in laboratory cultures of M. fructicola and/or M. laxa. Tolerance was not induced to
ferbam and dichlone, and all adapted isolates reverted to wild-type sensitivity after growing for two to five generations in the absence of fungicide.

The deliberate occasional use in the field of some alternative sprays has been
advocated, to minimise the likelihood of the emergence of pathogen strains
tolerant to a given spray (Evans, 1971; Dekker, 1972); another approach is to
use mixtures of fungicides (e.g. Jones, 1975). Since a fungicide acting
against a single biochemical 'site' is more likely to encounter resistance
problems (Wolfe, 1976), the second fungicide should preferably be one with
'multi-site' action. These are wise precautions.

It is thus now essential that alternatives to the benzimidazole group of fungicides should be available for use against the brown rot diseases, and the
merits and demerits of other fungicides are listed below, to assist in the
making of a rational choice.

The *captan* group (captan, captafol and folpet) are long-established protectant
fungicides of low mammalian toxicity and with 'multi-site' action, capable of
giving at least partial control of both blossom blight and fruit rot infection
of stone fruit by M. fructicola and M. laxa, but are generally inferior to the
benomyl group (e.g. Mitchell, Ravenscroft, Berger & Moore, 1963; Northover,
1972; Zehr, 1972, 1973, 1974; Jones, Burton & Tennes, 1973; Chandler, 1974b;
Heaton, 1974). Captan has also been used as a post-harvest dip (e.g. Smith,
Haller & McClure, 1956; Smith, 1971; Zehr, 1972; Jones & Burton, 1973; Jones
et al., 1973; Rohrbach, 1973). Captan sprays followed by benomyl-wax dips have
led to fruit injury (Chastagner & Ogawa, 1973). On peach fruit, dips (Smith,
1970) and sprays (Hutton & Kable, 1970) have sometimes resulted in injury.

Chlorothalonil is another candidate fungicide for control of brown rot of stone
fruit (Zehr, 1973, 1974; Heaton, 1974), although injury on two peach cultivars
has been reported (Zehr, 1974, pp. 40-41), and the fungicide is liable to russet fruit of some apple cultivars. Against M. fructicola on sweet cherries,
Jones (1975) found it inferior to several other fungicides as a spray, although
it had shown promise as a post-harvest dip (Jones et al, 1973). It rapidly
killed spores of M. fructicola in vitro (Turner & Battershell, 1970).

Dichlone has a long history of partial success against brown rot (e.g. Powell,
1951; Ogawa, Manji & Bose, 1968; Zehr, 1972) and is still recommended for use
against the blossom wilt stage on cherries (e.g. MacSwan & Koepsell, 1974).
It is somewhat liable to cause fruit spotting, and also to give rise to mild
dermatitis on the spray operator. It rapidly killed spores of M. fructicola
in vitro (Turner, 1970).

Dicloran is often included, as mentioned above, in sprays and dips against M.
fructicola and M. laxa on peaches, particularly when benzimidazole-type fungicides are used. The latter are not effective against Rhizopus spp., which may
be controlled by the dicloran. However, the compound has some activity in its
own right against the brown rot fungi both as a spray (e.g. Hansen & Beckman,
1967; Zehr, 1973) and as a post-harvest dip (e.g. Cappellini & Stretch, 1962;
Ogawa et al., 1968; Wells & Gerdts, 1971; Wells, 1972; Jones & Burton, 1973;
Phillips, 1975), although Smith (1971) found it of little value. Ravetto &
Ogawa (1972) showed its ability to penetrate peach fruits.

Dithianon is a sulphur-containing compound active as a protectant fungicide and capable of giving moderately good control of the brown rot diseases on both stone fruit and apple (e.g. MacSwan, 1969; Hutton & Kable, 1970; Byrde & Melville, 1971). It has also been used as a dip treatment for stone fruits (Jones & Burton, 1973), although in some countries at least, regulations demand an interval between spraying and harvest (Hutton & Kable, 1970). The compound can also cause skin irritation.

Dodine is a cationic fungicide frequently used against apple scab, often as a curative spray. It is also moderately effective against the brown rot fungi on stone fruits (e.g. Zehr, 1973) and is currently recommended against the blossom wilt stage in Oregon, U.S.A. (MacSwan & Koepsell, 1974). It rapidly killed spores of *M. fructicola in vitro* (Turner, 1970).

1-Isopropylcarbamoyl-3-(3,5-dichlorophenyl) hydantoin is a very promising new candidate fungicide against the brown rot diseases as a spray or dip (Lacroix *et al.*, 1974; Jones, 1975; Burgaud *et al.*, 1975). MacNab (1975) cited two other reports of its successful use.

Sulphur, in the form of a spray made from a wettable (dispersible) powder, has long been used against the brown rot fungi (Wormald, 1954; pp. 49-50), and is still recommended for use on stone fruits, especially against the fruit rot stage of the disease (e.g. MacSwan & Koepsell, 1974). Lime-sulphur sprays or sulphur dusts can also be used. These preparations have the advantage of less cost, but their efficacy is undoubtedly low by comparison with the better organic fungicides (e.g. Zehr, 1974), and they can delay fruit maturation and possibly reduce its size (P.F. Kable, priv. comm.). Sulphur dust has also been used as a post-harvest treatment (Smith *et al.*, 1956).

Triforine, initially introduced in 1969 for use against powdery mildews and apple scab, is a systemic fungicide which has since been shown to be effective against the brown rot diseases, but reports differ on the degree of efficacy. Thus Gilpatrick & Szkolnik (1972) considered the compound far superior to benomyl, captafol (Difolatan), captan, dichlozoline, thiabendazole, thiophanate-methyl, triarimol and a sulphur/ferbam mixture for control of *M. fructicola* on plum, and suggested that the complete and uniform wetting of the fruit by the triforine formulation might be a factor in its success. Gilpatrick (1973) confirmed its efficacy on stone fruits, but recorded damage to cherry fruit. In subsequent large-scale tests in the U.S.A. in which it was compared on a statistical basis with benomyl for blossom wilt or fruit rot control, it was rated significantly inferior in three reports and not significantly different in seven: exact comparisons are difficult in view of concentration variations (Zehr, 1973). Jones *et al.* (1973) found it a promising orchard spray against *M. fructicola* on prune and as a post-harvest dip on sweet cherry; Koffman & Kable (1975) rated it a better cherry dip than benomyl. As a spray, it gave 'good' protection of cherry fruit, but was inferior to benomyl (Jones, 1975). It has also proved effective against *M. fructigena* and *M. laxa* (Rohrbach, 1973; Kundert, 1975), and is clearly a promising candidate for brown rot control trials. It may encounter few resistance problems (Fuchs & Drandarevski, 1976).

Vinclozolin is a recent introduction of low mammalian toxicity, claimed to be active against *Monilinia* spp. both *in vitro* (Hess & Löcher, 1975) and against blossom and fruit infection of stone fruit in the field (Hess, Heimes & Löcher, 1975). The closely related compound *dichlozoline* (3-(3,5-dichlorophenyl)-5,5-dimethyl-2,4-oxazolidinedione) ('Sclex'), which was outstandingly effective against the disease (e.g. Zehr, 1972; Jones & Burton, 1973; Chandler, 1974*b*), has since been withdrawn.

Other fungicides have been used with varying degrees of success, e.g.

2-Aminobutane salts, used as a post-harvest treatment of peaches (Eckert & Kolbezen, 1964).

The *antibiotics* cycloheximide (e.g. Grover, 1962) and griseofulvin (e.g. Kagawa & Terui, 1962).

Copper fungicides (Wormald, 1954).

The *dithiocarbamate* group, comprising protectant fungicides, mostly long-established, capable of giving some control of the brown rot diseases (e.g. Wormald, 1954, pp. 50, 64; Hutton & Kable, 1970). Use of ferbam and ziram is still recommended in the U.S.A. (MacSwan & Koepsell, 1974), but other more recently introduced fungicides are generally more effective.

Mecarbinzid, a highly effective benzimidazole derivative (Chandler, 1974*b*) but no longer available.

Organo-mercury fungicides (Wormald, 1954).

Polymeric hexamethylene diguanide hydrochloride (Koffman & Kable, 1975).

'*RH 3928*', only just introduced, but promising (MacNab, 1975; I.C. MacSwan, priv. comm.).

Sodium hypochlorite, or the calcium salt, as a fruit dip (McClure, 1958; Phillips & Grendahl, 1973).

Sodium orthophenylphenate, used as a post-harvest dip (McClure, 1958).

Triarimol (2,4-dichloro-α-pyrimidin-5-yl-benzhydrol), which was withdrawn: it had given variable control on stone fruit (e.g. Zehr, 1972).

ERADICATION OF OVERWINTERING INOCULUM

The success of attempts by Keitt and his colleagues (e.g. Keitt & Palmiter, 1937) to control apple scab, caused by *Venturia inaequalis* (Cke) Wint. by destroying the inoculum on overwintering infected leaves led him and a number of investigators to attempt the control of the brown rot diseases in a similar manner. Horsfall (1945, pp. 46-47) discussed such an approach to disease control in general and postulated that such treatment was most likely to succeed for diseases with one generation in a year. This would minimise the likelihood of the pathogen recovering from winter depletion of its inoculum. The blossom wilt phase of the brown rot diseases, with its single very limited period of infection, is thus more likely to be successfully controlled than is infection of fruit (Ogawa, Hall & Koepsell, 1967). Although control of blossom infection was indeed achieved, dormant spraying never found favour, largely because of the comparatively high toxicity to animals and man of many of the compounds used experimentally; sodium arsenite is particularly hazardous, although monocalcium arsenite (Keitt & Palmiter, 1937; Wilson, 1942; Calavan & Keitt, 1948; Chitzanidis, 1971) is rather less so.

In the trials that were carried out, the targets were overwintering, mummified fruits and/or 'hold-over' cankers arising from blossom, fruit or twig infections; sprays were normally applied fairly late in the dormant season, but application too late could lead to phytotoxicity. Results with compounds for which most data are available are listed in Table 8.5 . There is evidence that control of blossom infection of stone fruits can lead in turn to a reduction in fruit rot (Dunegan & Goldsworthy, 1948; Powell, 1951; Kable, 1970). Youganova (1946) claimed a 50-fold increase in the yield of apricots following use of copper naphthenate sprays against twig infections by *M. laxa*.

There is now some renewed interest in this form of treatment, because of the anti-sporulant properties of the generally non-phytotoxic benzimidazole fungicides, and Kable (1976) has suggested that a single application of carbendazim during late dormancy, at a rate as low as 0.025%, is effective and economically acceptable.

Where apothecial production from fallen mummies is involved, ground applications of calcium cyanamide can effectively prevent the emergence of apothecia (Wormald, 1954, p. 55).

SUPPRESSION OF SPORULATION IN THE GROWING SEASON

At the time when most dormant season spraying was being attempted, no compound was known that would suppress sporulation in the growing season without causing acute phytotoxicity (Moore, 1950c). The introduction of benomyl and related compounds makes it possible to limit spore populations during the summer season also, without acute phytotoxicity, and the effectiveness of these compounds in practice may be partly due to this property, so well demonstrated by Kable (1976), as well as to their ability to penetrate fruit. Triforine has also been reported to have anti-sporulant properties (Gilpatrick, 1973), but this was not confirmed by Kable (1976).

FUNGICIDAL STUDIES WITH THE BROWN ROT FUNGI

Again because of their ease of culture and economic importance, *Monilinia* spp. have been used as 'models' in many studies of fungicidal activity, e.g.

(i) Effects on oxygen uptake and germination of conidia (McCallan, Miller & Weed, 1954); on respiration of mycelial pellets (McCallan & Miller, 1957a); and on mycelial growth and secretion of macerating enzymes (Grover & Moore, 1962);

(ii) Uptake of fungicides (Miller, McCallan & Weed, 1953; McCallan & Miller, 1958; Brown & Sisler, 1960);

(iii) Role of polyphenol oxidase in fungitoxicity of phenols and quinones (Rich & Horsfall, 1954);

(iv) Compounds inhibiting sporulation (Horsfall & Rich, 1955, 1959, 1960);

(v) Mechanisms of action of sulphur (McCallan & Miller, 1957b; Tweedy & Turner, 1966), of seven organic fungicides (Byrde & Woodcock, 1959), of zineb (Kitovskaya, Khariton & Kulik, 1973), and of an inhibitor of sterol biosynthesis (Kato, Tanaka, Ueda & Kawase, 1974, 1975);

(vi) Morphogenetic effects of an antibiotic (Barathova, Betina, Barath & Nemec, 1975);

(vii) Rate of action of fungicides (Turner, 1970), and the factors controlling it (Turner, 1971; Turner & Battershell, 1970).

TABLE 8.5. EFFECT OF SOME DORMANT-SEASON FUNGICIDES ON *MONILINIA* spp.

Compound	Species*	Host	Reduction of sporulation (%)	Type of disease+	Control (%)	References
Benomyl	Fc	Peach	48–100 ‡	–	–	Kable (1970, 1976)
	L	Almond	95–98	B.B.	44–69	Ramsdell & Ogawa (1973*a*)
Carbendazim	Fc	Peach	63–100 ‡	–	–	Kable (1976)
Copper naphthenate	L	Apricot	High	T.B.	Good	Youganova (1946)
Dinitro-*o*-cresol and salts	Fc	Peach	26–82	–	–	Kable (1970)
	L	Apricot, almond	48–95	B.B.	2–78	Wilson (1943)
Lime–sulphur plus oil	Fc	Peach	67–91	–	–	Kable (1970)
Pentachlorophenol and salts	Fc	Peach	55–93	–	–	Kable (1970)
	Fg	Apple	85	F.R.	0	Byrde (1954*b*)
	L	Almond	37–87	B.B.	31–73	Wilson (1950); see also Ramsdell & Ogawa (1973*a*)
Phenyl mercury chloride	Fc	Peach	78–99	–	–	Kable (1970)
	Fg	Apple, plum	85–95	F.R.	0–20	Marsh (1947); Byrde (1952)
Thiophanate–methyl	Fc	Peach	83–99	–	–	Kable (1976)

* Fc = *M. fructicola*; Fg = *M. fructigena*; L = *M. laxa*
+ B.B. = Blossom blight; F.R. = Fruit rot; T.B. = Twig blight. Blanks indicate disease not assessed.
‡ At very low concentration.

Chapter 9

CONTROL BY OTHER MEANS

Many methods other than fungicide application have been used in the past to check the brown rot diseases, or are worthy of future consideration, and these are listed below under eight headings. Much can be achieved in plant disease control by the adoption of an 'integrated' strategy, which involves a combination of cultural, genetic and chemical measures.

The frequency with which Wormald's (1954) monograph is cited indicates that most of the measures were discussed individually long ago, and that there has been comparatively little work recently.

REDUCTION OF FUNGAL INOCULUM - GENERAL HYGIENE

As mentioned in earlier Chapters, the brown rot fungi frequently overwinter in mummified fruits on the trees or in 'hold-over' cankers, on which they produce conidia in the following spring. Destruction of such inoculum by removal during pruning, and subsequent burning or deep burying, provided that it is thorough (Kennel, 1968), can considerably decrease disease (Anon., 1973), but not eradicate it (Dunegan, 1953). At least several inches of the twigs bearing cankers should be removed (Kable, 1971a). Clearly, the degree of success of such treatment is influenced by the same factors that apply to the use of eradicant fungicides (see Chapter 8). It is more difficult to detect infected spurs when pruning is normally done, i.e. during the dormant season, than during the late summer when the dead leaves contrast sharply with the healthy foliage (Wormald, 1954, p. 84).

Wormald (1954, p. 85) also emphasized that hygiene is easier and equally necessary during or after seasons of light infection. It can also reduce the population of spore vectors (Kable, 1971a).

In countries where the perfect stage occurs, fallen mummies should be ploughed in too deep for the apothecia to emerge.

Particular care is needed in packing and storage of fruit because the fungus can pass by growing from one fruit to others in contact. Damaged fruit should not be included, in case they have incipient brown rot infections (Wormald, 1954, p. 84; see also Ogawa, Bose, Manji & Schreader, 1972). Old storage and orchard boxes may bear mycelial pads of the fungi; sterilization of these with formalin solution (1:320, v/v) (Wormald, 1954, p. 84) or sulphur dust (MacSwan & Koepsell, 1974, p. 27) has been recommended.

THE IMPORTANCE AND POSSIBLE CONTROL OF SPORE VECTORS

Even though sources of spore inoculum may be present in or near healthy fruit or blossom, infection can occur only when the spores reach a susceptible site on the host. Were it possible to control vectors of spores (see Chapter 7), the disease could be more easily checked. The most important of these vectors are birds, wasps (*Vespula* spp.), beetles, especially the nitidulid beetles (*Carpophilus* spp.), dipterous flies including *Drosophila* spp. (Willison & Dustan, 1956; Kable, 1969a) and some butterflies (Lepidoptera). Birds may be

checked in orchards remote from houses by the use of explosive scarers; wasps'
nests should be sought out and destroyed. Direct control of the other vectors
(which are often attracted to rotten and damaged fruit) seems difficult to
achieve, but may well have accounted for the success of parathion (highly
toxic to mammals) when used against *M. fructigena* (Hardh, 1951).

CONTROL OF WOUND AGENTS

The living wound agents which have been implicated in subsequent brown rot infection, together with some suggested control measures, are listed in Table
9.1; wasps, red ants (*Myrmica* spp.) (L.E. Hawker, priv. comm.), the Egyptian
alfalfa beetle (*Hypera brunneipennis*) (Ogawa, Manji & Schreader, 1975) and the
weevil *Rhynchites bacchus* (Stojanovic, 1956) may also be important. In many
instances (e.g. Moore, 1950*b*; Croxall, Collingwood & Jenkins, 1951; Kable,
1971*a*), eradication of the wound agent has been one of the most effective ways
of controlling the fruit rot phase of the diseases. Clearly it is necessary
to determine the cause of the damage in a given orchard, and then to apply the
appropriate control measure.

Injuries may also result from weather conditions adverse to the host. Thus
hail can readily damage fruit (e.g. Moore, 1951; Kable, 1975) and it is useful
to apply a protectant fungicide without delay when such injury occurs. Alternation of wet and dry periods often results in the splitting of the skins of
fruits of cherries, plums, peaches and, less frequently, of apples: everything
possible should be done to maintain a constant water supply to the trees, e.g.
by careful irrigation (Renaud, 1967), and cut-grass mulches. Minute surface
cracks can also be present without such stress (Fogle & Faust, 1975) and rub-
bing by branches can lead to injury and infection (Moore, 1950*c*). On apples,
fruit russet may be so severe as to lead to cracking, allowing *M. fructigena* to
invade (Moore, 1950*c*). Careful choice of sprays, avoiding those that induce
russet formation, minimises such injury.

Care during picking and handling is also essential: fruit should be picked with
its stalk intact (Wormald, 1954, pp. 64, 70; see also Fig. 9.1). Mechanical
harvesting of peaches can lead to more severe rotting due to injuries (Zehr
et al., 1975). When such damage occurs, chemical treatment, such as dipping
in a fungicide (Zehr *et al.*, 1975), or in ethephon (which promotes abscission)
(Aebig & Dewey, 1974) is advisable.

ORCHARD AND STORE MANAGEMENT

The likelihood of severe outbreaks of the brown rot diseases can be reduced by
intelligent siting of orchards. Thus Ingram (1948) advised the planting of
susceptible cherry cultivars in open, sunny situations, and this is sound
advice for all plantings of top fruit in areas where the brown rot diseases
may be severe. Frost can increase blossom infection (Jenkins & Skene, 1968)
and orchards are best sited on slopes or high ground (Vitanov, 1961). Suggestions for the avoidance of 'single line' culture in annual crops (Browning &
Frey, 1969) may also have some relevance in orchards. However, interplanting
of susceptible cultivars maturing at different times has been deprecated
(Kable, 1971*a*) because inoculum builds up on the early-maturing cultivars and
puts at risk the fruit of other cultivars that ripen later. Ogawa, Hall &
Koepsell (1967) referred to outbreaks of disease in an orchard of a normally
resistant almond cultivar where this had been interplanted with a susceptible
one to ensure effective pollination.

TABLE 9.1. SOME WOUND AGENTS INVOLVED IN INFECTION BY SPORES OF THE BROWN ROT FUNGI (based on Wormald, 1954, pp. 32-34).

Common name	Latin name	Host	Current control measures	Reference to control measures
Animals:				
Birds	Various	Apple	Scarers	–
Codling moth	*Cydia pomonella*	Apple	Organophosphorus and carbamate insecticides	Anon. (1975)
Curculio	*Conotrachelus nenuphar*	Stone fruits	Organochlorine and organophosphorus insecticides	*
Earwig	*Forficula auricularia*	Apple	BHC, carbaryl	Anon. (1975); Croxall *et al.* (1951)
Japanese beetle	*Popillia japonica*	Peach	Organochlorine insecticides; chemo-sterilants	*
Leaf-curling plum aphid	*Brachycaudus helichrysi*	Plum	Range of insecticides	Anon. (1975)
Mediterranean fruit fly	*Ceratitis capitata*	Apricot, peach	Insecticide baits; chemo-sterilants	*
Nitidulid ('dried fruit') beetles	*Carpophilus* spp.; *Haptonchus luteolus*	Peach	Organophosphorus insecticides; hygiene	**Kable** (1971a); Tate & Ogawa (1973, 1975); see also Ogawa (1957)
Nut weevil	*Balaninus mucum*	Hazel nut	Lead arsenate	Moore (1950a)

/ cont.

TABLE 9.1 .. cont.

Common name	Latin name	Host	Current control measures	Reference to control measures
Oriental fruit moth	*Cydia molesta*	Peach	Organophosphorus insecticides; carbaryl	Tate & Ogawa (1973, 1975); see also Kable (1969*a*)
Red plum maggot	*Cydia funebrans*	Plum	Organophosphorus and carbamate insecticides	*
Fungi:				
Apple and pear scab	*Venturia inaequalis; V. pirina*	Apple; pear	Benomyl, captan, dithianon, dodine	Anon. (1975)
Stone fruit scab	*Cladosporium carpophilum*	Peach	Benomyl	Delp & Klöpping (1968)

* Indications in *Review of Applied Entomology*.
Consult current control manuals for country in question.

Fig. 9.1. Increased susceptibility of cherries to *M. laxa* when picked
without stalks (left).

Scions on different rootstocks produce fruit more or less liable to cracking
and russeting, and thus have different numbers of infection sites (Moore, 1932;
Wormald, 1954).

Limited benefit may also follow measures designed to alter the environment in
established orchards in the host's favour. Thus skilful pruning avoids excessive overcrowding of branches (e.g. Renaud, 1967), and the better air circula-
tion results in more rapid drying. In addition, the penetration of any sprays
is enhanced, minimising the number of fruits not receiving full spray coverage
(see Mitchell, 1948). Summer pruning is advocated in new high-density peach
orchards, and brown rot incidence has been less than in conventional plantings
(Phillips & Weaver, 1975).

Manuring can have some influence on brown rot: it is useful to withhold excessive nitrogen, since high nitrogen at the wound site increases infection by *M.
fructigena* (Vasudeva, 1930). Applications of potassium have brought about a
reduction in disease incidence, at least on apricots, where potassium status
seemed to be important (Wade, 1956*b*). Lefter & Pasc (1963) and Renaud (1967)
emphasized the need for nitrogen/potassium balance. By contrast, Millikan
(1968) reported no beneficial effect of potassium treatment on post-harvest rot
of peach, although there was negligible orchard infection in his experiments.
Soil drainage, too, may be beneficial, as an association with water-logging has
been reported (Angell, 1955; Jenkins & Skene, 1968). Jennings (1969) considered that overhead irrigation favoured *M. fructicola* on peach, and Kable (1971*a*)
warned of the need to restrict sprinkler irrigation so as to avoid long periods
of dampness, in particular at blossom time.

Once the fruit is picked, alteration of the environment to the selective disadvantage of the pathogen is much more easily achieved, and the use of hot-
water dips, for example, has often been used successfully, sometimes in combination with fungicide treatment. Thus Smith, Parsons, Anderson & Bassett
(1964) showed the value of hot water alone for peaches and nectarines, although
it was difficult to obtain complete inactivation of *M. fructicola* or *Rhizopus*
sp. without heat injury to the host (cf. Smith & Anderson, 1972, 1975; Smith &
Keil, 1972). Wells & Harvey (1970) and Daines (1970) demonstrated the value
of combining heat with dicloran treatment; benomyl has proved particularly effective used in this way (e.g. Smith, 1971; Wells, 1972). Jones & Burton
(1973) and Jones, Burton & Tennes (1973) found that a range of fungicides added to hot water (51.5°C, 125°F) at one-quarter of the recommended commercial
rates were at least as effective as these materials at full rate in unheated
water.

Hydrocooling, or hydrair cooling, is now extensively used for peaches after
harvest in the south-eastern U.S.A., but it is generally necessary to add a
fungicide to the chilled water (McClure, 1958; Wells & Bennett, 1975), or to
have already treated the fruit in a non-emulsifiable wax formulation of a
fungicide (Wells & Revear, 1976).

The artificial ripening of peach fruit at 94°-95°F, too warm for the growth of
M. fructicola, showed promise (Tindale, Jenkins & Peggie, 1958), and this method is in current use in Victoria, Australia with some success, although some
loss of fruit weight occurs (P.F. Kable, priv. comm.).

When fruit can be chilled below about 5°C (41°F) in transit and storage, the
growth of the brown rot fungi is very slow (Chapter 4). Attempts to control
the disease by modifying the gaseous composition of the store atmosphere have
not been successful (Smith & Anderson, 1972, 1975).

Gamma radiation has also been tried as a sterilant (Beraha, Ramsey, Smith &
Wright, 1959; Willison, 1963; Beraha, 1964; Kuhn, Merkley & Dennison, 1968;
Terui & Harada, 1969), but does not seem to be widely practised.

BREEDING FOR RESISTANCE

General principles of the manipulation of genes for host resistance have been
discussed at length by Van der Plank (1968, 1975) and, with special reference
to fruit, by Janick & Moore (1975), who make occasional mention of the brown
rot diseases.

Many factors, listed in Table 7.2, have been implicated in host resistance to
brown rot and blossom wilt. The genetic basis of these is poorly understood,
although Crossa-Raynaud (1969), from the performance of crosses, suggested that
resistance to *M. laxa* in apricot was polygenic. Renaud (1975) reported that
the susceptibility of flowers and young shoots of plum to *M. laxa* is inherited
as a dominant character. It should nevertheless be possible in the long term
to incorporate some of these characters, if their role in resistance is proven,
in commercially viable cultivars. Breeding for brown rot resistance is a major
objective in a German cherry breeding programme (Janick & Moore, 1975). However, other characters may conflict with commercial requirements, particularly
in dessert fruit; for example, thick skins are not popular with consumers, and
high acidity and phenolic content do not result in good flavour. Grover (1963)
suggested a method for resistance assessment *in vitro*, but Zwintzscher (1955),
Crossa-Raynaud & Gharieni (1967), Crossa-Raynaud (1969) and Khokhryakova (1971)

favoured a branch inoculation method for *M. laxa*. Crossa-Raynaud (1969) also stressed the need to repeat the tests over several years.

In practice many cultivars of fruit trees have proved more or less resistant to one or other of the brown rot fungi, and these are listed below.

Almonds (to *M. laxa*): Nonpareil (Ogawa, Hall & Koepsell, 1967; Crossa-Raynaud, 1969); Burbank (Crossa-Reynaud, 1969).

Apples (to *M. fructigena*): La Claimanteuse, Beauty of Boskoop, Jonathan, Grüner Fürster, Rote Jungfer (Wormald, 1954); Rheinischer Bohnapfel, Ribston Pippin (Mittmann-Maier, 1940*b*); Blenheim Orange (Mittmann-Maier, 1940*b*; Byrde, 1956); Edward VII (Byrde, 1956; Fawcett & Spencer, 1967); various cider apples (Byrde, 1956); Slavyanka, Pepin, Giafrapnyi, Borsdorf Kitaika (Sokolov, 1962); Serinka, Titovka (Skeivyte, 1964); Kekhura, Krasnyi Kal'vil, Tsigana, Kinula (Rekhviashvili, 1973); and (to *M. laxa* f. *mali*), Bramley's Seedling (Anon., 1973).

Apricots (to *M. laxa*): Luizet, hybrids of St. Ambroise (Wormald, 1954); Hamidi (Crossa-Raynaud, 1966, 1969); Addedi, Arengi II (Lakhoua, Crossa-Raynaud, Carraut & Chemli, 1967); Derby Royal (Crossa-Raynaud, 1969); Nugget (Janick & Moore, 1975). In general, the 'European' group of cultivars is more resistant (Janick & Moore, 1975).

Cherries (to *M. fructicola* or *M. laxa*): Merton Heart (Wormald, 1954; Brooks & Olmo, 1959); Beste Werdersche (Wormald, 1954); Krassa Severa, Griotte du Pays (Grover, 1963); Dalbastija, Burbanc, Lotovka, Umbra (Soskic & Zekovic, 1968); six Russian cultivars (Shestakov, 1971). In general, sweet cherries are more resistant than sour cherries (Zwintzscher, 1955).

Nectarines: Cavalier, Redchief, Globerta, Necta Red 2 and 3 (Brooks & Olmo, 1953, 1954, 1963); Harko (Layne, 1975*a*); Hardired (Layne, 1975*b*).

Peaches (to *M. fructicola* or *M. fructigena*): Elberta (Jordovic, 1954; Kable, 1974; but see also Zehr, 1974, Report 56); Red Bird (Jordovic, 1954); Stark Late Gold, Red Gold, La Gem, La Premiere (Brooks & Olmo, 1955, 1957, 1966); Cuberland (Rekhviashvili, 1973), Pullars Cling (Kable, 1974).

Pears (to *M. fructigena*): Khechechuri, Bere-gri, Williams, Zamtris Klerzho (Rekhviashvili, 1973).

Plums (to *M. fructicola* or *M. laxa*): Damsons, especially French and Shropshire (Wormald, 1954); Lantz (Brooks & Olmo, 1959); progeny of two plum crosses (Vitanov, 1974); Casselman, Late Santa Rosa (but only to blossom infection) (Moller, Ogawa, Nyland & Gerdts, 1976).

It is also possible that, in time, resistance genes present in wild species (e.g. Kovalev, 1940; Janick & Moore, 1975) could be incorporated.

Much remains to be done before cultivars showing high resistance to the brown rot fungi, yet with good commercial characters, can be developed. Many of the resistant cultivars that have been recognised may not now exist, and in most instances the basis of resistance is not known. Where characters have been suggested as of importance in resistance (Table 7.2), their significance is often unproven, and they have rarely been defined in precise terms. There is thus ample scope for a systematic effort, on a world-wide scale, to identify, preserve and incorporate the genes for resistance, perhaps with the establishment of a 'gene bank'. Because of the time that elapses before fruit trees bear crops, this form of control is inevitably a long-term one. Of more immediate relevance to fruit growers are the resistant cultivars already available.

THE POSSIBILITY OF BIOLOGICAL CONTROL

Biological control of plant pathogens is currently being attempted on an increasing scale following the demonstration by Rishbeth (1963) of the value of applying propagules of *Peniophora gigantea* on the surface of felled stumps to protect them from infection by *Fomes annosus*. A valuable general review of the topic has been published by Baker & Cook (1974).

Successful biological control depends on the use of an organism showing some form of antagonism or competition to the pathogen and at the same time able to flourish in the pathogen's environment. In general, attempts to control soil-borne pathogens have been much more successful than with air-borne pathogens (Yarwood, 1973).

Other relevant generalisations are that 'the more specialized the parasite, the more restricted the conditions under which it can cause disease, and the more susceptible it is apt to be to antagonistic micro-organisms', and 'rather than kill the pathogen, it may only be necessary to weaken it and make it more vulnerable to antagonism of the associated microflora' (Baker & Cook, 1974, pp. 173, 292).

With *Monilinia* spp., A.T.K. Corke (priv. comm.) noted the occurrence of *Trichoderma viride* on overwintered mummified plum fruits and observed that this fungus was very extensive on fruits treated with dinitro-*o*-cresol winter wash: reduction in sporulation of *M. fructigena* may have resulted from the increase in *T. viride*, perhaps owing to the selective fungicidal effect of the dinitro-*o*-cresol. A commercial preparation of *T. viride* (not yet approved for commercial use in the U.K.) has been shown to protect injuries in plum trees against infection by the silver leaf fungus *Stereum purpureum*, and might be worthy of trial against *Monilinia* spp. as a protectant spray. Corke, Hunter & Collins (1975) found a tendency for less infection of fruit by *M. fructigena* on container-grown plum trees experimentally inoculated in the trunk with *T. viride*, with or without *S. purpureum*, than on trees inoculated with *S. purpureum* only. Khasanov (1962) reported that volatile fractions of culture filtrates of *T. viride* were fungistatic to *M. fructigena*. Ale-Agha, Dubos, Grosclaude & Ricard (1974) demonstrated that heat-killed spores of *T. viride* inhibited *M. laxa* and *M. fructigena in vitro*.

Jenkins (1968*a,b*) described a method for isolating bacteria antagonistic to *M. fructicola* and reported a species of *Bacillus*, probably *B. cereus*, that was associated with conidia on trees. It seemed to reduce the development of brown rot when introduced on the surface of mature fruit. Another bacterium perhaps worthy of test is *B. subtilis*, often present on leaf scars of apple trees (Swinburne, 1973) and which produces two substances antagonistic to *M. fructicola* (Michener & Snell, 1949; Kröber, 1952). Other micro-organisms that could be examined include *Camarosporium* sp. from olive trees (Ribaldi, 1954), the antagonistic saprophytes mentioned by Akhavan (1973), and those mentioned in Chapter 6.

The possibility also exists of using avirulent isolates of the *Monilinia* sp. itself. Thus Grente (1970) claimed that an avirulent isolate of *Endothia parasitica*, on anastomosis with a virulent race, transmitted its (extra-nuclear) ability to trigger host (chestnut) defence mechanisms. By contrast, Howell (1972) considered that any avirulence factors in mutagen-treated isolates of *M. fructigena* would rapidly be selected out and lost following heterokaryosis and division. However, too little is known of the factors that attenuate the virulence of races of plant pathogens for this approach to be dismissed.

The exploitation of viruses, as agents capable of infecting fungi and sometimes reducing pathogenicity (Atanasoff, 1973; Lemke & Nash, 1974), also represents a possible method of control for the future.

As a general principle to be borne in mind in any attempted biological control of *Monilinia* spp., it is desirable that the antagonist should occupy the infection site in advance of the pathogen (Baker & Cook, 1974, p. 318). With a wound parasite, this is difficult to achieve unless a substantial population of the antagonist is at hand when the injury is made. It is also essential that the antagonist, and closely-related strains, are non-pathogenic to man and animals.

GOVERNMENT LEGISLATION

One of the most striking features of the brown rot diseases is the geographical localization of the three species, described in Chapter 1. It is clearly extremely important that this localization should be maintained and that, for example, *M. fructigena* should not invade North America nor *M. fructicola* become established in Western Europe. With the great increase in air travel and freight in the last decade, it is indeed surprising that this has not yet happened: Wormald (1954, pp. 16-17) described several occasions on which non-indigenous species have been intercepted; see also Anon. (1960). The position clearly calls for great vigilance on the part of Plant Health Authorities throughout the World.

DISEASE FORECASTING

Forecasting methods have now been devised for a number of important plant diseases, e.g. potato blight and apple scab. With the brown rot diseases, sufficient knowledge of the climatic conditions governing infection of a given injury are available in semi-quantitative form to enable forecasts to be made. However, one of the most important factors governing the likelihood of infection - the incidence of fruit injury - seems virtually impossible to quantify, since such a variety of wound agents exists.

When long-range weather forecasts of reasonable accuracy become available, it may well be possible to advise growers in rather general terms of the likelihood of a severe outbreak of the brown rot diseases, bearing in mind the role of alternating wet and dry periods in causing fruit cracking, the effect of humidity, and the comparatively high temperature optimum for the fungus. A pilot scheme is already in existence in the Murrumbidgee Irrigation Areas in Australia, where rainfall, necessary for infection, is comparatively infrequent. Almost all severe epidemics there were found to be associated with one of only four types of weather pattern. Fuller details were published by Kable (1971*a*, 1972). An experimental forecasting system in Eastern Europe has also been reported (Karova, 1974). Nevertheless, in many areas long-term weather forecasts are as yet insufficiently reliable for any practical scheme. The need for work on crop diseases, in preparation for a time when accurate long-range forecasts become available, has been emphasized by Hirst (1976).

Chapter 10

EVOLUTION AND STATUS

Fossil records of fungi are fragmentary and do not contribute significantly to studies on the evolution of fungal pathogens. Some reports in old literature can be interpreted as references to damage of crops by fungi, but these are uncertain records, especially as it was not suspected until the 17th Century that fungi were one of the causes of plant diseases. Thus reliable written records on fungal diseases have become available only in comparatively recent times. As a result of the lack of fossil and written records, an understanding of the evolution of fungi has lagged behind the interpretation of that of higher plants and animals.

Some suggestions on the way that the present day brown rot fungi could have evolved and their status as pathogens are outlined in this Chapter. These ideas have been included because a general study of a group of fungi is incomplete without some discussion on their evolution; also, it is hoped that the hypothesis outlined will stimulate thought and possibly lead to studies by workers in gene centres of the brown rot fungi and their hosts. However, it must be emphasized that the explanations presented are mainly speculative and may require considerable revision as more data become available in the future.

GENETIC VARIABILITY OF BROWN ROT FUNGI

Genetic variability is an important attribute of all plants and animals and it enables them to adapt to changing conditions. In a host-pathogen relationship the association is such that changes in the genotype of the one will affect the genotype of the other. Thus, if a host during its evolution develops a significant degree of resistance to a particular pathogen, then selection pressure is exerted on the latter so that new virulent strains or mutants are selected from within the existing population. It has been found that variability in hosts selects for corresponding variability in their pathogens; conversely, lack of change in host plants will lead to greatly reduced selection pressure on their pathogens.

During the process of sexual reproduction there is a recombination of characters to give progeny which are different from the parents, and in this way new genetic forms are constantly obtained. Many fungi produce sexual spores at some stage during their life cycles. These spores develop in large numbers and, as the life cycles of fungi are often short, more than one generation may be obtained in one season. Therefore new genetic forms are produced more rapidly by fungi than by most host plants. The perfect stage of M. *fructicola* has been reported on many occasions in North America, although it appears to be formed less frequently than the literature would suggest (Chapters 1 and 3). In other regions where this species occurs, ascocarps have been found with greater regularity recently than in the past (Chapter 1). There have been several reports of cultural variations between single ascospore isolates of the New World species (Sharvelle & Chen, 1943; Thind & Keitt, 1949). The apparent infrequent production of apothecia of M. *fructigena* and M. *laxa* suggests that this method of generating variability is not of importance to the Old World species today, although this probably did not apply to the ancestral forms of these fungi.

The existence of genetically different nuclei in cytoplasmic continuity with one another (heterokaryosis) is a phenomenon unique to fungi. Heterokaryosis is responsible for increased genetic variability in fungi (Davis, 1966). Also, in a multinucleate cytoplasm, recessive but potentially valuable genetic variations will probably survive in much the same manner as in heterozygous, diploid organisms. Heterokaryosis was thought to provide a plastic system by which changes in nuclear ratios may take place to give quick adjustment to environmental changes (Pontecorvo, 1946; Jinks, 1952), but later work suggests that heterokaryon incompatibility may limit the usefulness of this mechanism (Caten, 1971). Cytological studies on the vegetative mycelia of *M. fructicola* (Hall, 1963), *M. fructigena* and *M. laxa* (Hoffmann, 1970) have shown that single hyphal segments are multinucleate, and there is frequent migration of nuclei from one segment to another through the septal pores. Hoffmann (1972, 1974) concluded that more than one type of nucleus is present in the mycelia of *M. fructigena* and *M. laxa* and that they are therefore di- or hetero-karyotic. Anastomoses (hyphal fusions) are frequently observed in all species (Hoffmann, 1970) and these provide a means by which heterokaryons may be produced. However heterokaryon incompatibility in the brown rot fungi has not been studied. Thus it is not known to what extent the infection on a host consists of a population nor the importance of hyphal fusions in genetic changes of the fungi.

Pontecorvo (1954) demonstrated a parasexual cycle in the homothallic ascomycete, *Aspergillus nidulans*, which has also a typical sexual cycle. Other fungi have since been shown to possess parasexuality. It is not known if there is a parasexual cycle in the brown rot fungi, but the phenomenon, with some variations between species, could be widespread among filamentous fungi (Roper, 1966). Thus the fruit-rotting *Monilinia* species possess most of the machinery needed for the generation of variability. There are indications that the present day brown rot fungi are slow to adapt to changing conditions but, presumably, ancestral forms were able to adapt more quickly. The slow adaptation of these fungi to new habitats or changes in their environment could indicate that now the mean phenotype of the population of each species is close to optimal. However, in theory, severe selection should produce new viable forms and the recent identification in Australia of strains which are tolerant to the fungicide benomyl (Whan, 1976) could be interpreted as evidence in support of this.

ORIGINS OF HOSTS

Background knowledge on the origins and histories of apples, pears and stone fruits could give some understanding of the origins of the brown rot fungi since the evolution of specialized pathogens is closely associated with that of their hosts. Fortunately there is some information on the nature and distribution of the wild progenitors of fruit trees (Janick & Moore, 1975), although there remain many significant gaps and uncertainties in our knowledge.

The peach (*Prunus persica* L.) was first known in China and from there it spread westwards to Persia and then Southern Europe where it was known as the Persian apple. The Romans were responsible for the introduction of the peach into Western Europe and Britain. Nectarines do not form a distinct species from peaches and both fruits have a similar origin. The apricot (*P. armeniaca* L.) is believed to have primary centres of origin in China and the mountainous area of Central Asia. Apricots were taken through Persia into the Transcaucasian area and then westward into Greece and Italy. Probably the specific name *armeniaca* was derived from the Armenian traders who introduced the fruit into Southern Europe. The sweet cherry (*P. avium* L.) is thought to have come from Northern Persia and the Russian provinces south of the Caucasus. There have been valuable fruit-producing trees in these areas since the beginning of agriculture. The sour cherry (*P. cerasus* L.) is considered to be a native of Asia Minor and perhaps South East Asia. The native country of the common garden plum (*P. domestica* L.) is unknown, but it is found in the wild state in the Caucasus and the Transcaucasian region. There are many plum varieties in temperate zones of the World; *P. insititia* L. has given rise to the damson group and was probably cultured around Damascus, from which the name damson was given; *P. salicina* Lindl., the Japanese plum, was described as a native of China by Chandler (1951).

The cultivated apple (*Malus pumila* Mill.) is referred to in records dating back several hundred years B.C. and has been much associated with folk-lore and legends of the Greeks, Arabians and Norsemen. The apple is regarded as endemic in the area from the Balkans and South-eastern Russia eastwards through the Transcaucasus, Persia, Turkestan and north to Central Russia (Janick & Moore, 1975). Leppik (1970) suggested that the original area of the genus *Malus* is in Eastern Asia with four other centres of speciation of the genus in other regions, one of which is in North America. The native habitat of the progenitors of the common pear (*Pyrus communis* L.) that comprises all the well-known European varieties is claimed to be Southern Europe and Asia as far east as Kashmir. Wild pear trees grow abundantly along with wild apples in the Caucasus and Turkestan. The quince (*Cydonia oblongata* L. Mill.) was described as a native of the Near East by Vavilov (1930).

Cultivated apples, pears and stone fruits were taken to North America by the early colonists. Peaches were introduced by the Spaniards in the 16th Century and the trees became so well-established, even as far north as Philadelphia, that early English settlers thought the peach was a native plant. Also, apples were introduced from Europe and grew in a large area from the New England States to Virginia and westward to the Mississippi Valley (Gourley & Howlett, 1941). Intensive cultivation of fruits started in America during the early 19th Century.

CENTRES OF ORIGIN OF *MONILINIA*

Plants have long been exposed to the selective pressure of local pathogens in their centres of origin or gene centres. Natural resistance to specific diseases is usually found in centres of origin of the host plant and the sources of resistance used in plant breeding programmes have been obtained often from the gene centres of cultivated plants. The wild progenitors and the first cultivated species of the hosts of the brown rot fungi probably originated in two main centres – Eastern Asia (China and Japan) for peaches, nectarines and apricots, and the countries in South East Europe and South West Asia for apples, pears, plums and cherries. It seems reasonable to assume that the ancestor of the present-day brown rot fungi first became associated with wild fruit trees in one of these centres. It is not known in which region the initial association developed. Leppik (1970) described the Far East as the region with the largest numbers of wild *Pyrus*, *Prunus* and *Malus* species that are resistant to most of the general diseases of these crops. Leppik suggested that most fruit trees of the rosaceous subfamily Pomoideae and many of their pathogens have their origins in China or adjacent areas.

If the gene centre of the host plant is also the centre of origin of one of its pathogens, a greater diversity of this pathogen will be found there because of the reciprocal genetic interaction between host and parasite. Considerable diversity of the brown rot fungi has been reported from Japan. This may reflect to some extent the amount of mycological work that has been carried out there compared with that in other Asian countries but is, nevertheless, of interest in the present context. Some of the Japanese species were referred to by Wormald (1954) and include *Sclerotinia* (= *Monilinia*) *mali* Tak. (Shima, 1936); *S.* (= *M.*) *malicora* Muira (Susa, 1934); a variant form of *M. laxa* which produces disjunctors between conidia (Takahashi, 1911); and *S.* (= *M.*) *kusanoi* (Takahashi, 1911). Recently there have been reports of different forms of the brown rot fungi in Russia (Khokhryakova, 1969, 1973; Rekhviashvili, 1972). Of particular interest is the report by Khokhryakova (1969) of a form of *M. laxa* from the Soviet Far East that appears to be different in conidial size and colour, colony characteristics and pathogenicity from the fungus usually described as *M. laxa*. Apothecia were produced by this fungus and they are of interest because of the infrequent production elsewhere of the perfect stage by this species. The indications are that this is not *M. laxa*.

ANCESTRAL FORM

Some of the general characteristics that would be expected of an ancestral form include a wide host and tissue range and the ability to adapt quickly to changing conditions. Of the two common Old World species of brown rot, *M. laxa* has the wider host range and attacks a greater variety of host tissues; also this species is more adaptable to new habitats than is *M. fructigena*, as indicated by its establishment in the Western States of North America and in Australasia during the present Century. Studies on the pectolytic enzymes of the common brown rot fungi suggest that *M. laxa* possesses a larger number of forms of these enzymes that might confer greater adaptibility to new hosts on this species (Willetts, Byrde, Fielding & Wong, 1976). Also, the pectolytic enzyme patterns of *M. laxa* could be interpreted as general ones from which the patterns of the other species could have been derived.

Monilinia fructicola produces similar symptoms to, and has a common host range with, *M. laxa*. Moreover, these two species are found in the same habitats in some areas of North America and, as shown recently, in many parts of Australasia where the hosts are grown (Penrose, Tarran & Wong, 1976; Boesewinkel, 1972). These common features could indicate that *M. fructicola* and *M. laxa* have closer genetic affinities with each other than either has with *M. fructigena*. The latter species and *M. laxa* occur in the same regions of the Old World but there are significant differences in their pathogenicities to the hosts that they have in common (Ogawa & English, 1960). Probably, *M. laxa* is in a central position between *M. fructicola* and *M. fructigena* and it was from a fungus similar in many ways to the present-day *M. laxa* that *M. fructigena* and *M. fructicola* evolved.

POSSIBLE EVOLUTIONARY EVENTS

M. laxa

It is postulated that, in the Far East, an ancestral form of the brown rot fungi similar to *M. laxa* became a pathogen of the progenitors of stone fruit trees. After a period of adjustment in the wild state, a balanced relationship would be expected between host and pathogen, and only a low level of damage to the trees would occur each season. Presumably blossom and twig blight were conspicuous symptoms on wild plants with fruit rot of lesser importance. However, the perfect stage was probably regularly produced on infected fruits and contributed to the generation of genetic variability. The fruits of the wild progenitors were small, hard and sour but after a period of selection by man, cultivated varieties were obtained with large, fleshy and sugary fruits. Abundant mycelial growth and sporulation by the brown rot pathogen would take place on such succulent substrata. Possibly, as mummies became the providers of abundant asexual spores which were quickly produced over long periods if conditions were favourable, the perfect stage lost much of its importance in the life cycle of the pathogen. Consequently, after a period of selection, the ability of the fungus to produce ascocarps was greatly reduced. Apart from the effects of artificial selection of plant stock, use of different and intensive cultural practices and the growth of crops in new areas produced conditions that favoured the build-up of epiphytotics and influenced the evolutionary selection of the pathogens. When peaches and apricots were taken from the Far East to South West Asia, it was inevitable that the pathogens of the crops would be introduced eventually into the new areas of cultivation. Favourable conditions (growth and the presence of congenial crops, both those imported from elsewhere and indigenous *Prunus* species) enabled the brown rot fungus and variants of it to become successful pathogens of the region. The disease spread to other parts of Asia and to Europe as the cultivation of fruits become more extensive.

M. fructigena

It is suggested that the first brown rot fungus was a pathogen mainly of stone fruits in the Far East but that some strains were also able to infect the native *Malus* species. Some of the variant forms evolved *in situ* to give new subspecies and species that became pathogens of the local *Malus* plants. Possibly the apple pathogens of Japan referred to previously are examples. *M. fructigena* may also have evolved in the Far East but, unlike those apple pathogens that have been reported only in Japan, became established in Europe and the western areas of Asia.

However, *M. fructigena* may have its gene centre in Transcaucasia and adjacent areas where the species evolved from variant brown rot strains, either present in the population of the *M. laxa* type pathogen brought from the Far East, or forms that developed *in situ* from an introduced fungus. The change of habitat and contact with different *Malus* genotypes produced new selection pressures that led to the development of a species distinct from those found on apples in the Far East.

M. laxa f. *mali* could provide an evolutionary bridge between *M. laxa* and *M. fructigena*, although the former might be a variant of *M. laxa* that has become a pathogen of apple but has not given rise to new distinct species. There are great similarities between *M. laxa* and *M. laxa* f. *mali* but they have different patterns of pathogenicity as described in Chapter 1. It is not difficult to envisage the evolution of *M. fructigena* from an ancestor similar to *M. laxa* through a form like that of *M. laxa* f. *mali*. If *M. fructigena* evolved in the Transcaucasian region, the species was eventually taken to other areas, including the Far East, on diseased apple tissues.

M. fructicola

Apart from the few exceptions cited earlier (Chapter 1), *M. fructicola* is confined to the New World. The similarities between the brown rot species suggest that they have come from a common ancestor that originated, presumably, in the Old World. Probably *M. fructicola* evolved in North America, but there are no indications of when or how the initial introduction of a brown rot ancestral form was made to that Continent. The fungus may have been carried across the Pacific Ocean before or after the New World was discovered or taken across the Atlantic in post-Columbian times. Anderson (1956) concluded that *M. fructicola* was pathogenic on the wild plum of America before the country was colonized by Europeans and later the fungus found a congenial host on cultivated peaches. All that written records show is that *M. fructicola* began to cause significant losses to crops early in the 19th Century. It seems unlikely that this was due to the emergence of a new species at that time. If *M. fructicola* evolved from other species, it must have done so before these largely lost the ability to produce apothecia. As the New World species continues to form apothecia, an origin much less recent than the cultivation of stone fruits in North America is indicated. The assumption is made that *M. fructicola* had been established in North America for some considerable time before the country was colonized by Europeans and certainly long before the disease was reported as a troublesome pathogen there. The increased losses coincided with more intensive cultivation of fruit trees which favoured the build-up of epiphytotics. Also there was more awareness at that time of the role of fungi as pathogens of crops.

When there is a chance introduction of a fungus into a completely new region, the genetic variability of that population is much less than that of the large population of the fungus in the region from whence it originated. Consequently adaptation to a different and possibly hostile environment will be slow. In many instances the fungus is unable to compete successfully in the new habitat and will not survive. The large gene pool that develops in a fungus that has been endemic in an area for hundreds or thousands of years will confer on the species great potential for adaptation to new or changing conditions. Probably, the fungal strain from which *M. fructicola* evolved in the New World was produced in the Old World but was selected against there, because of some adverse factor of the environment. However, in the New World, the variants found congenial hosts such as native *Prunus* spp. and were able to become well-established; upon further selection the fungus became sufficiently different from the forms found elsewhere to be classed as a new species. In such a manner *M. fructicola* could have evolved in North America from an imported variant of one of the Old World species, probably *M. laxa* or a variant form of this species. Later the disease was introduced into South America and Australasia where growth conditions were favourable and hosts available, so that the fungus also became a pathogen of these regions.

STATUS AS PATHOGENS

Unspecialized fungal pathogens usually kill the tissues of their hosts at an early stage of invasion, their host ranges are relatively wide and the fungi tend to penetrate host tissues through wounds (Brian, 1967; Garrett, 1970; Lewis, 1974). On these criteria the brown rot fungi must be regarded as unspecialized pathogens. Most of the other members of the genus *Monilinia* also kill the tissues of their hosts and cause fruit rot, leaf spots and die-back. However, there is evidence of greater host specificity in some forms as, for example, *M. johnsonii* (Ellis & Everhart) Honey, which parasitizes hawthorn leaves and fruits, and *M. urnula* (Weinmann) Whetzel which kills the shoot tips of whimberry (*Vaccinium vitis-idaea*) and mummifies the fruits. There is a tendency in the life cycles of *Vaccinium*-inhabiting members of the genus for the separation of conidial and apothecial production and there are examples of heteroecism (i.e., two or more alternate hosts are required to complete the life cycles) among them. This is illustrated by *M. ledi* (Nowaschin) Whetzel and *M. rhododendri* (Fischer) Whetzel that produce their conidial stages on

Vaccinium spp. while the fungi overwinter in fruits of *Ledum* and *Rhododendron* respectively; apothecia develop on the fruits in the spring and ascospores are responsible for new infections of *Vaccinium* shoots (Dennis, 1968). The presence within conidial chains of disjunctors for the dissemination of the spores is regarded as a specialized feature in the genus *Monilinia* but these structures are not formed by the brown rot species. Therefore it appears that *M. laxa*, *M. fructigena* and *M. fructicola* should be classed as some of the less specialized members of their genus.

The brown rot fungi show some degree of host specificity in that they inhabit only fruit trees. All the main hosts are perennial rosaceous plants that usually bear heavy crops of fruits for many years; the trees are intensively cultivated in large orchards and extensive areas of wild fruit trees are found in some regions. Thus the pathogens have become associated with hosts that provide abundant susceptible tissue for fungal growth. Also there is an obvious adaptation to fruit parenchyma and, with the exception of *M. laxa*, the brown rot fungi rarely cause appreciable damage to woody tissue. Lewis (1974) suggested that the degree of specialization of a pathogen is related to its control over the secretion of wall-degrading enzymes and in highly evolved biotrophic host-parasite combinations the secretion and activities of pectolytic and cellulolytic enzymes are reduced to minimal levels. On this criterion the fruit-rotting *Monilinia* species show some degree of specialization, since they do not secrete detectable concentrations of cellulase while abundant pectolytic enzymes have been reported only *in vitro* and are somewhat restricted *in vivo* (Chapters 5 and 7). Furthermore, the fungi are well adapted to survive adverse periods either in fruit mummies or in dormant host tissues (Chapter 6). Under favourable conditions, abundant inocula are produced and the mycelia and spores are well placed to infect healthy parts of the plant or to be carried by wind, water splashes and animal vectors to susceptible tissues (Chapter 7).

Therefore, although on the usually accepted criteria the brown rot fungi show only limited specialization, they are well adapted to the ecological niche, i.e. fruit trees, where they are found.

POSSIBLE REASONS FOR PRESENT-DAY DISTRIBUTION

The distribution of the brown rot fungi has been outlined in Chapter 1. The reasons for the interesting distribution of these species are not known, but obviously there are some major factors that restrict them, particularly *M. fructigena* and *M. fructicola*, to their respective areas. Quarantine records show that the European species have been intercepted on many occasions on fruits entering America; *M. fructicola* has also been introduced into Europe and the Far East on stone fruits imported from America or Australasia. Although *M. laxa* is an important pathogen in North America it is restricted to certain regions of that Continent; in Australasia it is only in recent years that this species has become established although now the distribution appears to be spreading.

It seems unlikely that physical factors alone are responsible for the present-day distribution of the brown rot fungi. Their ability to thrive in some areas and their absence from others could be affected by a variety of biotic factors. Some of these could be: the types of micro-organisms that are antagonistic to them; the distribution of the antagonists in different areas of the World; the availability and types of wild hosts; the importance of wild hosts in overwintering of the diseases; and differences in the life cycles of the fungal species. A major difference between the Old and New World species is the frequent formation of the perfect stage by *M. fructicola*. Apothecia are produced only on well organized stromata and therefore the regular production of the perfect stage provides convincing evidence of the survival in soil of mummies of *M. fructicola*. Possibly the differences in the survival of stromata of the species are of significance in the distribution of the brown rot fungi.

A detailed study of the factors that have inhibited the establishment of *M. fructigena* in America and the reasons why *M. fructicola* is still mainly confined to countries of the New World could give an understanding of natural control of the diseases. Such data will have direct application to the development of biological control of the diseases on cultivated fruit crops. International co-operation is essential for the development of this type of work. Studies on isolates of the brown rot fungi from the Far East, Transcaucasia and neighbouring areas, and the east and west coastal areas of North America would be of particular interest. Also some of the techniques now in use in plant pathological studies such as electrophoresis, isoelectric focusing and serology could help resolve the affinities between species, give information on the diversity within species, and provide a better understanding of the evolution of the brown rot pathogens. Much of this information will be relevant to other fungi.

REFERENCES

(R.A.M. = Rev. appl. Mycol.; R.P.P. = Rev. Pl. Path.)

ABELENTSEV, V.I. (1973). *Khimiya v Sel'skom Khozjajstve* 11, 32-36.
(*R.P.P.* 54, 1581, 1975).

ADERHOLD, R. (1904). *Ber. dtsch. bot. Ges.* 22, 262-266.

ADERHOLD, R. & RUHLAND, W. (1905). *Arb. biol. Abt. (Asst Reichsanst) Berl.*
4, 427-442.

AEBIG, D.E. & DEWEY, D.H. (1974). *Hortscience* 9, 448-449.

AHARONI, Y. & STADELBACHER, G.J. (1973). *Phytopathology* 63, 544-545.

AINSWORTH, G.C. & SUSSMAN, A.S. (1965). *The Fungi. I. The Fungal Cell.*
New York & London: Academic Press. 748 pp.

AKHAVAN, A. (1973). *Iran. J. Pl. Path.* 9, 101-108. (*R.P.P.* 54, 1134, 1975).

ALBERSHEIM, P. & ANDERSON, A.J. (1971). *Proc. natn. Acad. Sci. U.S.A.* 68,
1815-1819.

ALBERSHEIM, P. & ANDERSON-PROUTY, A.J. (1975). *A. Rev. Pl. Physiol.* 26,
31-52.

ALE-AGHA, N., DUBOS, B., GROSCLAUDE, C. & RICARD, J.L. (1974). *Pl. Dis.
Reptr* 58, 915-917.

ALI, M.D.H. & MORSY, A.A. (1972). *Egypt J. Phytopathol.* 4, 91-92.

ALLEN, A.K. & NEUBERGER, A. (1973). *Biochem. J.* 135, 307-314.

AMERICAN PHYTOPATHOLOGICAL SOCIETY. (1943). *Phytopathology* 33, 627-632.

ANDERSON, H.W. (1956). *Diseases of Fruit Crops.* (p. 190). New York, Toronto,
London: McGraw-Hill.

ANGELL, H.R. (1955). *J. Aust. Inst. agric. Sci.* 21, 180-182.

ANON. (1960). *Orchard. N.Z.* 33, 247.

ANON. (1973). *Brown rot and blossom wilt of apples.* Ministry of Agriculture,
Fisheries & Food, U.K. Advisory Leaflet no. 155 (revised). 5 pp.

ANON. (1975). *Approved products for Farmers and Growers, 1975.* London:
H.M.S.O. 183 pp.

ARCHER, S.A. (1973a). *Trans. Br. mycol. Soc.* 60, 235-244.

ARCHER, S.A. (1973b). Ph.D. Thesis, Univ. of Bristol.

ARCHER, S.A., BYRDE, R.J.W. & FIELDING, A.H. (1972). *J. gen. Microbiol.* 73,
xviii-xix.

ARCHER, S.A., CLAMP, J.R. & MIGLIORE, D. (1976). In preparation.

ARCHER, S.A. & FIELDING, A.H. (1975). *J. Food Sci.* 40, 423-424.

ARCHER, S.A. & HISLOP, E.C. (1975). *Ann. appl. Biol.* 81, 121-126.

ATANASOFF, D. (1973). *Phytopath. Z.* 78, 182-186.

BAKER, F.C., BROOKES, C.J.W. & HUTCHINSON, S.A. (1975). *J. chem. Soc., chem.
Commun.,* 1975 (8), 293-294.

BAKER, J.E. & SMITH, W.L. (1970). *Phytopathology* 60, 869-874.

BAKER, K.F. & COOK, R.J. (1974). *Biological control of plant pathogens.*
San Francisco: Freeman. 433 pp.

BARATHOVA, H., BETINA, V., BARATH, Z. & NEMEC, P. (1975). *Folio Microbiol.
Praha* 20, 97-102. (*Biol. Abstr.* 60, 030151, 1975).

BARRETT, A.J. & NORTHCOTE, D.H. (1964). *Biochem. J.* 94, 617-627.

BARTNICKI-GARCIA, S. (1968). *A. Rev. Microbiol.* 22, 87-108.

BARTRAM, H.E. (1916). *Phytopathology* 6, 71-78.

de BARY, A. (1886). *Bot. Ztg* 44, 377, 393, 409, 433, 449, 465.

BARSS, H.P. (1923). *Oreg. Agric. Exp. Stn Circ.* 53.

BASHAM, H.G. & BATEMAN, D.F.   (1975).   *Physiol. Pl. Path.* 5, 249-261.
BATEMAN, D.F. & MILLAR, R.L.   (1966).   *A. Rev. Phytopathology* 4, 119-146.
BAUER, W.D., TALMADGE, K.W., KEEGSTRA, K. & ALBERSHEIM, P.   (1973).   *Pl. Physiol., Lancaster* 51, 174-187.
BAXTER, L.W., ZEHR, E.I. & EPPS, W.M.   (1974).   *Pl. Dis. Reptr* 58, 844-845.
BEATTIE, B.B. & OUTBRED, N.L.   (1970).   *Aust. J. exp. Agric. Anim. Husb.* 10, 651-656.
BEDI, K.S.   (1962).   *Proc. Indian bot. Soc.* 42, 66-73.
BEHRENS, J.   (1898).   *Zentbl. Bakt. ParasitKde* (Abt. 2) 4, 514-777 (intermittently).
BELL, F.H. & ALANDIA, S.   (1957).   *Pl. Dis. Reptr* 41, 646-649.
BENT, K.J.   (1967).   *Ann. appl. Biol.* 60, 251-263.
BERAHA, L.   (1964).   *Phytopathology* 54, 755-759.
BERAHA, L., RAMSEY, G.B., SMITH, M.A. & WRIGHT, W.R.   (1959).   *Phytopathology* 49, 354-356.
BIEHN, W.L., KUC, J. & WILLIAMS, E.B.   (1968).   *Phytopathology* 58, 1255-1260.
BIRIS, D.A.   (1968).   *Diss. Abstr.* 29B, 833-834.
BJÖRLING, K.   (1951).   *Phytopath. Z.* 18, 129-156.
BLOOMFIELD, B.J. & ALEXANDER, M.   (1967).   *J. Bact.* 93, 1276-1280.
BOEREMA, H., VAN KESTEREN, H.A., DORENBOSCH, M.M.J. & DE WEERT, E.   (1971).   *Versl. Meded. plziektenk. Dienst Wageningen* 145, pp. 142.
BOESEWINKEL, H.J.   (1972).   *Orchard. N.Z.* (March), 51-57.
BOESEWINKEL, H.J. & CORBIN, J.B.   (1970).   *Pl. Dis. Reptr* 54, 504-506.
BOLAY, A., NEURY, G., DUCROT, V. & GERMANIER, R.   (1972).   *Revue suisse Viticult. & Arboricult.* 4, 15-21.   (*R.P.P.* 51, 4176, 1972).
BOLLEN, G.J. & FUCHS, A.   (1970).   *Neth. J. Pl. Path.* 76, 299-312.
BONORDEN, H.F.   (1851).   *Handbuch der allgemeinen Mykologie.* p. 76, Stuttgart.
BOS, J.R.   (1903).   *Tijdschrift-over Plantenziekten* 9, 125-146.
BOUDIER, E.   (1907).   *Histoire et classification des Discomycetes d' Europe.* Librairie des Sciences Naturelles, Paris.   223 pp.
BRAUNER, L.   (1954).   *A. Rev. Pl. Physiol.* 5, 163-182.
BRIAN, P.W.   (1967).   *Proc. R. Soc.* B168, 101-118.
BRIERLEY, W.B.   (1918).   *Kew Bull.* 129-146.
BROOKS, R.M. & OLMO, H.P.   (1953).   *Proc. Am. Soc. hort. Sci.* 62, 513-526.
BROOKS, R.M. & OLMO, H.P.   (1954).   *Proc. Am. Soc. hort. Sci.* 64, 535-549.
BROOKS, R.M. & OLMO, H.P.   (1955).   *Proc. Am. Soc. hort. Sci.* 66, 445-454.
BROOKS, R.M. & OLMO, H.P.   (1957).   *Proc. Am. Soc. hort. Sci.* 70, 557-584.
BROOKS, R.M. & OLMO, H.P.   (1959).   *Proc. Am. Soc. hort. Sci.* 74, 758-785.
BROOKS, R.M. & OLMO, H.P.   (1963).   *Proc. Am. Soc. hort. Sci.* 83, 862-882.
BROOKS, R.M. & OLMO, H.P.   (1966).   *Proc. Am. Soc. hort. Sci.* 89, 773-789.
BROWN, I.F. & SISLER, H.D.   (1960).   *Phytopathology* 50, 830-839.
BROWN, W.   (1936).   *Bot. Rev.* 2, 236-281.
BROWNING, J.A. & FREY, K.J.   (1969).   *A. Rev. Phytopathology* 7, 355-382.
BRUSCHI, D.   (1912).   *Atti. Accad. naz. Lincei Rc. s.5, v.* 21, sem. 1, 225-230; 298-304.
BUCHWALD, N.F.   (1949).   *Åsskr. K. Vet.-Landbohøjsk* 32, 75-191.
BULL, A.T.   (1970a).   *Archs Biochem. Biophys.* 137, 345-356.
BULL, A.T.   (1970b).   *Enzymologia* 39, 333-347.
BURCHILL, R.T. & EDNEY, K.L.   (1972).   *Ann. appl. Biol.* 72, 249-255.
BURGAUD, L., CHEVREC, J., GUILLOT, M., MARECHAL, G., THIOLLIERE, J. & COLE, R.J.   (1975).   *Proc. 8th Br. Insectic. Fungic. Conf., 1975,* 2, 645-652.
BURNETT, J.H.   (1968).   *Fundamentals of mycology.*   New York: St Martin's Press.   546 pp.
BURTON, K.   (1956).   *Biochem. J.* 62, 315-323.
BUSSEL, J., MIRANDA, M. & SOMMER, N.F.   (1971).   *Phytopathology* 61, 61-64.
BYRDE, R.J.W.   (1952).   *J. hort. Sci.* 27, 192-200.

BYRDE, R.J.W.   (1954*a*).   *Rep. agric. hort. Res. Stn, Univ. Bristol,* 163.
BYRDE, R.J.W.   (1954*b*).   *J. hort. Sci.* 29, 226-230.
BYRDE, R.J.W.   (1956).   *J. hort. Sci.* 31, 188-195.
BYRDE, R.J.W.   (1957).   *J. hort. Sci.* 32, 227-238.
BYRDE, R.J.W.   (1958).   Unpublished results.
BYRDE, R.J.W.   (1966).   *Proc. 18th Symposium of the Colston Research Society,*
    289-297.   London: Butterworth.
BYRDE, R.J.W.   (1972).   In: *Systemic Fungicides* (ed. R.W. Marsh), pp. 237-254.
    London: Longman.
BYRDE, R.J.W. & FIELDING, A.H.   (1955).   *Biochem. J.* 61, 337-341.
BYRDE, R.J.W. & FIELDING, A.H.   (1965).   *Nature, Lond.* 205, 390-391.
BYRDE, R.J.W. & FIELDING, A.H.   (1968).   *J. gen. Microbiol.* 52, 287-297.
BYRDE, R.J.W., FIELDING, A.H., ARCHER, S.A. & DAVIES, E.   (1973).   In: *Fungal*
    pathogenicity and the plant's response (ed. R.J.W. Byrde & C.V. Cutting),
    pp. 39-54.   London & New York: Academic Press.
BYRDE, R.J.W., FIELDING, A.H. & WILLIAMS, A.H.   (1960).   In: *Phenolics in*
    plants in health and disease (ed. J.B. Pridham), pp. 95-99.   Oxford:
    Pergamon Press.
BYRDE, R.J.W., MARTIN, J.T. & NICHOLAS, D.J.D.   (1956).   *Nature, Lond.* 178,
    638-639.
BYRDE, R.J.W. & MELVILLE, S.C.   (1971).   *Pl. Path.* 20, 48-50.
BYRDE, R.J.W. & WOODCOCK, D.   (1958).   *Biochem. J.* 69, 19-21.
BYRDE, R.J.W. & WOODCOCK, D.   (1959).   *Ann. appl. Biol.* 47, 332-338.
CALAVAN, E.C. & KEITT, G.W.   (1948).   *Phytopathology* 38, 857-882.
CALONGE, F.D.   (1969).   *Arch. Mikrobiol.* 67, 209-225.
CALONGE, F.D., FIELDING, A.H. & BYRDE, R.J.W.   (1969).   *J. gen. Microbiol.*
    55, 177-184.
CALONGE, F.D., FIELDING, A.H., BYRDE, R.J.W. & AKINREFON, O.A.   (1969).
    J. exp. Bot. 20, 350-357.
CAPPELLINI, R.A. & STRETCH, A.W.   (1962).   *Pl. Dis. Reptr* 46, 31-33.
CARLILE, M.J.   (1965).   *A. Rev. Pl. Physiol.* 16, 175-202.
CARLILE, M.J.   (1970).   In: *Photobiology of Microorganisms* (ed. Per Halldal),
    pp. 309-344.   London & New York: Wiley-Interscience.
CARLILE, M.J. & SELLIN, M.A.   (1963).   *Trans. Br. mycol. Soc.* 46, 15-18.
CARTER, G.A., GARRAWAY, J.L., SPENCER, D.M. & WAIN, R.L.   (1963).   *Ann. appl.*
    Biol. 51, 135-151.
CARTER, G.A., GARRAWAY, J.L., SPENCER, D.M. & WAIN, R.L.   (1964).   *Ann. appl.*
    Biol. 54, 115-127.
CATEN, C.E.   (1971).   *Heredity* 26, 299-312.
CATLING, W.S.   (1971).   *Proc. 6th Br. Insectic. Fungic. Conf., 1971* 2,
    103-109.
CHANDLER, W.A.   (1968).   *Pl. Dis. Reptr* 52, 695-697.
CHANDLER, W.A.   (1974*a*).   *Hortscience* 9, 332-333.
CHANDLER, W.A.   (1974*b*).   *Pl. Dis. Reptr* 58, 208-211.
CHANDLER, W.H.   (1951).   *Deciduous Orchards.*   Philadelphia: Lea & Febiger.
CHASTAGNER, G.A. & OGAWA, J.M.   (1973).   *Abstr. Papers 2nd Int. Cong. Pl.*
    Path., Minneapolis, 0052.
CHET, I.   (1969).   *Can. J. Bot.* 47, 593-595.
CHET, I., HENIS, Y. & MITCHELL, R.   (1967).   *Can. J. Microbiol.* 13, 137-141.
CHITZANIDIS, A.   (1971).   *Annls Inst. phytopath. Benaki* 10, 119-124.
CIFERRI, R.   (1953).   *Notiz. Mal. Piante* 23, 3-19.   (*R.A.M.* 33, 436, 1954).
CLAYTON, C.N.   (1942).   *Phytopathology* 32, 921-943.
COBB, N.A.   (1897).   *Agric. Gaz. N.S.W.* 8, 281.
COBB, N.A.   (1904).   *Agric. Gaz. N.S.W.* 15, 1.
COCHRANE, V.W.   (1958).   *Physiology of fungi.*   New York: Wiley.   524 pp.
COCHRANE, V.W. & COCHRANE, J.C.   (1966).   *Pl. Physiol.* 41, 810-814.

COHEN, G. (1955). *Israel F.A.O. Pl. Prot. Bull.* **3**, 93–94.

COLE, J.S. (1956). *Ann. Bot.* **20**, 15–38.

COLE, M. (1958). *Nature, Lond.* **181**, 1596–1597.

COLE, M. & WOOD, R.K.S. (1961a). *Ann. Bot.* **25**, 417–434.

COLE, M. & WOOD, R.K.S. (1961b). *Ann. Bot.* **25**, 435–452.

COLE, R.J., COX, T.W. & SOPER, D. (1973). *Proc. 7th Br. Insectic. Fungic. Conf. 1973,* **2**, 623–630.

COLE, R.J., GILCHRIST, A.J. & SOPER, D. (1971). *Proc. 6th Br. Insectic. Fungic. Conf., 1971,* **1**, 118–125.

COLEY-SMITH, J.R. (1959). *Ann. appl. Biol.* **47**, 511–518.

COLEY-SMITH, J.R. & COOKE, R.C. (1971). *A. Rev. Phytopathol.* **9**, 65–92.

COLLARD, J.W. (1918). *N.Z. Jl Agric.* **16**, 275–283.

CONNERS, I.L. (1967). *Canada Dep. Agric. Res. Branch Publication no. 1251.* 381 pp.

COOKE, R.C. (1969). *Trans. Br. mycol. Soc.* **53**, 77–86.

COOLEY, J.S. (1914). *Ann. Mo. bot. Gdn* **1**, 291–326.

CORBIN, J.B. (1963). *Aust. J. agric. Res.* **14**, 51–60.

CORBIN, J.B. & CRUICKSHANK, I.A.M. (1963). *Aust. J. biol. Sci.* **16**, 99–110.

CORBIN, J.B., OGAWA, J.M. & SCHULTZ, H.B. (1968). *Phytopathology* **58**, 1387–1394.

CORKE, A.T.K. (1958). *Pl. Path.* **7**, 56.

CORKE, A.T.K., HUNTER, T. & COLLINS, S.A. (1975). *Rep. agric. hort. Res. Stn, Univ. Bristol, 1974,* 131–132.

CORNER, E.J.H. (1950). *A Monograph of Clavaria and Allied Genera.* London & New York: Oxford University Press. 756 pp.

CREELMAN, D.W. (1962). *Canad. Pl. Dis. Surv.* **42**, 23–102.

CROSSA-RAYNAUD, P. (1966). *Annls Inst. natn. Rech. agron. Tunisie* **39**(3), 10 pp. (*R.A.M.* **46**, 2277, 1967).

CROSSA-RAYNAUD, P.H. (1969). *J. Am. Soc. hort. Sci.* **94**, 282–284.

CROSSA-RAYNAUD, P. & GHARIENI, R. (1967). *Annls Inst. natn. Rech. agron. Tunisie* **40**(9), 16 pp. (*R.A.M.* **48**, 1845, 1969).

CROSSE, R., McWILLIAM, R. & RHODES, A. (1964). *J. gen. Microbiol.* **34**, 51–65.

CROXALL, H.E., COLLINGWOOD, C.A. & JENKINS, J.E.E. (1951). *Ann. appl. Biol.* **38**, 833–843.

CROXALL, H.E., GWYNNE, D.C. & JENKINS, J.E.E. (1953). *Ann. appl. Biol.* **40**, 600–603.

CRUICKSHANK, I.A.M. (1966). *World Rev. Pest Contr.* **5**, 161–175.

CRUICKSHANK, I.A.M. & PERRIN, D.R. (1961). *Aust. J. biol. Sci.* **14**, 336–348.

CRUICKSHANK, I.A.M. & PERRIN, D.R. (1968). *Life Sciences* **7**, 449–458.

CRUICKSHANK, I.A.M., VEERARAGHAVAN, J. & PERRIN, D.R. (1974). *Aust. J. Pl. Physiol.* **1**, 149–156.

CUNNINGHAM, G.H. (1922a). *N.Z. Jl Agric.* **24**, 83–93.

CUNNINGHAM, G.H. (1922b). *N.Z. Jl Agric.* **25**, 177.

CUNNINGHAM, G.H. (1922c). *N.Z. Jl Agric.* **25**, 225–230.

CURTIS, K.M. (1928). *Ann. Bot.* **42**, 39–68.

DAINES, R.H. (1970). *Pl. Dis. Reptr* **54**, 764–767.

DANDENO, J.B. (1908). *Rep. Mich. Acad. Sci.* **10**, 51–53.

DARBY, R.T. & GODDARD, D.R. (1950). *Am. J. Bot.* **37**, 379–387.

DAVIDSE, L.C. (1973). *Pestic. Biochem. & Physiol.* **3**, 317–325.

DAVIS, R.H. (1966). In: *The Fungi*, vol. 2 (ed. G.C. Ainsworth & A.S. Sussman), pp. 567–588. New York & London: Academic Press.

DAVISON, F.R. & WILLAMAN, J.J. (1927). *Bot. Gaz.* **83**, 329–361.

DEKKER, J. (1972). In: *Systemic Fungicides* (ed. R.W. Marsh), pp. 156–174. London: Longman.

DELP, C.J. & KLÖPPING, H.L. (1968). *Pl. Dis. Reptr* **52**, 95–99.

DEMAIN, A.L. & PHAFF, H.J. (1957). *Wallerstein Labs Commun.* **20**, 119–140.

DENNIS, R.W.G. (1956). *C.M.I. Mycological Papers No. 62*, 216 pp.
DENNIS, R.W.G. (1968). *British Ascomycetes*. Cramer, Lehre: Verlag. 456 pp.
DICKSON, H. (1939). *Ann. Bot.* 3, 131-136.
DODGE, B.O. (1932). *Bull. Torrey bot. Club* 59, 347-360.
DOSHUMOV, U. (1958). *Trud. vsesoyuz. Inst. Zashch. Rast.* 11, 144-151. (*R.A.M.* 38, 154).
DOWLER, W.M., SHAW, P.D. & GOTTLIEB, D. (1963). *J. Bact.* 86, 9-17.
DRAYTON, F.L. (1932). *Mycologia* 24, 345-348.
DRAYTON, F.L. (1934). *Mycologia* 26, 46-72.
DRAYTON, F.L. (1937). *Mycologia* 29, 305-318.
DRUMMOND, R. (1934). *J. Pomol.* 12, 105-109.
DRUMMOND-GONCALVES, R. (1956). *Biológico* 23, 237-240.
DUMONT, K.P. & KORF, R.P. (1971). *Mycologia* 63, 157-168.
DUNEGAN, J.C. (1950). *U.S. National Peach Council, Peach Annual, 1950*, 23-24.
DUNEGAN, J.C. & GOLDSWORTHY, M.C. (1948). *Pl. Dis. Reptr* 32, 136-137.
DUTTA, S.K. & OJHA, M. (1972). *Molec. gen. Genetics* 114, 232-240.
ECKERT, J.W. & KOLBEZEN, M.J. (1964). *Phytopathology* 54, 978-986.
ECKERT, J.W. & SOMMER, N.F. (1967). *A. Rev. Phytopathol.* 5, 391-432.
EDGINGTON, L.V., KHEW, K.L. & BARRON, G.L. (1971). *Phytopathology* 61, 42-44.
EHRENBERG, C.G. (1818). *Sylvae mycologicae Ber.* 22.
ELLIOTT, M.E. (1964). *Can. J. Bot.* 42, 1393-1395.
ELLIOTT, M.E. (1965). *Can. J. Bot.* 43, 641-645.
ELLSMANN, E. (1939). *Forschungsdienst* 7, 361-366. (cited by Wormald, 1954).
ENGLISH, H., MOLLER, W.J. & NOME, S.F. (1967). *Pl. Dis. Reptr* 51, 212-214.
ERDELSKA, O. (1965). *Biologia, Bratisl.* 20, 90-99. (*R.A.M.* 44, 1905, 1965).
ESAM, G. (1917). *N.Z. Jl Agric.* 15, 84-89.
EVANS, E. (1971). *Pestic. Sci.* 2, 192-196.
EVANS, E.J. (1969). *Proc. 5th Br. Insectic. Fungic. Conf., 1969*, 2, 420-426.
EZEKIEL, W.N. (1924). *Bull. Md agric. Exp. Stn* 271, 87-142.
EZEKIEL, W.N. (1925). *Phytopathology* 15, 535-542.
FAWCETT, C.H. & SPENCER, D.M. (1967). *Ann. appl. Biol.* 60, 87-96.
FAWCETT, C.H. & SPENCER, D.M. (1968). *Ann. appl. Biol.* 61, 245-253.
FEATHER, M.S. & MALEK, A. (1972). *Biochim. biophys. Acta* 264, 103-105.
FIELDING, A.H. & BYRDE, R.J.W. (1969). *J. gen. Microbiol.* 58, 73-84.
FISKE, C.Y. & SUBBA ROW, Y. (1925). *J. biol. Chem.* 66, 375-400.
FOGLE, H.W. & FAUST, M. (1975). *J. Am. Soc. hort. Sci.* 100, 74-77.
FOSTER, J.W. (1949). *Chemical activities of fungi.* 648 pp. New York: Academic Press.
FRAMPTON, V.L. & MARSH, P.L. (1941). *Phytopathology* 31, 9.
FRIPP, Y.J. & DETTMAN, E.B. (1969). *Aust. J. exp. Agric. Anim. Husb.* 9, 9-11.
FROGGATT, W.W. (1909). *Agric. Gaz. N.S.W.* 20, 202.
FUCHS, A. & DRANDAREVSKI, C.A. (1976). *Neth. J. Pl. Path.* 82, 85-87.
FUCHS, A., JOBSEN, J.A. & WOUTS, W.M. (1965). *Nature, Lond.* 206, 714-715.
FUCKEL, L. (1869). *Symbolae mycologicae* 23-24, 1-459.
GARRETT, S.D. (1950). *Biol. Rev.* 25, 220-254.
GARRETT, S.D. (1956). *Biology of Root-infecting Fungi.* London & New York: Cambridge Univ. Press.
GARRETT, S.D. (1970). *Pathogenic Root-Infecting Fungi.* London & New York: Cambridge Univ. Press. 294 pp.
GAÜMANN, E. (1950). *Principles of plant infection*, p. 442. London: Crosby Lockwood. 543 pp.
GILPATRICK, J.D. (1973). *Pl. Dis. Reptr* 57, 457-459.
GILPATRICK, J.D. & SZKOLNIK, M. (1972). *Pl. Dis. Reptr* 56, 456-457.

GLODEANU, C., GLODEANU, E. & MARINESCU, G. (1973). *Anal. Univ. Craiova Biol. Stiint. agric. (A)* 3, 352-358.

GLODEANU, C., MARINESCU, G. & GLODEANU, E. (1973). *Anal. Univ. Craiova Biol. Stiint. agric. (A)* 3, 280-284.

GOLDENBERG, C.W. & COLE, H. (1973). *Phytopathology* 63, 201-202.

GOOD, D. & MacNEILL, B.H. (1972). *Proc. Can. Phytopathol. Soc.* 39, 31.

GOOD, H.M. & ZATHURECZKY, P.G.M. (1967). *Phytopathology* 57, 718-722.

GOURLEY, J.H. & HOWLETT, F.S. (1941). *Modern Fruit Growing.* New York: Macmillan & Co.

GREGORY, P.H. (1938). *Trans. Br. mycol. Soc.* 22, 201-203.

GREGORY, P.H. (1941). *Trans. Br. mycol. Soc.* 25, 26-40.

GREGORY, P.H. (1966). In: *The Fungi,* vol. 2 (ed. G.C. Ainsworth & A.S. Sussman), pp. 709-732. New York & London: Academic Press.

GREGORY, P.H., GUTHRIE, E.J. & BUNCE, M.E. (1959). *J. gen. Microbiol.* 20, 328-354.

GRENTE, J. (1970). *Summaries of Papers, VIIth Int. Cong. Plant Prot., Paris, 1970,* 538-539.

GRINDLE, M. & GOOD, H.M. (1961). *Trans. Br. mycol. Soc.* 44, 549-558.

GROVER, R.K. (1962). *Res. Bull. Panjab Univ. Sci.* 13, 103-114.

GROVER, R.K. (1963). *Indian Phytopath.* 16, 205-209.

GROVER, R.K. & MOORE, J.D. (1961). *Phytopathology* 51, 399-401.

GROVER, R.K. & MOORE, J.D. (1962). *Phytopathology* 52, 876-880.

GROVES, J.W. & DRAYTON, F.L. (1939). *Mycologia* 31, 485-489.

GROVES, J.W. & ELLIOTT, M.E. (1961). *Can. J. Bot.* 39, 215-231.

HALKILAHTI, A.H. (1962). *Maataloust. Aikakausk.* 34, 154-161.

HALL, M.P. (1933). *Ann. Bot.* 47, 543-578.

HALL, R. (1963). *Cytologia* 28, 181-193.

HALL, R. (1967a). *Aust. J. biol. Sci.* 20, 471-474.

HALL, R. (1967b). *Phytopath. Z.* 58, 131-136.

HALL, R. (1969). *Bot. Rev.* 35, 285-304.

HALL, R. (1971a). *Phytopath. Z.* 72, 245-254.

HALL, R. (1971b). *Phytopath. Z.* 72, 281-290.

HALL, R. (1972). *Phytopath. Z.* 73, 27-38.

HALL, R. (1973). *Bull. Torrey bot. Club* 100, 253-259.

HAMMERSCHLAG, R.S. & SISLER, H.D. (1973). *Pestic. Biochem. & Physiol.* 3, 42-54.

HANSEN, M.C. & BECKMAN, K.M. (1967). *Pl. Dis. Reptr* 51, 578-581.

HANSEN, N.H. & RIEMANN, H. (1963). *J. appl. Bact.* 26, 314-333.

HARDH, H.J.E. (1951). *Maataloust. Aikakausk.* 23, 79-87.

HARRISON, T.H. (1922). *J. Proc. R. Soc. N.S.W.* 55, 215-219.

HARRISON, T.H. (1928). *J. Proc. R. Soc. N.S.W.* 62, 99-151.

HARRISON, T.H. (1933). *J. Proc. R. Soc. N.S.W.* 67, 132-177.

HARRISON, T.H. (1935). *Mycologia* 27, 302-318.

HASHMI, M.H., MORGAN-JONES, G. & KENDRICK, B. (1972). *Can. J. Bot.* 50, 2419-2421.

HASPEL-HORVATOVIC, E. (1965). *Biologia, Bratisl.* 20, 14-24.

HASPEL-HORVATOVIC, E. (1972). *Phytopath. Z.* 74, 1-12.

HAWKER, L.E. (1950). *Physiology of fungi.* London: University Press. 360 pp.

HAWKER, L.E. (1957). *Symp. Soc. gen. Microbiol.* 7, 238-258.

HAWKINS, L.A. (1915). *Am. J. Bot.* 2, 71-81.

HEATON, J.B. (1974). *Qd J. agric. anim. Sci.* 31, 237-244.

HESS, C., HEIMES, R. & LÖCHER, F. (1975). *Mitt. biol. BundAnst. Ld- u. Forstw.* 165, 145-146.

HESS, C. & LÖCHER, F. (1975). *Proc. 8th Br. Insectic. Fungic. Conf., 1975,* 2, 693-696.

HEUBERGER, J.W. (1934). *Bull. Md agric. Exp. Stn* 371, 167-189.

HEYNS, A.J. (1967). *Decid. Fruit Grow.* 17, 326-329.
HEYNS, A.J. (1968). *Decid. Fruit Grow.* 18, 363-367.
HIROE, J. & MATSUO, A. (1957). *Trans. Tottori Soc. agric. Sci.* 11, 195-199.
HIRST, J.M. (1952). *Ann. appl. Biol.* 39, 257-265.
HIRST, J.M. (1953). *Trans. Br. mycol. Soc.* 36, 375-393.
HIRST, J.M. (1961). *Trans. Br. mycol. Soc.* 44, 138-139.
HIRST, J.M. (1976). *Proc. 8th Br. Insectic. Fungic. Conf., 1975,* 3, 721-729.
HIRST, J.M. & STEDMAN, O.J. (1962). *Rep. Rothamsted exp. Stn, 1961,* 114-115.
HISLOP, E.C. (1967a). *Rep. agric. hort. Res. Stn, Univ. Bristol, 1966,* 184-189.
HISLOP, E.C. (1967b). *Ann. appl. Biol.* 60, 265-279.
HISLOP, E.C., ARCHER, S.A. & HOAD, G.V. (1973). *Phytochemistry* 12, 2081-2086.
HISLOP, E.C., BARNABY, V.M., SHELLIS, C. & LABORDA, F. (1974). *J. gen. Microbiol.* 81, 79-99.
HISLOP, E.C., HOAD, G.V. & ARCHER, S.A. (1973). In: *Fungal pathogenicity and the plant's response.* (ed. R.J.W. Byrde & C.V. Cutting), pp. 87-117. London & New York: Academic Press.
HISLOP, E.C., SHELLIS, C., FIELDING, A.H., BOURNE, F.J. & CHIDLOW, J.W. (1974). *J. gen. Microbiol.* 83, 135-143.
HOFFMANN, G.M. (1970). *Phytopath. Z.* 68, 143-154.
HOFFMANN, G.M. (1972). *Phytopath. Z.* 73, 326-340.
HOFFMANN, G.M. (1974). *Phytopath. Z.* 79, 193-202.
HONEY, E.E. (1928). *Mycologia* 20, 127-157.
HONEY, E.E. (1936). *Amer. J. Bot.* 23, 100-106.
HORSFALL, J.G. (1945). *Fungicides and their action.* Waltham, Mass., U.S.A.: Chronica Botanica. 239 pp.
HORSFALL, J.G. (1956). *Principles of fungicidal action.* Waltham, Mass., U.S.A.: Chronica Botanica. 274 pp.
HORSFALL, J.G. & RICH, S. (1955). *Trans. N.Y. Acad. Sci. (2)* 18, 69-80.
HORSFALL, J.G. & RICH, S. (1959). *Phytopathology* 49, 541-542.
HORSFALL, J.G. & RICH, S. (1960). *Phytopathology* 50, 646.
HOWELL, H.E. (1972). Ph.D. Thesis, Univ. of Bristol.
HOWELL, H.E. (1975). *J. gen. Microbiol.* 90, 32-40.
HRDLICKA, J., CURDA, D. & BAUER, T. (1971). *Sb. vys. Sk. chem-technol. Praze, Potraviny* 30, 25-29. (*Biol. Abstr.* 55, 001856, 1973).
HUBER, F.M. & GOTTLIEB, D. (1969). *Mycopath. Mycol. appl.* 37, 49-56.
HUMPHREY, J.E. (1893). *Bot. Gaz.* 18, 85-93.
HUNTER, R.E. (1974). *Physiol. Pl. Path.* 4, 151-159.
HUTTON, K.E. & KABLE, P.F. (1970). *Pl. Dis. Reptr* 54, 776-780.
INGOLD, C.T. (1960). *Pl. Path.* 3, 137-168.
INGOLD, C.T. (1966). In: *The Fungi,* vol. 2 (ed. G.C. Ainsworth & A.S. Sussman), pp. 679-707. New York & London: Academic Press.
INGOLD, C.T. (1971). *Fungal Spores.* Oxford: Clarendon Press. 320 pp.
INGRAM, C. (1948). *Ornamental cherries.* London: Country Life. 259 pp.
ISHII, K. (1970). *Summaries of Papers, VIIIth Int. Cong. Plant Prot., Paris, 1970,* 200.
JACKSON, H.S. (1915). *Bienn. Crop Pest hort. Rep. Ore.* 2, 271-272.
JANICK, J. & MOORE, J.N. (ed.) (1975). *Advances in fruit breeding.* Purdue, U.S.A.: University Press. 640 pp.
JANITOR, A. (1970). *Česká Mykol.* 24, 198-206.
JARVIS, W.R. (1962). *Trans. Br. mycol. Soc.* 45, 549-559.
JEHLE, R.A. (1910). M.S. thesis, Univ. of Minnesota.
JEHLE, R.A. (1914). Ph.D. thesis, Cornell Univ.
JENKINS, P.T. (1965a). *Aust. J. agric. Res.* 16, 141-144.
JENKINS, P.T. (1965b). *Aust. J. agric. Res.* 16, 626-633.

JENKINS, P.T.   (1968a).   *Aust. J. biol. Sci.* 21, 937–945.
JENKINS, P.T.   (1968b).   *Aust. J. exp. Agric. Anim. Husb.* 8, 434–435.
JENKINS, P.T. & REINGANUM, C.   (1965).   *Aust. J. agric. Res.* 16, 131–140.
JENKINS, P.T. & REINGANUM, C.   (1968).   In: *Report of the Research Work on Brown Rot of Stone Fruits* (ed. Australian Brown Rot Research Committee), p. 48.   Melbourne: Government Printer.
JENKINS, P.T. & SKENE, K.   (1968).   In: *Report of the Research Work on Brown Rot of Stone Fruits* (ed. Australian Brown Rot Research Committee), p. 52.   Melbourne: Government Printer.
JENNINGS, J.P.   (1969).   *J. Agric. S. Aust.* 73, 62–65.
JEREBZOFF, S.   (1961).   Thèse Sciences Imprimerie du Sud, Toulouse.
JEREBZOFF, S.   (1965).   In: *Circadian Clocks* (ed. J. Aschoff), pp. 183–189.   Amsterdam: North-Holland Publ. Co.
JEREBZOFF, S. & JACQUES, R.   (1972).   *Pl. Physiol., Lancaster* 50, 187–190.
JEROME, S.M.R.   (1958).   *J. Aust. Inst. agric. Sci.* 24, 132–140.
JINKS, J.L.   (1952).   *Proc. R. Soc.* B140, 83–106.
JOHNSTON, T.H.   (1910).   *Agric. Gaz. N.S.W.* 21, 194.
JONES, A.L.   (1975).   *Pl. Dis. Reptr* 59, 127–130.
JONES, A.L. & BURTON, C.   (1973).   *Pl. Dis. Reptr* 57, 62–66.
JONES, A.L., BURTON, C.L. & TENNES, B.R.   (1973).   *Mich. State Univ. agric. Exp. Stn, East Lansing Res. Rep.* no. 209, 10 pp.
JONES, D., FARMER, V.C., BACON, J.S.D. & WILSON, M.J.   (1972).   *Trans. Br. mycol. Soc.* 59, 11–23.
JONES, D.R., GRAHAM, W.G. & WARD, E.W.B.   (1975).   *Phytopathology* 65, 1409–1416.
JONES, D.R., UNWIN, C.H. & WARD, E.W.B.   (1975).   *Phytopathology* 65, 1417–1419.
JORDOVIC, M.   (1954).   *Arh. poljopr. Nauke Teh.* 7, 96–99.   (*R.A.M.* 34, 603–604, 1955).
JUNG, J.   (1956).   *Phytopath. Z.* 27, 405–426.   (*R.A.M.* 36, 197, 1957).
KAARS SIJPESTEIJN, A.   (1972).   In: *Systemic Fungicides* (ed. R.W. Marsh), pp. 132–155.   London: Longman.
KABLE, P.F.   (1965a).   *Aust. J. exp. Agric. Anim. Husb.* 5, 166–171.
KABLE, P.F.   (1965b).   *Aust. J. exp. Agric. Anim. Husb.* 5, 172–175.
KABLE, P.F.   (1969a).   *Aust. J. agric. Res.* 20, 301–316.
KABLE, P.F.   (1969b).   *Aust. J. agric. Res.* 20, 317–323.
KABLE, P.F.   (1970).   *J. hort. Sci.* 45, 143–152.
KABLE, P.F.   (1971a).   *Agric. Gaz. N.S.W.* 82, 194–201.
KABLE, P.F.   (1971b).   *Phytopath. Z.* 70, 173–176.
KABLE, P.F.   (1972).   *Aust. J. agric. Res.* 23, 1035–1044.
KABLE, P.F.   (1974).   *Agric. Gaz. N.S.W.* 85, 43–44.
KABLE, P.F.   (1975).   *J. hort. Sci.* 50, 143–150.
KABLE, P.F.   (1976).   *J. hort. Sci.* (in press).
KABLE, P.F. & PARKER, K.G.   (1963).   *Pl. Dis. Reptr* 47, 1104.
KAGAWA, H. & TERUI, M.   (1962).   *Bull. Fac. Agric. Hirosaki Univ.* 8, 24–28.   (*R.A.M.* 43, 1695, 1964).
KAMAT, M.N. & PANDE-CHIPLONKAR, A.   (1971).   *Revue de Mycologie* 36, 257–276.
KAROVA, V.   (1974).   *Gradinarska i Lozarska Nauka* 11, 101–106.   (*R.P.P.* 54, 3396, 1975).
KARSTEN, P.A.   (1871).   *Mycologia Fennica.* Pars prima. Discomycetes.   (Helsingfors). 1–264.
KARSTEN, P.A.   (1885).   *Acta Soc. Faun. Fl. Fenn.* 2, pp. 1–174.
KATO, T., TANAKA, S., UEDA, M. & KAWASE, Y.   (1974).   *Agric. Biol. Chem. (Jap.)* 38, 2377–2384.
KATO, T., TANAKA, S., UEDA, M. & KAWASE, Y.   (1975).   *Agric. Biol. Chem. (Jap.)* 39, 169–174.

KATSER, A. (1933). *Phytopath. Z.* 6, 177-227.
KEEGSTRA, K., TALMADGE, K.W., BAUER, W.D. & ALBERSHEIM, P. (1973). *Pl. Physiol., Lancaster* 51, 188-196.
KEIL, J. (1950). *Naturwissenschaften* 37, 476-477. (*R.A.M.* 30, 237-238).
KEITT, G.W. & PALMITER, D.H. (1937). *J. agric. Res.* 55, 397-437.
KENNEL, W. (1968). *Z. PflKrankh. PflPath. PflSchutz.* 75, 585-591.
KHAN, M. (1966). *Nature, Lond.* 212 (5062), 640.
KHASANOV, O.K. (1962). *Uzbek. biol. Zh.* 6, 62-67. (*R.A.M.* 42, 443, 1963).
KHOKHRYAKOVA, T.M. (1964). *Zashch. Rast., Moskva* 9, 17-19. (*R.A.M.* 43, 2321, 1964).
KHOKHRYAKOVA, T.M. (1969). *Mikol. & Fitopat.* 3, 235-242.
KHOKHRYAKOVA, T.M. (1971). *Trudy prikl. Bot. Genet. Selek.* 43, 241-245. (*R.P.P.* 51, 1656, 1972).
KHOKHRYAKOVA, T.M. (1973). *Nauch.Tr. Krym. Opyt.-Selekts. St.* 7, 288-294.
KILLIAN, K. (1921). *Zbl. Bakt.* 53, 560-597.
KIMBROUGH, J.W. (1972). *Persoonia* 6, 395-404.
KIMURA, J. (1967). *Ann. Phytopath. Soc. Japan* 33, 126-128.
KINNEY, L.F. (1897). *Rep. Rhode Isl. agric. Exp. Stn, 1896*, 191-192.
KIRK, T.W. (1905). *Rep. N.Z. Dep. Agric. 1905*, p. 425.
KIRTLAND, J.R. (1855). *Florist and Hort. J.* 4, 34-36.
KITOVSKAYA, M.I., KHARITON, K.S. & KULIK, M.F. (1973). *Izv. Akad. Auk. mold. S.S.R., Ser. Biol. Khim. Nauk.* (1), 76-78. (*Biol. Abstr.* 56, 057159, 1973).
KNEE, M. (1975). *Phytochemistry* 14, 2181-2188.
KNEE, M., FIELDING, A.H., ARCHER, S.A. & LABORDA, F. (1975). *Phytochemistry* 14, 2213-2222.
KOCH de BROTOS, L. & BOASSO, C. (1955). *Publ. Minist. Ganad. Agric. Montevideo* 106, 65 pp.
KÖCK, G. (1910). *Z. landw. VersWes. Ost.* 13, 889-890. (cited by Wormald, 1954).
KOFFMAN, W. (1973). *Aust. J. exp. Agric. Anim. Husb.* 13, 205-207.
KOFFMAN, W. & KABLE, P.F. (1975). *Pl. Dis. Reptr* 59, 586-590.
KORF, R.P. & DUMONT, K.P. (1968). *J. Elisha Mitchell scient. Soc.* 84, 242-247.
KOSASIH, B.D. & WILLETTS, H.J. (1975). *Ann. Bot.* 39, 185-191.
KOVAL', N.D. (1969). *Mikol. & Fitopat.* 3, 44-46. (*R.A.M.* 48, 1817, 1969).
KRÖBER, H. (1952). *Höfchenbr. Bayer PflSchutz-Nachr.* 5 (4), 171-217.
KSENDZOVA, E.N. & NILOVA, V.P. (1975). *Mikol. & Fitopat.* 9, 77-80. (*R.P.P.* 64, 3832, 1975).
KUC, J. (1972). *A. Rev. Phytopathol.* 10, 207-232.
KUHN, G.D., MERKLEY, M.S. & DENNISON, R.A. (1968). *Fd Technol.* 22, 91-92.
KUNDERT, J. (1972). *Schweiz. Z. Obst.- u. Weinb.* 108, 44-52. (*R.P.P.* 51, 2665, 1972).
KUNDERT, J. (1975). *Schweiz. Z. Obst.- u. Weinb.* 111, 161-167. (*R.P.P.* 54, 5470, 1975).
KUNZE, G. & SCHMIDT, J.C. (1817). *Mycologische Hefte* 1, 80.
KUO, M.J. & ALEXANDER, M. (1967). *J. Bact.* 94, 624-629.
KYBAL, J. (1964). *Phytopathology* 54, 244-245.
LABORDA, F., ARCHER, S.A., FIELDING, A.H. & BYRDE, R.J.W. (1974). *J. gen. Microbiol.* 81, 151-163.
LABORDA, F., FIELDING, A.H. & BYRDE, R.J.W. (1973). *J. gen. Microbiol.* 79, 321-329.
LACOK, P., STANOVA, M. & BACIGALOVA, K. (1975). *Biologia, Bratisl.* 30, 497-503.
LACOK, P., STANOVA, M. & NIZNANSKA, A. (1972). *Biologia, Bratisl.* 27, 757-762.

LACROIX, L., BIC, G., BURGAUD, L., GUILLOT, M., LE BLANC, R., RIOTTOT, R. & SAULI, M. (1974). *Phytiat.-Phytopharm.* 23, 165-174.

LAKHOUA, H., CROSSA-RAYNAUD, P., CARRAUT, A. & CHEMLI, A. (1967). *Rapport d'activités du laboratoire d'arboriculture fruitierè de l'INRAT, 1966.* 32 pp.

LANGCAKE, P., BRATT, P.M. & DRYSDALE, R.B. (1973). *Physiol. Pl. Path.* 3, 101-106.

LANGLEY, B. (1729). *Pomona.* London: Strahan *et al.*

LAYNE, R.E.C. (1975a). *Hortscience* 10, 532.

LAYNE, R.E.C. (1975b). *Hortscience* 10, 532-533.

LE TOURNEAU, D. (1966). *Mycologia* 58, 934-942.

LEFTER, G. & PASC, I. (1963). *Gradina Via Livada* 12, 49-53. (*R.A.M.* 43, 2343, 1964).

LEMKE, P.A. & NASH, C.H. (1974). *Bact. Rev.* 38, 29-56.

LEPPIK, E.E. (1970). *A. Rev. Phytopathol.* 8, 323-344.

LEWIS, D.H. (1974). In: *Evolution in the Microbial World* (ed. M.J. Carlile & J.J. Skehel), pp. 367-392. Cambridge: University Press.

LEWIS, D.H. & SMITH, D.C. (1967). *New Phytol.* 66, 143-184.

LIEN, E.J., KONG, C.-T. & LUKENS, R.J. (1974). *Pestic. Biochem. & Physiol.* 4, 289-298.

LIN, C.-K. (1940). *Mem. Cornell Univ. agric. Exp. Stn* 233, 33 pp.

LIN, K.-H. (1942). *Phytopathology* 32, 239-245.

LIN, K.-H. (1948). *Lingnan Sci. J.* 22, 139.

LOCKWOOD, J.L. (1960). *Phytopathology* 50, 787-789.

LOVISOLO, O. (1956). *Boll. Staz. Pat. veg. Roma Ser. 3,* 13, 7-40.

LUND, B.M. & MAPSON, L.W. (1970). *Biochem. J.* 119, 251-263.

McALPINE, D. (1902). *Fungus diseases of stone fruit trees in Australia and their treatment.* Dep. Agric. Melbourne, Victoria. p. 53, p. 85.

McCALLAN, S.E.A. (1930). *Mem. Cornell Univ. agric. Exp. Stn* 128, 8-79.

McCALLAN, S.E.A. (1946). *Contr. Boyce Thompson Inst. Pl. Res.* 14, 105-116.

McCALLAN, S.E.A. & MILLER, L.P. (1957a). *Contr. Boyce Thompson Inst. Pl. Res.* 18, 483-495.

McCALLAN, S.E.A. & MILLER, L.P. (1957b). *Contr. Boyce Thompson Inst. Pl. Res.* 18, 497-506.

McCALLAN, S.E.A. & MILLER, L.P. (1958). *Adv. Pest Control Res.* 2, 107-134.

McCALLAN, S.E.A., MILLER, L.P. & WEED, R.M. (1954). *Contr. Boyce Thompson Inst. Pl. Res.* 18, 39-68.

McCALLAN, S.E.A. & WILCOXON, F. (1939). *Contr. Boyce Thompson Inst. Pl. Res.* 11, 5-20.

McCLENDON, J.H. (1975). *Phytochemistry* 14, 377-382.

McCLURE, T.T. (1958). *Phytopathology* 48, 322-323.

MacNAB, A.A. (1975). *Fungicide and Nematicide Tests,* 30, 39-49.

MacSWAN, I.C. (1969). *Fungicide and Nematicide Tests,* 24, 29-30.

MacSWAN, I.C. & KOEPSELL, P.A. (1974). *Oregon Plant Disease Control Handbook.* Extension Service, Oregon State University, Corvallis, U.S.A. 187 pp.

MADER, E.O. & SCHNEIDER, C.L. (1948). *Phytopathology* 38, 17.

MAJERNIK, O. & NIZNANSKY, A. (1962). *Biologia, Bratisl.* 17, 321-331.

MANARESI, A. (1920). *Riv. Patol. veg.* 10, 14 pp.

MARSH, P.B. (1945). *Phytopathology* 35, 54-61.

MARSH, R.W. (1947). *J. Pomol.* 23, 185-205.

MARTIN, H. (1972). (ed.) *Pesticide Manual.* Droitwich, U.K.: British Crop Protection Council. 535 pp.

MASRI, S.S. (1967). *Phytopathology* 57, 997.

MASURAT, G., PESCHEL, R. & STEPHAN, S. (1966). *Nachr. Bl. dt. PflSchutzdienst., Berl.* N.F. 20, 121-142. (*R.A.M.* 46, 1844, 1967).

MATHENY, W.A. (1913). *Bot. Gaz.* 56, 418-432.

MAZUR, P. (1968) In: *The Fungi*, vol. 3 (ed. G.C. Ainsworth & A.S. Sussman), pp. 325-394. New York & London: Academic Press.

MAZUR, P. (1970). *Science, N.Y.* 168, 939-949.

MEYER, J.A. & RENARD, J.L. (1969). *Phytopathology* 59, 1409-1411.

MICHENER, H.D. & SNELL, N. (1949). *Archs Biochem.* 22, 208-214.

MILLER, H.J. (1944). *Phytopathology* 34, 1009.

MILLER, L.P., McCALLAN, S.E.A. & WEED, R.M. (1953). *Contr. Boyce Thompson Inst. Pl. Res.* 17, 173-195.

MILLIKAN, C.R. (1968). In: *Report of the Research Work on Brown Rot of Stone Fruits*. (ed. Australian Brown Rot Research Committee), pp. 75-96. Melbourne: Government Printer.

MITCHELL, A.E. (1948). *Rep. Mich. St. hort. Soc., 1947*, 77-100.

MITCHELL, J.E., RAVENSCROFT, A.V., BERGER, R.D. & MOORE, J.D. (1963). *Pl. Dis. Reptr* 47, 548.

MITTMANN-MAIER, G. (1940a). *Z. PflKrankh. PflPath. PflSchutz.* 50, 84-95.

MITTMANN-MAIER, G. (1940b). *Gartenbauwissenschaft* 15, 334-361.

MIURA, M. (1929). *Flora of Manchuria and East Mongolia. Part III. Cryptogams, Fungi.* 93-98.

MOLLER, W.J. & CARTER, M.V. (1975). *Aust. Pl. Path. Soc. Newsletter* 4, 5.

MOLLER, W.J., OGAWA, J.M., NYLAND, G. & GERDTS, M.H. (1976). *Guide to field diseases on peaches, nectarines and plums.* Univ. Calif. Div. agric. Sci. Leaflet 2822.

MOORE, M.H. (1932). *J. Pomol.* 10, 271-294.

MOORE, M.H. (1950a). *J. hort. Sci.* 25, 213-224.

MOORE, M.H. (1950b). *J. hort. Sci.* 25, 225-234.

MOORE, M.H. (1950c). *Rep. E. Malling Res. Stn, 1949*, 169-173.

MOORE, M.H. (1951). *Rep. E. Malling Res. Stn, 1950*, 131.

MOORE, M.H. (1952). *Rep. E. Malling Res. Stn, 1951*, 148.

MORSCHEL, J.R.G. (1955). *Agric. Gaz. N.S.W.* 66, 146-150.

MÜLLER, K.O. (1956). *Phytopath. Z.* 27, 237-254.

MÜLLER, K.O. (1958). *Aust. J. biol. Sci.* 11, 275-300.

NAQVI, S.H.Z. & GOOD, H.M. (1957). *Can. J. Bot.* 35, 635-645.

NEGRU, A., MIRCEA, E. & CRIŞAN, A. (1957). *Studii Cerc. Agron. Cluj* 8, 93-98. (*R.A.M.* 38, 608, 1959).

NORTHOVER, J. (1972). *Proc. Can. phytopath. Soc.* 39, 37-38.

NORTON, J.B.S. (1902). *Trans. Acad. Sci. St. Louis* 12, 91-97.

NORTON, J.B.S. & EZEKIEL, W.N. (1924). *Phytopathology* 14, 31-32.

NORTON, J.B.S., EZEKIEL, W.N. & JEHLE, R.A. (1923). *Bull. Md agric. Exp. Stn* 271, 87-142.

OGAWA, J.M. (1957). *Phytopathology* 47, 530.

OGAWA, J.M. (1958). *Phytopathology* 48, 396.

OGAWA, J.M., BOSE, E., MANJI, B.T. & SCHREADER, W.R. (1972). *Phytopathology* 62, 579-580.

OGAWA, J.M. & ENGLISH, H. (1960). *Phytopathology* 50, 550-558.

OGAWA, J.M., HALL, D.H. & KOEPSELL, P.A. (1967). *Symp. Soc. gen. Microbiol.* 17, 247-267.

OGAWA, J.M., MANJI, B.T. & BOSE, E. (1968). *Pl. Dis. Reptr* 52, 722-726.

OGAWA, J.M., MANJI, B.T. & SCHREADER, W.R. (1975). *Pl. Dis. Reptr* 59, 876-880.

OGAWA, J.M., YATES, W.E., MANJI, B.T. & COWDEN, R.E. (1972). *Phytopathology* 62, 781.

O'HARA, T. & NASUNO, S. (1972). *Agric. Biol. Chem.* 36, 1797-1802.

OUCHTERLONY, O. (1968). *Immunodiffusion and Immunoelectrophoresis*. Michigan: Ann Arbor Science Publs.

OWENS, R.G. (1953). *Contr. Boyce Thompson Inst. Pl. Res.* 17, 273-282.

OWENS, R.G.   (1969).   In: *Fungicides*, vol. 2 (ed. D.C. Torgeson), pp. 147-301.
   New York & London: Academic Press.
OWENS, R.G., NOVOTNY, H.M. & MICHELS, M.   (1958).   *Contr. Boyce Thompson Inst.*
   Pl. Res. 19, 355-374.
OZAWA, J.   (1952).   *Rep. Ohara Inst. agric. Res.* 40, 110-112.
PARK, D.   (1965).   In: *Ecology of Soil-Borne Pathogens - Prelude to Biological*
   Control (ed. K.F. Baker & W.C. Snyder), pp. 82-97. Berkeley, California:
   Univ. of California Press.
PARK, D.   (1968).   In: *The Fungi*, vol. 3 (ed. G.C. Ainsworth & A.S. Sussman),
   pp. 5-39. New York & London: Academic Press.
PARTRIDGE, A.D. & RICH, A.E.   (1962).   *Phytopathology* 52, 1000.
PAUVERT, P., FOURNET, J. & RAPILLY, F.   (1969).   *Annls Phytopath.* 1, 491-493.
PAXTON, J., GOODCHILD, D.J. & CRUICKSHANK, I.A.M.   (1974).   *Physiol. Pl. Path.*
   4, 167-171.
PAYNTER, V.A. & JEN, J.J.   (1974).   *J. Food Sci.* 39, 1195-1199.
PAYNTER, V.A. & JEN, J.J.   (1975).   *Biochem. Physiol. Pflanzen* 167, 219-231.
PECK, C.H.   (1881).   *Rep. N.Y. St. Mus. nat. Hist.* 34, 34-36.
PEGG, G.F. & VESSEY, J.C.   (1973).   *Physiol. Pl. Path.* 3, 207-222.
PENROSE, L.J., TARRAN, J. & WONG, A.-L.   (1976).   *Aust. J. agric. Res.* (in
   press).
PERSOON, C.H.   (1796).   *Observationes Mycologicae* p. 26.
PERSOON, C.H.   (1801). *Synopsis Methodica Fungorum* p. 63, Gottingae.
PERSOON, C.H.   (1822). *Mycologia Europea* 1, 24-25.
PETERSON, P.D.   (1941).   *Phytopathology* 31, 1108-1116.
PETERSON, D.H. & McGLOHON, N.E.   (1967).   *Pl. Dis. Reptr* 51, 750-751.
PHILLIPS, D.J.   (1975).   *Phytopathology* 65, 255-258.
PHILLIPS, D.J. & GRENDAHL, J. (1973).   *Pl. Dis. Reptr* 57, 814-816.
PHILLIPS, D.J. & HARVEY, J.M.   (1975).   *Phytopathology* 65, 1233-1236.
PHILLIPS, J.H.H. & WEAVER, G.M.   (1975).   *Hortscience* 10, 580-582.
PITT, D. & COOMBES, C.   (1969).   *J. gen. Microbiol.* 56, 321-329.
POLLOCK, J.B.   (1909).   *Rep. Mich. Acad. Sci.* 11, 48-54.
POLLOCK, J.B.   (1918).   *Rep. Mich. Acad. Sci.* 20, 279-280.
PONTECORVO, G.   (1946).   *Cold Spring Harbor Symp. Quant. Biol.* 11, 193-201.
PONTECORVO, G.   (1954).   *Caryologia* (Suppl.) 6, 192-200.
POTGIETER, H.J. & ALEXANDER, M.   (1966).   *J. Bact.* 91, 1526-1532.
POWELL, D.   (1951).   *Pl. Dis. Reptr* 35, 76-77.
PREECE, T.F.   (1967).   *Pl. Path.* 16, 176-180.
PRING, R.J. & RICHMOND, D.V.   (1975).   *Trans. Br. mycol. Soc.* 65, 291-294.
PURDY, L.H.   (1967).   In: *Sourcebook of Laboratory Exercises in Plant*
   Pathology, p. 41. San Francisco & London: Freeman.
RAMSDELL, D.C. & OGAWA, J.M.   (1973*a*).   *Phytopathology* 63, 830-836.
RAMSDELL, D.C. & OGAWA, J.M.   (1973*b*).   *Phytopathology* 63, 959-964.
RAPER, J.R.   (1968).   In: *The Fungi*, vol. 3 (ed. G.C. Ainsworth & A.S.
   Sussman), pp. 677-693. New York & London: Academic Press.
RATTIGAN, A. & AYRES, P.G.   (1975).   *Trans. Br. mycol. Soc.* 65, 315-317.
RAVETTO, D.J. & OGAWA, J.M.   (1972).   *Phytopathology* 62, 784.
REEVE, R.M.   (1957).   *Stain Technol.* 34, 209-211.
REHM, H.   (1887-1896).   *Rabenhorst's Kryptogamen-Fl. Deutschl., Oesterr.*
   Schweiz 1, 1-1275.
REINGANUM, C.   (1964).   *Aust. J. biol. Sci.* 17, 705-718.
REKHVIASHVILI, L.M.   (1972).   *Trudy Inst. Zashch. Rast., Tbilisi* 23, 261-265.
   (*R.P.P.* 53, 2433, 1974).
REKHVIASHVILI, L.M.   (1973).   *Trudy Inst. Zashch. Rast., Tbilisi* 25, 143-147.
   (*R.P.P.* 54, 3379, 1975).
RENARD, J.L. & MEYER, J.A.   (1969).   *Trans. Br. mycol. Soc.* 53, 455-461.
RENAUD, R.   (1967).   *Revue Zool. agric. appl.* 66, 58-64.

RENAUD, R. (1968). *Revue Zool. agric. appl.* 67, 81-86.
RENAUD, R. (1970). *Summaries of Papers, VIIth Int. Cong. Pl. Prot., Paris, 1970,* 267.
RENAUD, R. (1975). *Acta horticult.* 48, 79-82.
REYES, F. & BYRDE, R.J.W. (1973). *Biochem. J.* 131, 381-388.
RIBALDI, M. (1954). *Annali Sper. agr.* 8, 1043-1053. (*R.A.M.* 35, 213, 1956).
RICH, S. & HORSFALL, J.G. (1954). *Proc. natn. Acad. Sci. U.S.A.* 40, 139-145.
RICH, S. & HORSFALL, J.G. (1961). *Bull. Conn. agric. Exp. Stn 639.* 95 pp.
RICHARDSON, L.T. & THORN, G.D. (1969). *Can. J. Bot.* 47, 241-245.
RIDGWAY, R. (1912). *Color Standard and Color Nomenclature.* Washington, D.C. 43 pp.
RISHBETH, J. (1963). *Ann. appl. Biol.* 52, 63-77.
ROBERTS, D.W.A. (1969). *Int. Rev. Cytol.* 26, 303-328.
ROBERTS, J.W. & DUNEGAN, J.C. (1927). *Mycologia* 19, 195-205.
ROBERTS, J.W. & DUNEGAN, J.C. (1932). *Tech. Bull. U.S. Dep. Agric.* 328, 59 pp.
ROHRBACH, K.U. (1973). *Proc. 7th Br. Insectic. Fungic. Conf., 1973,* 2, 631-636.
ROPER, J.A. (1966) In: *The Fungi,* vol. 2. (ed. G.C. Ainsworth & A.S. Sussman), pp. 589-617. New York & London: Academic Press.
ROSIK, J., KUBALA, J., LACOK, P. & STANOVA, M. (1969). *Biologia, Bratisl.* 24, 298-306.
SACCARDO, P.A. (1884). *Bot. Centralbl.* 18, 213-220, 247-256.
SACCARDO, P.A. (1889). *Sylloge Fungorum omnium hucusque cognitorum* 8, 1-1143.
SACCARDO, P.A. (1906). *Sylloge Fungorum* 18, 41.
SACCARDO, P.A. & VOGLINO, P. (1886). *Sylloge Fungorum* 4, 35.
SAREJANNI, J.A., DEMETRIADES, S.D. & ZACHOS, D.G. (1953). *Annls Inst. phytopath. Benaki* 7, 5-10.
SCHELLENBERG, H.C. (1908). *Flora, Jena* 98, 257-308.
SCHMIDT, J.C. (1918). *Deutschlands Schwamme* 225.
SCHRÖTER, C.J. (1893). *Cohn, Krypt.-Fl. Schles.* 3, 67.
SHARVELLE, E.G. & CHEN, S.-M. (1943). *Phytopathology* 33, 1118.
SHEPHERD, C.J. (1968). In: *Report of the Research Work on Brown Rot of Stone Fruits* (ed. Australian Brown Rot Research Committee), pp. 25-45. Government Printer, Melbourne.
SHESTAKOV, I.I. (1971). *Trudy prikl. Bot. Genet. Selek.* 43, 241-245. (*R.P.P.* 51, 1657, 1972).
SHIBATA, Y. & NISIZAWA, K. (1965). *Archs Biochem. Biophys.* 109, 516-521.
SHIMA, Y. (1936). *J. Fac. Agric. Hokkaido (imp.) Univ.* 39, 143-270. (*R.A.M.* 16, 325-327).
SKEIVYTE, S.A. (1964). *Liet. TSR Mokslu Akad. Darb., Ser. C, 1964,* 55-62. (*R.A.M.* 44, 1149, 1965).
SLEZARIK, A. & REXOVA, L. (1967). *Biologia, Bratisl.* 22, 407-413.
SMITH, M.A. (1936). *Phytopathology* 26, 1056-1060.
SMITH, W.L. (1971). *Pl. Dis. Reptr* 55, 228-230.
SMITH, W.L. & ANDERSON, R.E. (1972). *Phytopathology* 62, 790.
SMITH, W.L. & ANDERSON, R.E. (1975). *J. Am. Soc. hort. Sci.* 100, 84-86.
SMITH, W.L. & BLOMQUIST, M. (1970). *Phytopathology* 60, 866-868.
SMITH, W.L., HALLER, M.H. & McCLURE, T.T. (1956). *Phytopathology* 46, 261-264.
SMITH, W.L. & KEIL, H.L. (1972). *Phytopathology* 62, 672.
SMITH, W.L., MILLER, W.H. & BASSETT, R.D. (1965). *Phytopathology* 55, 604-606.
SMITH, W.L., PARSONS, C.S., ANDERSON, R.E. & BASSETT, R.D. (1964). *U.S.D.A. Mktg Res. Rep. no. 643,* 22pp.

SOKOLOV, A.M. (1962). *Sb. nauch. Trud. ivanov. sel.'-khoz. Inst. 1962* ,
     63-67. (*R.A.M.* 43, 1974, 1964).
SOLKINA, A. (1931). *Pl. Prot. Leningr.* 8, 309-310. (*R.A.M.* 11, 310).
SOSKIC, M. & ZEKOVIC, P. (1968). *Zast. Bilja* 19, 111-117. (*R.A.M.* 48,
     1849, 1969).
SPENCE, J.A. (1961). *Ann. appl. Biol.* 49, 723-734.
STADELMANN, E.J. & KINZEL, H. (1972). *In: Methods in cell physiology*, vol.
     5 (ed. D.M. Prescott), pp. 325-372. London & New York: Academic Press.
STAHMANN, M.A. (1973). In: *Fungal pathogenicity and the plant's response*.
     (ed. R.J.W. Byrde & C.V. Cutting), pp. 156-157. London & New York:
     Academic Press.
STEPHENS, G.J. & WOOD, R.K.S. (1975). *Physiol. Pl. Path.* 5, 165-181.
STOESSL, A., UNWIN, C.H. & WARD, E.W.B. (1972). *Phytopath. Z.* 74, 141-152.
STOJANOVIC, D. (1956). *Plant Protection, Belgrade*, no. 34, 63-65. (*Rev. appl.
     Ent.* 46, 287, 1958).
STONE, J.G., WADE, N.L. & BEATTIE, B.B. (1971). *Agric. Gaz. N.S.W.* 82,
     375-377.
STORCK, R. (1966). *J. Bact.* 91, 227-230.
STOYANOV, I. (1975). *Ovoshtarstvo, Sofia* 54, 42-44. (*R.P.P.* 54, 4033,
     1975).
STRINGER, A. & LYONS, C.H. (1974). *Pestic. Sci.* 5, 189-196.
SUSA, T. (1934). *Rep. Aomori hort. Exp. Stn* Kuroishi, Aomori-Kiev, Japan.
SUSSMAN, A.S. (1968). In: *The Fungi*, vol. 3 (ed. G.C. Ainsworth & A.S.
     Sussman), pp. 447-486. New York & London: Academic Press.
SUSSMAN, A.S. (1974). *Taxon* 23, 301-323.
SUSSMAN, A.S. & HALVORSEN, H.O. (1966). *Spores: Their Dormancy and Germi-
     nation*. New York: Harper. 356 pp.
SUTTON, T.B. & CLAYTON, C.N. (1972). *Phytopathology* 62, 1369-1373.
SWEENEY, B.M. (1963). *A. Rev. Pl. Physiol.* 14, 411-440.
SWINBURNE, T.R. (1973). *Trans. Br. mycol. Soc.* 60, 389-403.
SWINBURNE, T.R. (1975). *Phytopath. Z.* 82, 152-162.
TAKAHASHI, Y. (1911). *Mirjabe-Festschrift* 135-155. (Résumé in English in
     Mykol. Zbl. 3, 246-248, 1913).
TALMADGE, K., KEEGSTRA, K., BAUER, W.D. & ALBERSHEIM, P. (1973). *Pl. Physiol.,
     Lancaster* 51, 158-173.
TATE, K.G. & OGAWA, J.M. (1973). *Abstr. Papers 2nd Int. Cong. Pl. Path.,
     Minneapolis*, 0576.
TATE, K.G. & OGAWA, J.M. (1975). *Phytopathology* 65, 977-983.
TATE, K.G., OGAWA, J.M., MANJI, B.T. & BOSE, E. (1974). *Pl. Dis. Reptr* 58,
     663-665.
TEHRANI, G. & DICKSON, G.H. (1973). *Hortscience* 8, 340.
TERUI, M. & HARADA, Y. (1963). *Bull. Fac. Agric. Hirosaki Univ.* 9, 1-6.
TERUI, M. & HARADA, Y. (1964). *Bull. Fac. Agric. Hirosaki Univ.* 10, 41-45.
TERUI, M. & HARADA, Y. (1965). *Bull. Fac. Agric. Hirosaki Univ.* 11, 14-22.
TERUI, M. & HARADA, Y. (1966a). *Ann. phytopath. Soc. Japan* 32, 291-294.
TERUI, M. & HARADA, Y. (1966b). *Bull. Fac. Agric. Hirosaki Univ.* 12, 31-35.
TERUI, M. & HARADA, Y. (1966c). *Ann. phytopath. Soc. Japan* 32, 4.
TERUI, M. & HARADA, Y. (1966d). *Trans. mycol. Soc. Japan* 7, 309-311.
TERUI, M. & HARADA, Y. (1969). *Bull. Fac. Agric. Hirosaki Univ.* 15, 21-31.
TERUI, M. & HARADA, Y. (1970). *Bull. Fac. Agric. Hirosaki Univ.* 16, 123-130.
TERUI, M. & HARADA, Y. (1971). *Bull. Fac. Agric. Hirosaki Univ.* 17, 59-67.
THANOS, A. (1951). *Phytopathology* 41, 35.
THIND, K.S. & KEITT, G.W. (1949). *Phytopathology* 39, 621-636.
TILTON, J. (1807). *Mem. Phila. Soc. Promoting Agr.* 1, 192-197.
TINDALE, G.B., JENKINS, P.T. & PEGGIE, I.D. (1958). *J. Dep. Agric. Vict.*
     56, 107-111.

TORGESON, D.C. (ed.) (1969). *Fungicides*, vol. 2. New York & London: Academic Press. 742 pp.

TRIBE, H.T. (1955). *Ann. Bot.* 19, 351–368.

TUBAKI, K. (1958). *J. hattori bot. Lab.* 20, 142–244.

TULASNE, L.E. (1851). *Ann. Sci. nat.*, Sept. 3, 15.

TURIAN, G. (1966). In: *The Fungus Spore* (ed. M.F. Madelin), p. 61. London: Butterworths.

TURNER, B.L. (1969). *Taxon* 18, 134–151.

TURNER, N.J. (1970). *Contr. Boyce Thompson Inst. Pl. Res.* 24, 227–229.

TURNER, N.J. (1971). *Contr. Boyce Thompson Inst. Pl. Res.* 24, 357–361.

TURNER N.J. & BATTERSHELL, R.D. (1969). *Contr. Boyce Thompson Inst. Pl. Res.* 24, 139–147.

TURNER, N.J. & BATTERSHELL, R. (1970). *Contr. Boyce Thompson Inst. Pl. Res.* 24, 203–212.

TURNER, N.J., LIMPEL, L.E., BATTERSHELL, R.D., BLUESTONE, H. & LAMONT, D. (1964). *Contr. Boyce Thompson Inst. Pl. Res.* 22, 303–310.

TURNER, W.B. (1971). *Fungal Metabolites*. London & New York: Academic Press. 446 pp.

TWEEDY, B.G. & TURNER, N. (1966). *Contr. Boyce Thompson Inst. Pl. Res.* 23, 255–265.

UPHAM, P.M. & DELP, C.J. (1973). *Phytopathology* 63, 814–820.

VALENTA, V. (1950). *Ochr. Rost.* 23, 205–210. (cited by Sutton & Clayton, 1972).

VALLEAU, W.D. (1915). *J. agric. Res.* 5, 365–396.

VAN BRUMMELAN, J. (1972). *Persoonia* 6, 389–394.

VAN DEN ENDE, G. (1964). *Neth. J. Pl. Path.* 70, 37–52.

VAN DEN ENDE, G. (1969). *Phytopath. Z.* 64, 68–76.

VAN DEN ENDE, G. & COOLS, P.J.M. (1967). *Phytopath. Z.* 59, 122–128.

VAN DEN ENDE, G. & CORNELIS, J.J. (1970). *Neth. J. Pl. Path.* 76, 183–191.

VAN DER PLANK, J.E. (1968). *Disease resistance in plants*. New York & London: Academic Press. 206 pp.

VAN DER PLANK, J.E. (1975). *Principles of plant infection*. New York & London: Academic Press. 216 pp.

VASEV, A. (1973). *Gradinarska i Lozarska Nauka* 10, 35–41. (*R.P.P.* 53, 612, 1974).

VASUDEVA, R.S. (1930). *Ann. Bot.* 44, 469–493.

VAVILOV, N.I. (1930). *Rep. Proc. IX int. Hort. Cong. London*, 271–286.

VESSELL, E.S. (1972). In: *Metabolic Inhibitors*, vol. 3. (ed. R.M. Hochster et al.), pp. 383–425. New York & London: Academic Press.

VESTERBERG, O. (1971). In: *Methods in Microbiology*, vol. 5B (ed. J.R. Norris & D.W. Ribbons), pp. 595–614. New York & London: Academic Press.

VITANOV, M. (1961). *Ovoshtarstvo, Sofia* 8, 20–24. (*R.A.M.* 40, 543–544, 1961).

VITANOV, M. (1974). *Comptes Rendus de l'Academie Agricole Georgi Dimitrov* 7, 17–20. (*R.P.P.* 54, 194, 1975).

VIZAROVA, G. (1975). *Biologia Pl.* 17, 380–382.

VON THÜMEN, F. (1875). *Österr. Landwirtsch. Wochenblott*, 41–48.

VON THÜMEN, F. (1879). *Fungi Pomicoli*, pp. 22, 25.

WADE, G.C. (1956a). *Aust. J. agric. Res.* 7, 504–515.

WADE, G.C. (1956b). *Aust. J. agric. Res.* 7, 516–526.

WADE, G.C. (1960). *Tasm. J. Agric.* 31, 242–249.

WADE, G.C. & CRUICKSHANK, R. (1973). *Abstr. Papers 2nd Int. Cong. Pl. Path.*, 0006.

WADE, N.L. & GIPPS, P.G. (1973). *Aust. J. exp. Agric. Anim. Husb.* 13, 600–603.

WAFFELAERT, P. (1969). *Phytiat.-Phytopharm.* 18, 51-55.
WAHL, B. (1926). *Verlag. Bundesanst. PflSchutz. Wien II*, 28 pp.
WALKER, J. & McLEOD, R.W. (1970). *Agric. Gaz. N.S.W.* 81, 452-458.
WALKER, J.R.L. (1969). *Phytochemistry* 8, 561-566.
WALLROTH, F.G. (1833). *Flora Crypt.* German pt. 11, pp. 182-183 .
WARD, E.W.B. (1976). *Phytopathology* 66, 175-176.
WARD, E.W.B., UNWIN, C.H. & STOESSL, A. (1973). *Can. J. Bot.* 51, 2327-2332.
WARD, E.W.B., UNWIN, C.H., HILL, J. & STOESSL, A. (1975). *Phytopathology* 65,
    859-863.
WEAVER, L.O. (1950). *Phytopathology* 40, 1136-1153.
WEBB, S.J. (1965). *Bound Water in Biological Integrity.* Springfield,
    Illinois: Thomas.
WELLMAN, R.H. & McCALLAN, S.E.A. (1942). *Contr. Boyce Thompson Inst. Pl.
    Res.* 12, 431-449.
WELLMAN, R.H. & McCALLAN, S.E.A. (1946). *Contr. Boyce Thompson Inst. Pl.
    Res.* 14, 151-160.
WELLS, J.M. (1972). *Phytopathology* 62, 129-133.
WELLS, J.M. & BENNETT, A.H. (1975). *Pl. Dis. Reptr* 59, 931-935.
WELLS, J.M. & GERDTS, M.H. (1971). *Pl. Dis. Reptr* 55, 69-72.
WELLS, J.M. & HARVEY, J.M. (1970). *Phytopathology* 60, 116-120.
WELLS, J.M. & REVEAR, L.G. (1976). *Hortscience* 11, 107-108.
WESTERDIJK, J. (1912). *Meded. phytopath. Lab. Willie Commelin Scholten.* 3,
    39-41.
WHAN, J.H. (1976). *Pl. Dis. Reptr* (in press).
WHETZEL, H.H. (1943). *Lloydia* 6, 18-52.
WHETZEL, H.H. (1945). *Mycologia* 37, 648-714.
WILLAMAN, J.J. (1920). *Bot. Gaz.* 70, 221-229.
WILLAMAN, J.J. (1926). *Proc. Soc. exp. Biol. Med.* 23, 680-681.
WILLAMAN, J.J., PERVIER, N.C. & TRIEBOLD, H.O. (1925). *Bot. Gaz.* 80,
    121-144.
WILLER, K.-H. (1967). *Phytopath. Z.* 58, 193-199.
WILLER, K.-H. (1970). *Z. wiss. Mikrosk.* 70, 49-57. (*R.P.P.* 50, 770, 1971).
WILLETTS, H.J. (1968*a*). *Ann. Bot.* 32, 219-232.
WILLETTS, H.J. (1968*b*). *Trans. Br. mycol. Soc.* 51, 625-632.
WILLETTS, H.J. (1968*c*). *Trans. Br. mycol. Soc.* 51, 633-642.
WILLETTS, H.J. (1968*d*). *J. gen. Microbiol.* 51, 271-273.
WILLETTS, H.J. (1969*a*). *Arch. Mikrobiol.* 69, 48-53.
WILLETTS, H.J. (1969*b*). *Trans. Br. mycol. Soc.* 52, 309-314.
WILLETTS, H.J. (1969*c*). *Mycologia* 61, 332-339.
WILLETTS, H.J. (1971). *Biol. Rev.* 46, 387-407.
WILLETTS, H.J. (1972). *Biol. Rev.* 47, 515-536.
WILLETTS, H.J., BYRDE, R.J.W., FIELDING, A.H. & WONG, A.-L. (1976). In
    preparation.
WILLETTS, H.J. & CALONGE, F.D. (1969*a*). *New Phytol.* 68, 123-131.
WILLETTS, H.J. & CALONGE, F.D. (1969*b*). *Arch. Mikrobiol.* 64, 279-288.
WILLETTS, H.J. & WONG, A.-L. (1971). *Trans. Br. mycol. Soc.* 57, 515-524.
WILLIAMS, A.H. (1963). In: *Enzyme chemistry of phenolic compounds.* (ed. J.B.
    Pridham), pp. 87-95. Oxford: Pergamon Press.
WILLISON, R.S. (1963). *Can. Pl. Dis. Surv.* 43, 39-53.
WILLISON, R.S. & DUSTAN, G.G. (1956). *Can. J. agric. Sci.* 36, 233-240.
WILSON, E.E. (1942). *J. agric. Res.* 64, 561-594.
WILSON, E.E. (1943). *Phytopathology* 33, 506-516.
WILSON, E.E. (1950). *Phytopathology* 40, 567-583.
WILSON, J.K. (1948). *Mycologia* 40, 605-613.
WILSON, R.W. (1970). *Can. J. Microbiol.* 16, 629-634.
WILSON, E.E. & BAKER, G.A. (1948). *J. agric. Res.* 72, 301-327.

WILTSHIRE, S.P. (1920). *Rep. agric. hort. Res. Stn, Univ. Bristol, 1919*, 34-36.

WINTER, G. (1883). *Hedwigia* 22, 67-72, 129-131.

WOLF, C.N., SCHULDT, P.H. & BALDWIN, M.M. (1955). *Science, N.Y.* 121, 61-62.

WOLFE, M.S. (1976). *Proc. 8th Br. Insectic. Fungic. Conf.*, 1975, 3, 813-822.

WONG, A.-L. & WILLETTS, H.J. (1974). *J. gen. Microbiol.* 81, 101-109.

WONG, A.-L. & WILLETTS, H.J. (1975). *J. gen. Microbiol.* 88, 339-344.

WOOD, R.K.S. (1967). *Physiological Plant Pathology.* Oxford: Blackwell.

WOOD, R.K.S., BALLIO, A. & GRANITI, A. (ed.) (1972). *Phytotoxins in plant diseases.* London & New York: Academic Press. 530 pp.

WOODCOCK, D. (1972). In: *Systemic Fungicides* (ed. R.W. Marsh), pp. 34-85. London: Longman.

WORMALD, H. (1919). *Ann. Bot.* 33, 361-404.

WORMALD, H. (1920). *Ann. Bot.* 34, 143-171.

WORMALD, H. (1921). *Ann. Bot.* 35, 125-135.

WORMALD, H. (1927). *Ann. Bot.* 41, 287-299.

WORMALD, H. (1945). *Gdnrs' Chron.* 117, 115 and *Rep. E. Malling Res. Stn for 1944*, 75-76.

WORMALD, H. (1954). *Tech. Bull. Minist. Agric. Fish. Fd, Lond.* no. 3. London: H.M.S.O. 113 pp.

WORONIN, M. (1888). *Mém. Acad. Sci. St-Petersb. (Zap. imp. russk. tekh. Obshch.)* (VIIe sér.) 36, 1-49.

WORONIN, M. (1895). *Mém. Acad. Sci. St-Petersb. (Zap. imp. russk. tekh. Obshch.)* (VIIIe sér.) 2, 1-27.

WORONIN, M. (1900). *Mém. Acad. Sci. St-Petersb. (Zap. imp. russk. tekh. Obshch.)* (VIIIe sér.) 10, 1-38.

YARWOOD, C.E. (1950). *Am. J. Bot.* 37, 636-639.

YARWOOD, C.E. (1973). *Phytopathology* 63, 1324-1325.

YODER, D.M. (1950). Ph.D. thesis, Cornell Univ.

YOUGANOVA, O.M. (1946). *Pub. Crimean Res. Inst. Plant Prot.* 71 pp.

ZEHR, E.I. (ed.) (1972). *Fungicide and Nematicide Tests* 27, 41-56.

ZEHR, E.I. (ed.) (1973). *Fungicide and Nematicide Tests* 28, 38-50.

ZEHR, E.I. (ed.) (1974). *Fungicide and Nematicide Tests* 29, 31-41.

ZEHR, E.I., SMITH, W.L., WEBB, B.K., HOOD, C.E., GAMBRELL, C.E. & SIMS, E.T. (1975). *Hortscience* 10, 144.

ZOBERI, M.H. (1961). *Ann. Bot.* 25, 53-64.

ZUCKERKANDLE, F. & PAULING, L. (1965). *J. Theoret. Biology* 8, 357-366.

ZWINTZSCHER, M. (1955). *Rep. XIVth Int. hort. Cong.*, 1955, 716-734.

ZWYGART, T. (1970). *Phytopath. Z.* 68, 97-130.

INDEX

The names of individual countries are not indexed; see
under appropriate continent (e.g. for Japan, see Asia).

For the three main species, and their main hosts, only the
principal entries are indexed.